Mathematics First Course

Second Edition

Mathematics

First Course

John A. Brown

University of Delaware

Bona Lunn Gordey

Orville Wright Junior High School
Tulsa, Oklahoma

Dorothy Sward

Silvarado Junior High School
Napa, California

Consultant and General Editor:

John R. Mayor

American Association for the
Advancement of Science, and
the University of Maryland

Prentice-Hall, Inc.
Englewood Cliffs, N. J.

Photo Acknowledgments

Courtesy of Beloit Public Schools, Beloit, Wisconsin, 20, 32. Courtesy of Fairbanks Morse and Company, 230. Courtesy of International Business Machine Corporation, 144, 276. Courtesy of National Aeronautics and Space Administration, 285. Courtesy of New York World's Fair 1964-1965 Corporation, 15, 102. Courtesy of Rocketdyne, a division of North American Aviation, 279.

Cover and title page photos courtesy of Jack Pitkin.

Mathematics, First Course, *Second Edition*
John A. Brown, Bona Lunn Gordey, Dorothy Sward, John R. Mayor

Library of Congress Catalog Card No. 65-10256

Printed in the United States of America
56239-E

Preface

The mathematics experiences of junior high school students should be a very important part of their education. Junior high school mathematics serves as a bridge between the study of arithmetic in the elementary school and the study of algebra and geometry in the senior high school. Mathematics at this level also provides much of the foundation for the study of high school science. If an understanding of mathematics is obtained in junior high school, the student will be much better prepared for the great variety of applications of mathematics which he will want to make in his more advanced studies in many fields and in experiences throughout life.

MATHEMATICS, FIRST COURSE and MATHEMATICS, SECOND COURSE are planned for the seventh and eighth grades for all students. There is sufficient material to challenge the most gifted, and careful attention is given to the needs of those who have not been so successful in earlier mathematical study. The emphasis in these texts on unifying principles, the use of the inductive method, and the bringing together of ideas of arithmetic, geometry, and algebra should enable the student to study mathematics with greater enjoyment and greater success. This will be due in considerable part to the opportunity for the pupil to develop further understanding of previously studied materials, and of the many new topics which are included.

The materials are written in the spirit of modern mathematics whenever feasible, with attention given to structure and to some of the newer vocabulary, such as sets and number statements. The recommendations of the Commission on Mathematics for the Junior High School have been followed. Numeration, bases other than ten, has been introduced

early and is made use of where appropriate in exercises throughout the text. The choice of new topics is based on an experimental study carried out at a major university laboratory school by one of the authors even before much of the current widespread work on secondary school curriculum had been started.

Special features of the text are the Quick Quizzes, which appear throughout both courses, and the Appendix materials, which contain many exercises both for maintenance of skills and for the introduction to new topics which might not be included in a basic course for all students. There is less emphasis on the so-called social applications of mathematics than is traditional, although additional work is provided on these topics by means of appendices. Time taken from these traditional topics is given to the interpretation of principles of number systems and ideas of geometry which are fundamental to the study of mathematics at this level.

The authors wish to express appreciation particularly to the many students who have been in their junior high school classes and to the many teachers with whom they have had the privilege of exchanging ideas in local and state curriculum committees, teachers' meetings, and meetings of the National Council of Teachers of Mathematics. The authors wish to thank especially the following reviewers: Mrs. Lina Walters, Paterson State College, Paterson, New Jersey; Dr. James H. Zant, Professor of Mathematics, Oklahoma A & M College, Stillwater, Oklahoma; Dr. John J. Kinsella, School of Education, New York University, New York, New York; James L. Chedester, Principal, Pattonville High School, Pattonville, Missouri.

Contents

CHAPTER ONE THE BASIS OF NUMBERS 1

The Egyptian Numerals, 3. The Roman Numerals, 5. The Hindu-Arabic Numerals, 7. Exponents, 10. Expressing Numbers Using Exponents, 12. Using Exponents in Expressing Numbers in Polynomial Form, 12. Grouping by Fives, 13. Changing A Numeral From Base Five to a Numeral in Base Ten, 15.

CHAPTER TWO EXPLORING LINES 19

Constructing Line Segments of Certain Length, 22. Bisecting Line Segments with a Ruler, 23. Bisecting Line Segments with Compasses and Straight Edge, 24. Drawing Perpendicular Line Segments with Straight Edge and Right Angle, 26. Constructing Perpendicular Line Segments with Straight Edge and Compasses, 27. Drawing Parallel Line Segments with a Ruler and Right Angle, 28.

CHAPTER THREE EXPLORING ANGLES 31

Measuring a Right Angle, 33. Kinds of Angles, 34. Drawing and Measuring Angles, 37. More About Angles, 39.

CHAPTER FOUR ADDITION 45

Reading Large Numbers, 49. Fun With Numbers, 51. Rounding Numbers, 52. Meaning of Fractions and Terms Used with Fractions, 54.

Rules of Divisibility, 57. Simplifying Improper Fractions, 58. Adding Fractions, 58. Changing to Like Fractions, 59. More on Adding Fractions, 60. Addition of Decimal Fractions, 63. Adding Denominate Numbers, 66.

CHAPTER FIVE SUBTRACTION 71

Method I: The Take Away Process, 72. Method II: The Additive Process, 73. Subtracting Common Fractions, 76. Subtracting Decimal Fractions, 80. Subtracting Denominate Numbers, 83. Subtracting Measures of Time, 84. Standard Time, 84. The Missing Number, 87.

CHAPTER SIX EXPLORING TRIANGLES AND QUADRILATERALS 91

The Triangle, 91. The Quadrilateral, 96.

CHAPTER SEVEN MULTIPLICATION 101

Multiplying by 10 and 100 and Multiples of 10 and 100, 104. Multiplication of Common Fractions, 108. Multiplication of Mixed Numbers, 113. Multiplication of Decimal Fractions, 116. Multiplying by 10, 100, or 1000, 117. Multiplication of Denominate Numbers, 119.

CHAPTER EIGHT DIVISION 123

Division and Other Processes, 124. Estimating Quotients, 126. Methods of Division, 127. Finding an Average, 129. More About Division with Whole Numbers, 130. Short Division, 131. Common Fractions in Division, 133. Division of Decimal Fractions, 138. Dividing by a Decimal, 140. Rounding Decimals, 142. Dividing Decimals by 10, 100, or 1000, 145. Changing Fractions to Decimals and Decimals to Fractions, 147. Division of Denominate Numbers, 151. Fun with Numbers, 152.

CHAPTER NINE COMPARING QUANTITIES 155

Comparing Quantities by Division, 156. Practice Using Ratios, 158. Using Bar Graphs to Make Comparisons, 161.

CHAPTER TEN PERIMETERS AND AREAS 167

Perimeters of Squares and Rectangles, 167. Perimeters of Triangles, 170. Areas of Rectangles and Squares, 172. Areas of Parallelograms, 176.

CHAPTER ELEVEN EXPLORING PER CENTS 183

Changing Fractions to Per Cents, 186. Changing Per Cents to Decimals and Fractions, 188. Table of Equivalents, 189. Using Per Cents in

Solving Problems, 189. Finding the Per Cent of a Quantity, 191. Using More Difficult Per Cents, 194. Per Cents Greater than 100%, 195. Per Cents Less than 1%, 197. Other Applications of Per Cents, 199. Per Cent of Increase or Decrease, 204. Using Per Cents in Sports, 206.

CHAPTER TWELVE BUSINESS USES OF PER CENT 211

Commission, 211. Discount, 216. Interest, 220. Finding the Amount, 221. Writing a Formula for Finding Interest, 222. Finding Interest When Time Is Given in Days, 224.

CHAPTER THIRTEEN EXPLORING THE CIRCLE 227

Making Designs with Circles, 228. The Relation of the Circumference to the Diameter of a Circle, 230. The Formula for Finding the Areas of Circles, 234.

CHAPTER FOURTEEN POLYGONS AND RECTANGULAR SOLIDS 239

Some Kinds of Polygons, 239. Perimeter of a Regular Pentagon, 242. Volume of Rectangular Solids, 243.

CHAPTER FIFTEEN GRAPHS 249

Pictographs, 249. Bar Graphs, 251 Broken-line Graphs, 254. Circle Graphs, 256. Making Circle Graphs, 260. The Number Line, 262. Lines in a Plane, 265. Assigning Numbers to Points on the Plane, 268.

CHAPTER SIXTEEN ESTIMATING AND CENTRAL TENDENCY 275

Estimating Sums and Products, 275. Estimating with Per Cents, 277. Averages, 278. Other Measures of Central Tendency, 282. Computation with Approximate Numbers, 284.

APPENDIX 289

Tables of Measure, 312.

INDEX 315

CHAPTER ONE  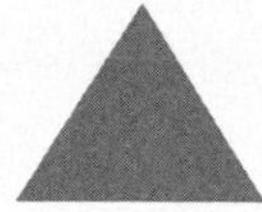  

The Basis of Numbers

Arithmetic is a language of numbers. It is a system of ideas invented by people to help solve problems involving numbers. Our arithmetic of today developed slowly through history.

The daily life of the earliest man did not require a bookkeeping system based upon numbers. His possessions, since they were meager, were not extensive enough to demand a record of his wealth.

As man gained more property it became wise for him to keep records. For instance, he may have had "many" sheep and "many" tools among his wealth. Since "many" does not indicate an exact amount, a more definite system was needed. One way a shepherd kept an account of his sheep was to let one stone represent one sheep. The sheep were counted by using the principle of one-to-one correspondence, that is, there was one stone for each sheep and one sheep for each stone. The counting resulted in a collection of stones. The total collection indicated the number of sheep in the flock.

In communicating his wealth to other people, such as merchants or the tax collector, it was necessary for man to have a spoken word and a written expression to indicate the size of the pile of stones. The spoken word or the written expression may be referred to as a verbal expression. In our discussion, the pile of stones will be referred to as a "model group." The pile of stones is an imitation of the flock of sheep. The written name of the model group is a *numeral.*

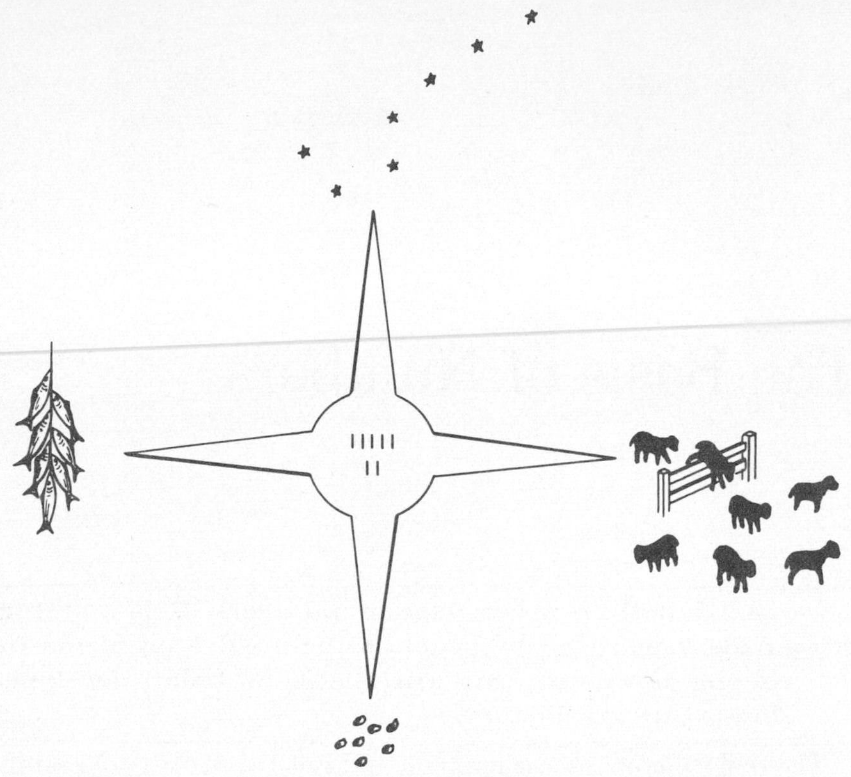

Examples

(a) The marks represent a model for counting. One may name this group by the verbal expressions "seven" or "five plus two." A numeral for the model is "7," or "5 + 2."

(b) The feet of a bird may be thought of as a model. The verbal expressions could be "two," "a pair," or "one plus one." Examples of numerals for the model group are "2" or "1 + 1."

(c) 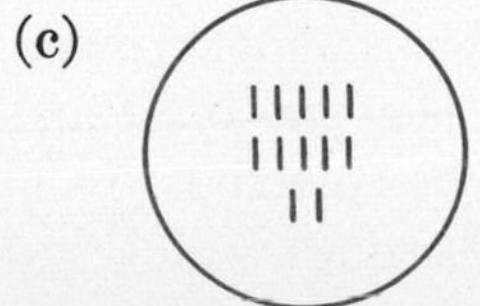

This model could be called a "dozen," "twelve," or "ten and two more." Numerals to name the model could be "12" or "10 + 2."

EXERCISES—Represent the following model by (a) a verbal expression and (b) a numeral.

Example xxxxx
xxx (a) Eight or five plus three.
(b) 8

1. xxxxx

2. xxxxxx
xxxx

3. xxxx
xxxx
xxxx

4. xxxxxx
xxxxxx
xxxxxx
xxxxxx

5. xxxxxxxxxx
xxxxxxxxxx

6. oooooo
oooooo
oooooo
oooooo
oooo

7. ooooooooooooo
ooooooooooooo

8. xxxxxxxxxx
xxxxx

The Egyptian Numerals

Two systems of writing numerals, besides our own, will be studied in this chapter. The study of these systems will reveal the role of symbols and the role of the principles involved in using these symbols to represent number.

The Egyptians had an advanced civilization many years before the birth of Christ. Among their accomplishments was a set of number symbols. The following table illustrates our verbal expression of the model and the Egyptian numeral for the model:

Table I

One	𓏺
Ten	𓎆
One hundred	𓍢
One thousand	𓆼
Ten thousand	𓂭
One hundred thousand	𓆐
One million	𓁨

Notice that the Egyptians did not use a symbol for a model group for each quantity that they wished to express. For example, they did not have a single numeral for twelve. Accepting the principles of (a) repetition and (b) addition, the seven numerals could be used to write numerals for any quantities.

The system followed a simple pattern. One stroke (|) was "one"; two strokes (||), using the principles of repetition and addition, meant "two," that is, one plus one; three strokes (|||) using the two principles, meant "three," and so on to nine (|||||||||). Ten was written as ∩. This symbol replaced the ten strokes.

Examples

1. Represent the number in the group using Egyptian numerals.

   xxxxxx
   xxxxxx
   x

   Explanation: This follows from ∩ = 10 and | = 1 and by applying the principles of repetition and addition, ∩ + | + | + | would be written ∩||| . Notice that the plus sign was understood in the writing of the numeral. Also, the symbol with the largest value was written first.

2. Change 9∩∩∩||||||| from the Egyptian system to our own system.

   9∩∩∩||||||| = 100 + 10 + 10 + 10 + 7 = 137

3. Write 236 in the Egyptian system.

   236 = 99∩∩∩||||||

EXERCISES—In Exercises 1 through 5, represent the number of the items in the groups by using Egyptian numerals.

1. xxxxx

2. xxxx
   xxxx

3. xxxxxx
   xxxxxxxx

4. oooooo
   oooooo
   oooooo
   ooooo

5. oooooooooo
   oooooooooo
   oooooooooo
   ooooo

In Exercises 6 through 9, change the numerals from the Egyptian system to our own system.

6. 𓎆𓎆𓎆𓎆𓎆𓏺𓏺𓏺

7. 𓍢𓍢𓎆𓏺𓏺

8. 𓆼𓍢𓏺𓏺𓏺𓏺

9. 𓍢𓍢𓍢𓍢𓍢𓍢𓎆𓎆𓎆𓎆𓎆𓎆𓎆𓏺𓏺𓏺𓏺𓏺𓏺𓏺𓏺𓏺

In Exercises 10 through 14, write the numerals in the Egyptian system.

10. Fourteen.

11. Three hundred eight.

12. Nineteen fifty-seven.

13. 2351

14. 6004

15. What number relationships exist among the seven models used in the Egyptian numeration system?

The Roman Numerals

The Romans used seven symbols in their numeration system, most of which were different from the ones accepted by the Egyptians. The numerals used for the Roman model groups have changed during the years. The table below shows the modern adaptation of the symbols used by the Romans.

Table II

One	I
Five	V
Ten	X
Fifty	L
One hundred	C
Five hundred	D
One thousand	M

Like the Egyptian system, the model groups did not represent all quantities that one would want to count and record. In order to have numerals for these quantities, the Romans used the principles of (a) repetition, (b) addition, (c) subtraction, and (d) multiplication.

In the numeral III, repetition and addition are used to write $1 + 1 + 1$. In the numeral IV, subtraction is used to write four, that is, five minus one. When subtraction is used, the symbol representing the number to be subtracted is written before the symbol representing the larger numeral. A bar over a numeral multiplies the number represented by the numeral by one thousand. For instance, $\overline{\text{V}}$, would be five thousand and $\overline{\text{XLIII}}$ would be forty-three thousand.

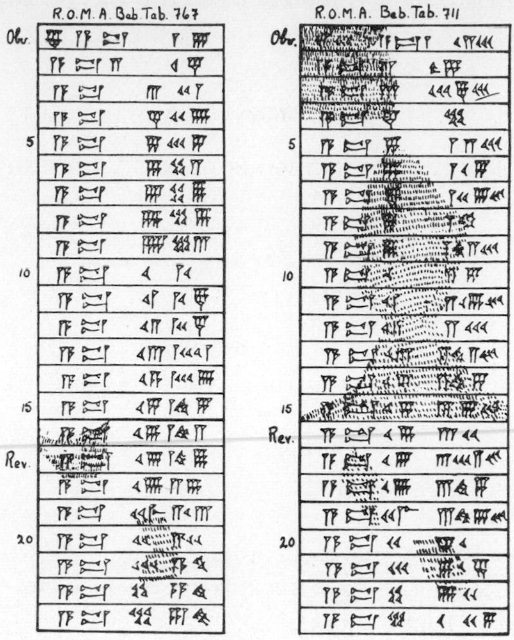

Babylonian multiplication tables.

One notices that a numeration system requires numerals for the model groups together with a set of principles. Both the symbols and the principles are arbitrarily chosen. For other systems of numeration such as the Greek and Babylonian systems, the same is true. A set of numerals together with principles are arbitrarily chosen to make the system operational.

Examples

1. Represent the group using Roman numerals.

xxxxxx xxxxxx	XII	This number is represented with one ten, X, plus two ones, II. The principles of repetition and addition are used.
ooooo ooooo oooo	XIV	This number is represented with one ten, X, plus four ones. The subtraction principle is used to write four, that is, five minus one.

2. Change the Roman numerals to a numeral in our system.

$$\text{LXXIV} = 50 + 10 + 10 + 4 = 74$$

3. Write the following in Roman numerals.

Three hundred twenty-four = CCCXXIV

EXERCISES—In Exercises 1 through 4, represent the groups in the Roman number system.

1. ooooo
   ooo

2. oooooo
   oooooo
   oooooo

3. xxxxxxxxxx
   xxxxxxxxxx
   xxx

4. xxxxx xxxxx
   xxxxx xxxxx
   xxxxx xxxx

In Exercises 5 through 9, change the Roman numerals to numerals in our own system.

5. XXVIII
6. CX
7. CIV
8. DCCIX
9. MCDII

In Exercises 10 through 13, write the numbers in the Roman system.

10. Sixty-eight.
11. Ninety-nine.
12. Four hundred seventy.
13. 1957.
14. Explain how the principles of the Roman system are used to write 3109.
15. Explain how the principles of the Roman system are used to write 42,300.
16. What relationships exist among the seven numerals of the Roman system?

The Hindu-Arabic Numerals

The numeration system we use today is called the "Hindu-Arabic" system. Generally it is agreed that the Hindu people first used a set of nine symbols together with the principles of (a) addition and (b) place value. Arabian scholars traveling through India noticed this unusual system and introduced it into their homeland. After many years someone invented zero as the tenth symbol. The zero, used as a place holder, was a most important invention in making the whole system more useful.

The ten symbols were arbitrarily chosen just like the choices made by the Egyptians and the Romans. The symbols changed in appearance many times. Table III illustrates some of these changes.

Table III

Two	Three	Four	Five	Seven
[illegible]	[illegible]	[illegible]	[illegible]	7
[illegible]	3	[illegible]	[illegible]	∧
7	3	4	4	7
2	3	4	5	

The characteristics of the Hindu-Arabic system which make it so different from other systems are the principle of place value and the use of zero. The principle of place value was recognized in the use of the abacus. The abacus is an instrument in which strings of beads are used for counting. The numerical value of one bead depends on the string that it is on.

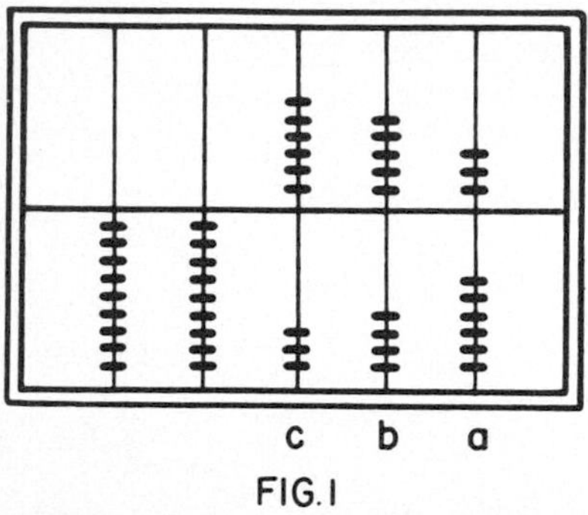

FIG. 1

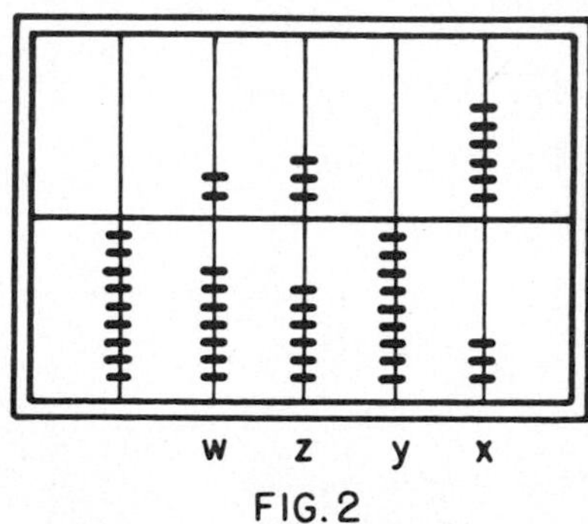

FIG. 2

In figure 1, column *a* shows the number of units (ones), in this case three (in the upper part); column *b* shows the number of tens, in this case five; and column *c* shows the number of one hundreds, in this case six. By using the principle of addition the number is 6 hundreds plus 5 tens plus 3 units or 653.

In figure 2, the x column (in the upper part) shows 6 units, the y column shows zero tens, the z column shows 3 hundreds, and w column shows 2 thousands. The number can be written as 2306.

The numbers indicated in the above illustrations may also be written in the form $6(100) + 5(10) + 3$ and $2(1000) + 3(100) + 0(10) + 7$. This form of writing numbers will be called the *polynomial form*. In elementary arithmetic it is not necessary for one to have a careful definition of this term. Notice this polynomial is a sum of terms, each of which may be a product. [6(100), 5(10) and 3 are examples of terms.] These two numbers written as 653 and 2307 are said to be written in *positional notation.* Each digit represents a certain value by virtue of its position in the number. The 7, in 2307, represents 7 units; the 3 represents 3(100) or 300; and the 2 by its position represents 2(1000) or 2000. By using 0 in the tens position, the place value of the 3 and the 2 is determined.

Example—Using the principles of the Hindu-Arabic system write 236 in polynomial form.

$$236 = 2(100) + 3(10) + 6 \text{ or}$$
$$2 \text{ hundreds} + 3 \text{ tens} + 6 \text{ units}$$

Note: 2(100) means 2 times 100. This could also be written, 2×100.

EXERCISES—In Exercises 1 through 5, write the number represented by each abacus. In Exercises 6 through 15, write the numbers in polynomial form.

1.

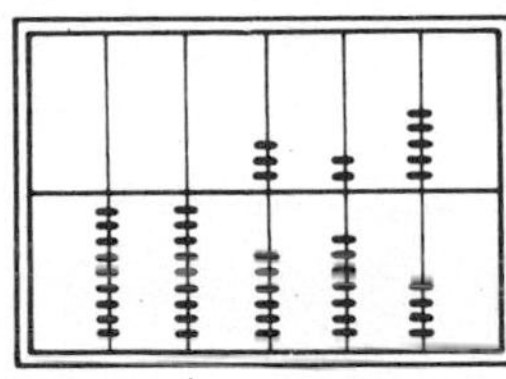

2.

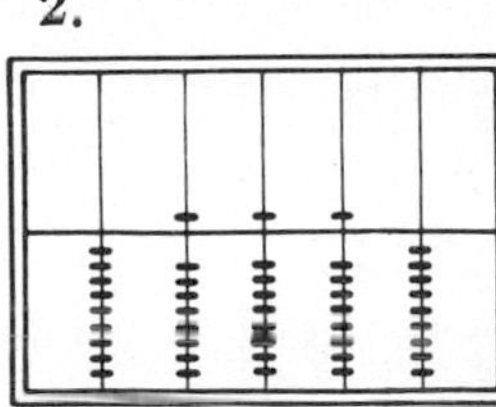

3.

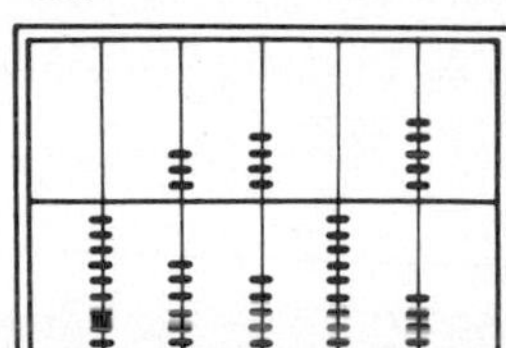

4.

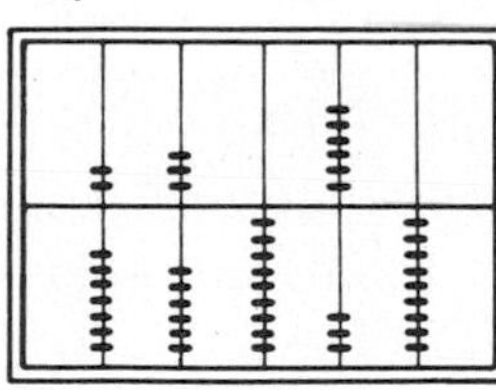

5.

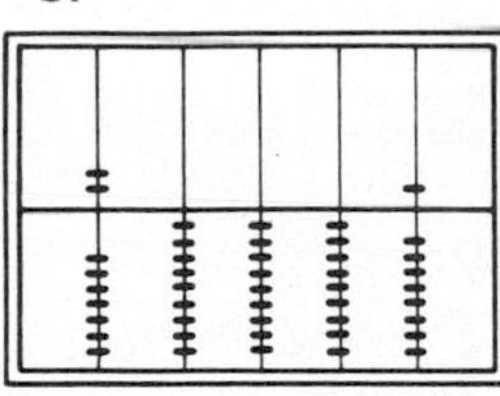

6. 54
7. 88
8. 234
9. 603
10. 2326
11. 4039
12. 3672
13. 9007
14. 32,162
15. 1,000,001

In Exercises 16 through 20, represent the number models in polynomial form.

16. xxxxxx
    xxxxxx
    xx

17. ooooooo
    ooooooo
    ooooooo

18. xxxxxxxxxx
    xxxxxxxxxx
    xxxxxxxxxx
    xxxxx

19. ooooo ooooo
    ooooo ooooo
    ooooo ooooo
    ooooo ooooo
    ooooo ooooo
    ooo

20. xxxxxxxxx
    xxxxxxxxxx
    xxxxx
    xxxxxxxxxxx

We see that: $3(1000) + 4(100) + 6(10) + 8 = 3468$

$$4(1000) + 2(10) = 4020$$

Notice that a zero in the units place and a zero in the hundreds place gives value to the 2 and 4 by virtue of the place of the 2 and the 4 in the number written in positional notation.

Change from polynomial form to positional notation.

21. $3(100) + 4(10) + 2$
22. $6(1000) + 2(100) + 9(10) + 7$
23. $7(1000) + 3(100) + 4(10) + 8$
24. $6(100) + 5$
25. $5(1000) + 3(100)$
26. $9(1000) + 4(10)$
27. $8(10{,}000) + 3(1000) + 4(100) + 6$
28. $6(10{,}000)$
29. $1(10{,}000) + 1$
30. $3(10{,}000) + 1(100)$
31. $7(10{,}000) + 6(1000)$
32. $8(100{,}000) + 7(10{,}000) + 5(10)$

In Exercises 33 through 37, change the answers of Exercises 16 through 20 to positional notation.

Exponents

Man is always trying to simplify and refine his written expressions of symbols. Descartes, a famous French mathematician of the 17th century, is given the credit for the invention of a short way of writing certain numbers. In the Descartes system, a number like $2 \times 2 \times 2$ is written as 2^3 and a number like $5 \times 5 \times 5 \times 5$ is written as 5^4. Written this way the 2^3 and 5^4 are called powers. 2^3 is read "two cube" or "two to the third power," and the 5^4 is read "five to the fourth power." The small ^{3} and the ^{4} are called *exponents* and the 2 and 5 are called *bases*. Notice that this is a short way of writing multiplication when equal numbers are multiplied together. One of the equal numbers is the base and the number of equal numbers in the product is the exponent. Thus, $10^2 = 10 \times 10 = 100$ and $6^3 = 6 \times 6 \times 6 = 216$. When ^{1} is an exponent it is usually not written. It is understood that, if the symbol representing a number does not have an exponent indicated, the exponent is 1.

Examples—For the following numbers (a) write a verbal expression for the number and (b) find the value of the number: 2^4, 10^3, a^3.

2^4 (a) Two to the fourth power
(b) $2^4 = 2 \times 2 \times 2 \times 2 = 16$

10^3 (a) Ten cube
(b) $10^3 = 10 \times 10 \times 10 = 1000$

a^3 (a) *a* cube
(b) $a^3 = a \times a \times a$

In the last example *a* is a symbol for a number. Various number values may be assigned to *a*. You probably have used letters as symbols for numbers.

EXERCISES—In the following, (a) first write a verbal expression for the numbers and, (b) then find the value of the numbers in Exercises 1 through 10.

1. 2^2
2. 3^3
3. 10^2
4. 10^3
5. 4^2
6. 5^2
7. 12^2
8. 10^5
9. 2^4
10. 3^5
11. a^2
12. x^4
13. a^5
14. 2^6
15. (a) Identify the base of each power in Exercises 1 through 7.
(b) Identify the exponent of each power in Exercises 1 through 7.

Expressing Numbers Using Exponents

Certain numbers may easily be written by the use of exponents.

For example: $100 = 10 \times 10 = 10^2$

$$9 = 3 \times 3 = 3^2$$

$$64 = 8 \times 8 = 8^2$$

$$64 = 4 \times 4 \times 4 = 4^3$$

$$64 = 2 \times 2 \times 2 \times 2 \times 2 \times 2 = 2^6$$

EXERCISES—Write the following using exponents.

1. 4
2. 25
3. 36
4. 81
5. 49
6. 8
7. 16
8. 1000
9. 10,000
10. 100,000
11. $x \cdot x \cdot x$
12. $a \cdot a \cdot a \cdot a$
13. $x \cdot x \cdot x \cdot x \cdot x \cdot x$

Note: A dot may be used to indicate multiplication.

Using Exponents in Expressing Numbers in Polynomial Form

Exponents may be used to express numbers in polynomial form. A number such as 342 written as a polynomial is 3 one hundreds plus 4 tens plus 2 units or ones. Since one hundred is 10^2 and ten is 10, the polynomial may be written $3(10^2) + 4(10) + 2$. Notice that using parentheses is another way to indicate multiplication, that is, 4(10) means 4 times ten and $3(10^2)$ means $3 \times 10 \times 10$.

Examples—Write 4256 in polynomial form using exponents.

$$4256 = 4(10^3) + 2(10^2) + 5(10) + 6$$

EXERCISES—Write the following in polynomial form using exponents.

1. 372
2. 408
3. 6231
4. 7003
5. 10,328
6. 40,444
7. 57,360
8. 5000
9. 39,704
10. 60,007
11. 100,101
12. 10,000,000

*13. Notice that the exponents of the polynomial, reading from left to right, decrease by one for each place. Also, notice that the last term, the units place, does not show a power of ten. If ten were used in parentheses for the units place, what would have to be its exponent in order to fit into the order of descending exponents?

Grouping by Fives

Since ten is the base of the powers in a number expressed as $6(10^3) + 4(10^2) + 5(10) + 6$, it is said that the base of this system of grouping is ten. This tells one that the size of the groups which are added are powers of ten. Ten was arbitrarily chosen as a base. It is possible to add groups which are powers of five, two, twelve, or any number.

If one grouped by fives, the first size of the groups would be units; the second would be fives; the third twenty-fives, that is, 5×5; the fourth would be one hundred twenty-fives, that is, $5 \times 5 \times 5$. This can be extended to any power of 5.

Examples—Represent the groups in polynomial form using powers of 5.

(a) xxxxx
xxxxx $= 2(5) + 3$
xxx

(b) ooooo ooooo
ooooo ooooo $= 1(25) + 1(5) + 2$
ooooo ooooo or
oo $1(5^2) + 1(5) + 2$

EXERCISES—In Exercises 1 through 4 represent the groups in polynomial form using powers of 5.

1. xxxxx
xxx

2. ooooooo
ooooooo

3. oooooooo
oooooooo
oooooooo
oooooooo

4. xxxxxxxxxx
xxxxxxxxxx
xxxxxxxxx

5. If the groups in Exercises 2 and 3 were combined into a single group, represent the new group in polynomial form using powers of 5's.
6. Write a polynomial using powers of 5's to represent a group twice the size of the number in Exercise 4.
7. Triple the group in Exercise 3 and write this new group as a polynomial in powers of 5's.

The above groups were written in polynomial form. The groups may also be expressed in positional notation. In expressing $3(10^2) + 5(10) + 7$ in positional notation, the 3, 5, and 7 were written in their proper place to give 357.

If a polynomial is in base 5, that is powers of 5, the same procedure applies. For example, $3(5) + 4$ in positional notation is 34; $4(5^2) + 2(5) + 3$ written in positional notation is 423. Since one would not like to confuse 423, base 5, with 423, base 10, it is necessary to introduce a scheme of writing numerals to avoid confusion. In a commonly used method, the base is written to the right, such as, 34 (base five) and 423 (base five). If the base is 10, we do not write the base.

Examples—(a) Represent the group as a polynomial in powers 5, and (b) represent the group in positional notation.

a. xxxxx
xxxxx
xxxxx
xxxx

(a) $3(5) + 4$

(b) 34 (base five) *Note:* This is read "3 fives plus 4."

b. ooooooo
ooooooo
ooooooo
ooooooo

(a) $1(5^2) + 3$

(b) 103 (base five) Read as "one twenty-five plus three." Note that the zero must be written in the fives place. Why?

In the base five system, place value is determined by the powers of five just as in the base ten system, place value is determined by the powers of ten.

EXERCISES—In Exercises 1 through 4, (a) represent the groups as a polynomial in powers of 5, and (b) represent the groups in positional notation.

1. xxxxx
xxxx
xxx

2. xxxxxx
xxxx
xx
xx

3. oooooo
oooooo
oooooo
oooooo

4. xxxxxxxxx
xxxxxxxxx
xxxxxxxxx
xxxxxxxxx

5. Represent in positional notation the group obtained by adding 2 to the group in Exercise 2.
6. Represent the group obtained by adding 3 to the group in Exercise 4.
7. Represent in positional notation the sum of the groups in Exercises 4 and 6.
8. Double the group in Exercise 2 and write the new group in positional notation.
9. Combine the groups in Exercises 2 and 4 into a single group and represent the new group in polynomial form, base 5, and positional notation, base 5.

New York World's Fair. Pavilion of New Jersey.

Changing a Numeral from Base Five to a Numeral in Base Ten

A numeral such as 32 (base five) can be changed to base ten by writing $3(5) + 2 = 15 + 2 = 17$.

A numeral such as 123 (base five) may be changed to base 10 by first changing the numeral to polynomial form in base 10, $1(5^2) +$

$2(5) + 3$, and then determining $25 + 10 + 3 = 38$. That is, 38 (base 10) is equal to 123 (base 5).

Example—Change 1304 (base five) to base 10.

$$\begin{aligned} 1304 \text{ (base five)} &= 1(5^3) + 3(5^2) + 0(5) + 4 \\ &= 125 + 75 + 0 + 4 = 204 \end{aligned}$$

EXERCISES—In Exercises 1 through 7, change the numerals to numerals in base 10.

1. 13 (base five)
2. 24 (base five)
3. 32 (base five)
4. 321 (base five)
5. 304 (base five)
6. 440 (base five)
7. 2113 (base five)
8. Write the first twenty counting numbers with numerals in base 5. (Hint: 1, 2, 3, 4, 10, 11, and so on.)
9. Write the largest two digit numeral in base 5.
10. Write the largest three digit numeral in base 5.
11. Is 34 (base five) an odd or even number?
12. Is 33 (base five) an odd or even number?

Review of . . .
NUMBERS AND NUMERALS

1. List the principles of the Hindu-Arabic numeration system.
2. What principle is common to all numeration systems that we have studied?
3. Express the following group in (a) Roman numerals, (b) in the Egyptian system, and (c) in the Hindu-Arabic system.

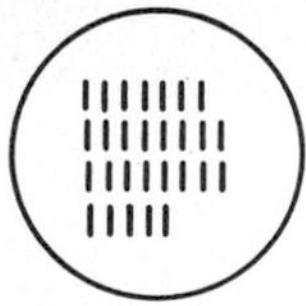

4. Express the following group (a) as a polynomial, base 5, and (b) in positional notation, base 5.

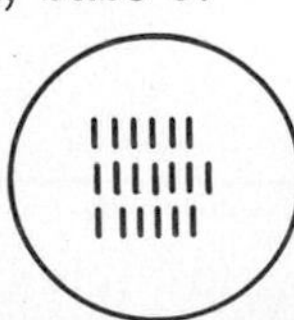

5. What is the base of our numeration system?
6. Write the following by using exponents:
   (a) $A \cdot A \cdot A$
   (b) $3 \cdot 3 \cdot 3 \cdot 3$
   (c) $2 \cdot 2 \cdot 2 \cdot 2 \cdot 2 \cdot 2$
   *(d) $2A \cdot 2A \cdot 2A$
7. Find the value of the following:
   (a) 2^3
   (b) 10^4
   (c) 6^3
   (d) 4^0
   (e) 5^2
   (f) 8^3
8. Write the following using exponents:
   (a) 27 (b) 32 (c) 100 (d) 64
9. Write 3654 as a polynomial.
10. Write 4000 as a polynomial.
11. Write 213 (base five) as a polynomial.
12. Change 32 (base five) to base ten.
13. Change 123 (base five) to base ten.
14. Change 201 (base five) to base ten.
*15. Change 124 (base six) to base ten.
*16. Change 201 (base eight) to base ten.

Chapter Test

1. Express the number of the group (a) in Roman numerals, (b) in polynomial form, base ten, and (c) in positional notation, base ten.

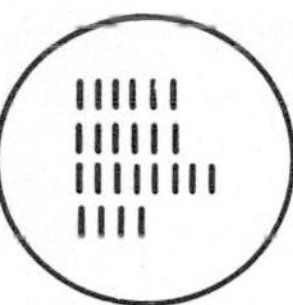

2. Express the number of the following group (a) in polynomial form, base five, and (b) in positional notation, base five.

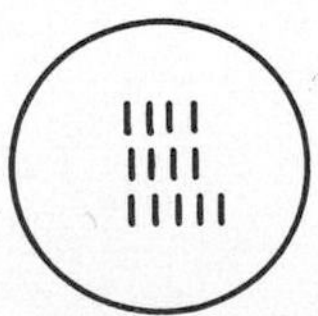

3. What principle makes our system of writing numerals differ from others that we have studied?
4. What is the role of zero in the numeral 504?

5. What is the base of 10^4? What is the exponent?
6. Write 2045 as a polynomial, base ten.
7. Change 42 (base five) to base ten.
8. Is 33 (base five) an odd or even number? Prove your answer.
9. Find the value of 4^3.
10. Change 104 (base five) to base ten.

CHAPTER TWO  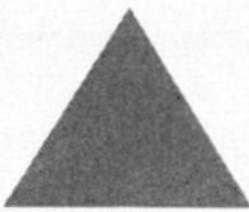  

Exploring Lines

During this year, you will continue to learn more about the processes dealing with numbers and will begin the study of geometry. In geometry, we will study points, lines, angles, surfaces, and solids.

We will study lines in objects about us.

EXERCISE 1. Look about you in the classroom and see how many uses of each kind of line, illustrated below, that you can find.

Straight lines are named according to their position or direction. If a weight is tied to a string, and allowed to hang freely, the string will take a straight up and down position. This is called a plumb line.

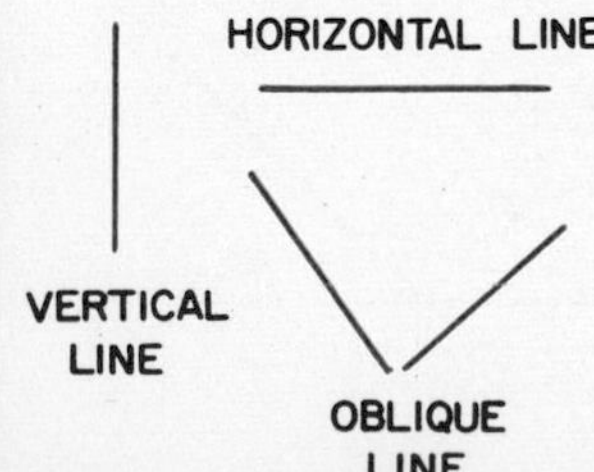

A vertical line has the direction of a plumb line (straight up and down).

A horizontal line has the same direction as the top of the blackboard.

Oblique or slanting lines are neither vertical nor horizontal.

When lines are printed in the book or drawn on paper we may refer to them as vertical or horizontal even though they are not actually in the direction of a plumb line or the top of the blackboard. Usually we mean that such lines would be vertical or horizontal if the book or tablet were held in a vertical position.

EXERCISE 2. How many uses of these lines can you find in your classroom?

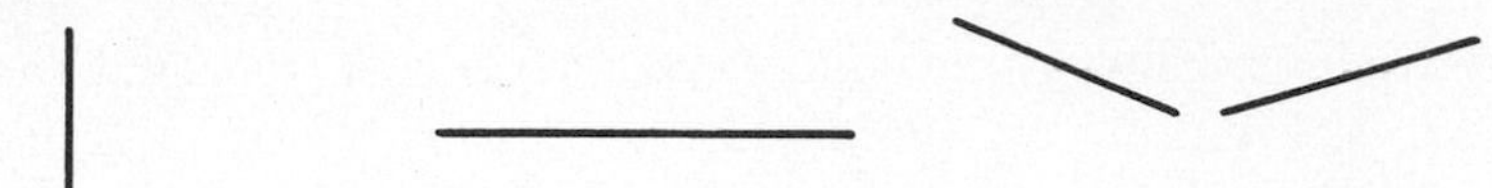

The lines printed on a writing tablet appear to be the same distance apart. These are called *parallel* lines. Parallel lines have the

High school parking lot shows the use of parallel lines.

same direction and never meet. Parallel lines may be vertical, horizontal, or oblique.

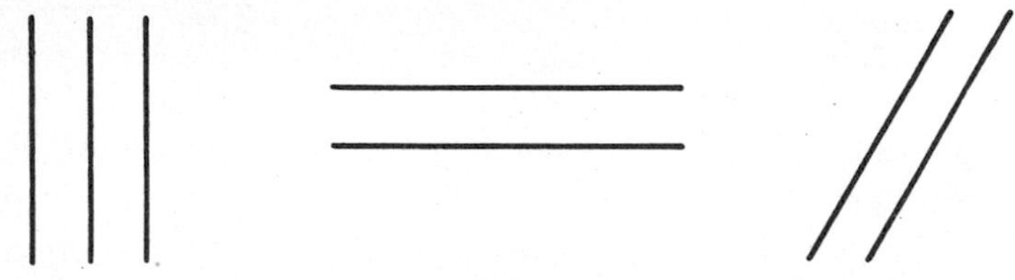

Lines that meet or cross are called intersecting lines.

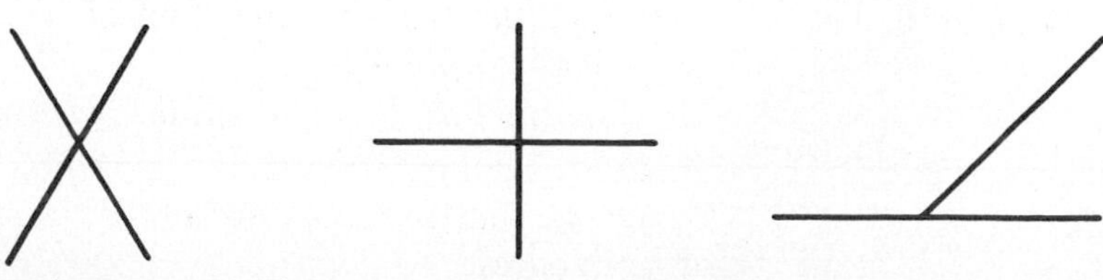

When two lines intersect, like the edges of a box, they are called *perpendicular* lines, and are said to be at right angles.

EXERCISE 3. How many uses of parallel lines and perpendicular lines can you find in your classroom?

Throughout the book, you will find important words listed for you. You should learn to spell these words as well as know what they mean.

Many lines are used in this beautiful window. See if you can find parallel lines, perpendicular lines, horizontal lines, vertical lines, oblique lines, and curved lines.

Words you should understand:

1. horizontal line
2. vertical line
3. oblique line
4. parallel lines
5. perpendicular lines
6. intersecting lines

EXERCISE 4

(a) Choose one of the following and explain the uses of lines in (1) the bedroom, (2) the kitchen, (3) the living room, (4) the yard, (5) the automobile, or (6) the church.

(b) Find in the world about you illustrations of the various kinds of lines.

(c) Copy the statements and fill in the following blanks:

1. Two lines that have the same direction and can never meet are _______ lines.
2. Two lines which meet forming square corners (right angles) are _______ lines.

Constructing Line Segments of Certain Length

Have you noticed that when you draw a line you could extend it in both directions? A straight line has no end points. This means that it is unlimited in extent. The part of a line with two end points is called a line segment. In construction work we always use a straight edge such as a ruler to draw line segments.

Tools you will need:

1. ruler (straight edge) **2. compasses**
3. right angle

EXERCISE 1. With your ruler measure the line segments below and construct lines of the same length on your paper. Notice we use capital letters at the ends of the line segments to name them. We call the first example line segment *AB*. Name your line segments the same as these.

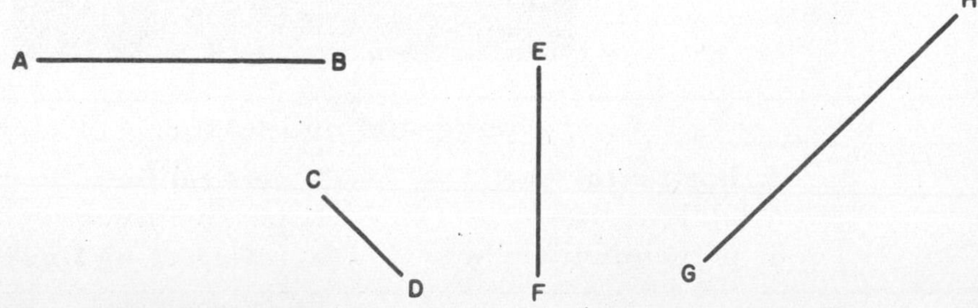

EXERCISE 2. Use compasses and a straight edge to construct a line segment equal in length to another line segment, AB, Exercise 1.

Step 1. Draw line segment MC.

Step 2. To measure line segment AB with compasses put the metal point of the compasses on point A and open the compasses until the point of the pencil is on point B. This length is called a *radius*.

Step 3. To mark the length of this radius on line segment MC, place the point of the compasses on point M. Draw an arc (a curved line made with the compasses) cutting MC at point N.

Check: Measure with a ruler to see if the line segment MN on line segment MC is equal in length to given line segment AB.

EXERCISE 3. Construct a line segment with compasses and straight edge equal in length to line segment CD in Exercise 1.

***EXERCISE 4.** Construct a line segment with compasses and straight edge equal in length to line segment EF in Exercise 1.

***EXERCISE 5.** Construct a line segment with compasses and straight edge equal in length to line segment GH in Exercise 1.

Compasses can be used to draw circles. Any part of the curved line drawn, which is the circle, is called an *arc* of the circle. The distance from the center of the circle to any point on the arc of the circle is the radius of the circle. The word *construct* refers to making a figure with straight edge and compasses.

Bisecting Line Segments with a Ruler

The word bisect is made up of two syllables, bi meaning two and sect meaning parts. The word bisect means to cut anything into two equal parts.

EXERCISE 1. With your ruler, draw line segment AB about two inches in length. Since line segment AB is two inches in length, where will you mark point O so that OA is equal in length to OB? Measure AO with compasses and see if it is equal in length to OB. To measure with compasses put metal point on point A and open

A O B

the compasses so that the pencil point touches point O. Keep the compasses fixed and place the metal point on O and see if the pencil point touches B.

EXERCISE 2. Draw line segment CD with a length of $2\frac{1}{2}$ inches and bisect it with a ruler. How long must each part be?

***EXERCISE 3.** Draw line segment EF with a length of $1\frac{1}{2}$ inches and bisect it with a ruler. How long must each part be?

***EXERCISE 4.** Draw line segment GH with a length of $1\frac{3}{4}$ inches and bisect it with a ruler. How long must each part be?

Bisecting Line Segments with Compasses and Straight Edge

EXERCISE 1. Bisect AB with compasses and straight edge.

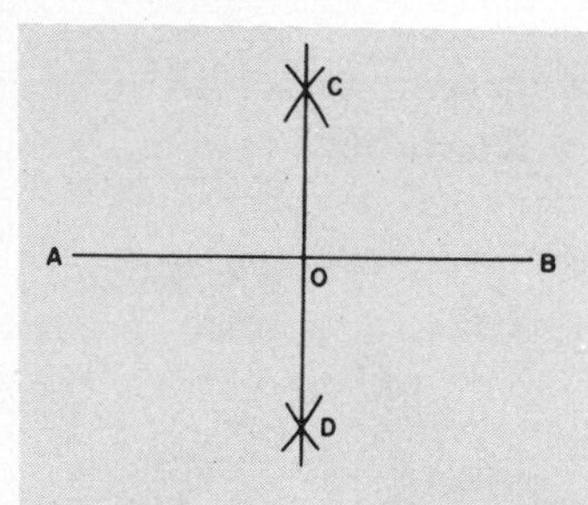

Step 1. Draw line segment AB.

Step 2. Place metal point of the compasses on point A and open the compasses so that the opening is longer than half of AB.

Step 3. With the metal point of your compasses still on point A, draw arcs above and below line segment AB.

Step 4. Using the same radius as in Step 2, place the metal point of the compasses on point B and draw arcs above and below line segment AB cutting the first arcs at points C and D.

Step 5. Connect points C and D with a line crossing line segment AB at O.

Check: Measure OA with your compasses and see if it is equal to OB.

EXERCISE 2. Draw a horizontal line segment EF and bisect it with compasses.

***EXERCISE 3.** Draw a vertical line segment GH and bisect it with compasses.

***EXERCISE 4.** Draw an oblique line segment JK and bisect it with compasses.

Quick Quiz No. 1

1. The underlined digit in 44,<u>4</u>44 represents 4_______.
2. XLII is _______ in Hindu-Arabic numerals.
3. XC means _______ less than 100 or _______.
4. In the number 3,245, which represents the greater value—the 4 or the 3?
5. How many 100's are there in 1000?
6. Round 7,526 to the nearest thousand.
7. Write 62 in Roman numerals.
8. Write the largest number you can with 4 digits.
9. How many digits are there in the number 364?
10. Write the following in Hindu-Arabic numerals:
    Fifty thousand two hundred one.

Keeping Records

In the book there are Quick Quiz exercises. You should keep a record of your rating on the exercises so that you can see if you are improving in your work.

A table or chart is useful in keeping records. A table of number facts which has been collected and classified and which is used to show comparisons is called a statistical table. A drawing or line picture called a graph can be used to show the information in the table. Often a graph gives a more meaningful or clearer picture than the table.

Here and on the next page is Sally Hughes' progress record for the first half year on the Quick Quiz Exercises in both table and graph form.

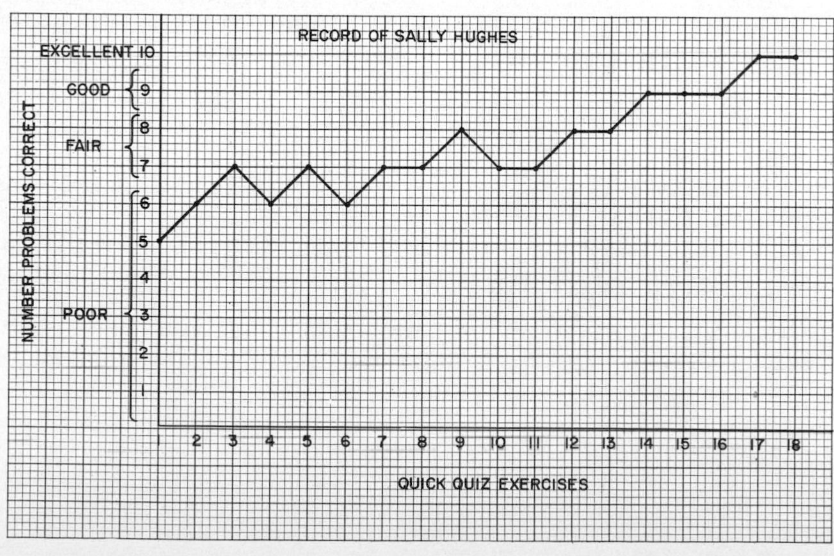

Record of Sally Hughes

Quick Quiz	1	2	3	4	5	6	7	8	9	10	11	12	13	14	15	16	17	18
Correct	5	6	7	6	7	6	7	7	8	7	7	8	8	9	9	9	10	10

Sally used "cross-section" or graph paper to make the graph. She drew two line segments, a vertical line called the vertical axis and a horizontal line called the horizontal axis. The numbers on the horizontal axis represent the numbers of the quizzes and the numbers on the vertical axis represent the number of correct answers. Each point is located by a pair of numbers. The first point is located by 1 on the horizontal axis and 5 on the vertical axis.

Prepare a table and also a graph on which to keep your record. Keep in a safe place and each time you take a Quick Quiz, record your score and watch your progress.

Drawing Perpendicular Line Segments with Straight Edge and Right Angle

EXERCISE 1. Draw a perpendicular to *AB* with straight edge and right angle.

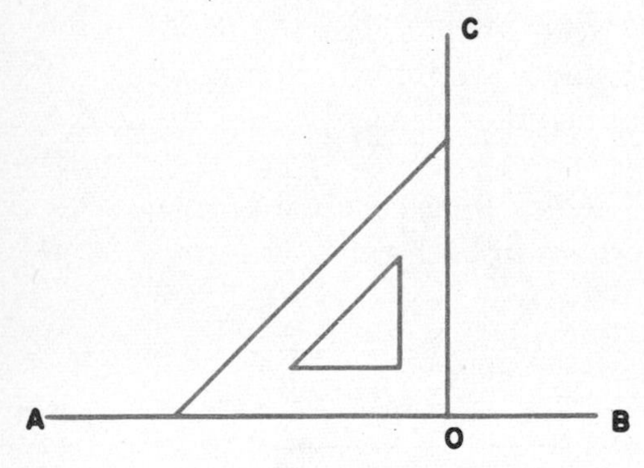

Step 1. Draw line segment *AB* and place point *O* on the line.

Step 2. Place the square corner (right angle) so that the base line lies on *OA* and the right angle is at point *O*.

Step 3. Draw line segment *CO* along the vertical side of the right angle. We write this $CO \perp AB$, and read it as *CO* is perpendicular to *AB*.

EXERCISE 2. Draw a vertical line segment *EF* and place point *O* anywhere on it. Draw a line segment perpendicular to *EF* at point *O* using a straight edge and a right angle.

EXERCISE 3. Draw an oblique line segment *GH* and place point *O* anywhere on it. Draw a line segment perpendicular to *GH* at point *O*.

Notice the lines formed by the pipes in an oil refinery.

Constructing Perpendicular Line Segments with Straight Edge and Compasses

EXERCISE 1. Construct a perpendicular to AB with a straight edge and compasses.

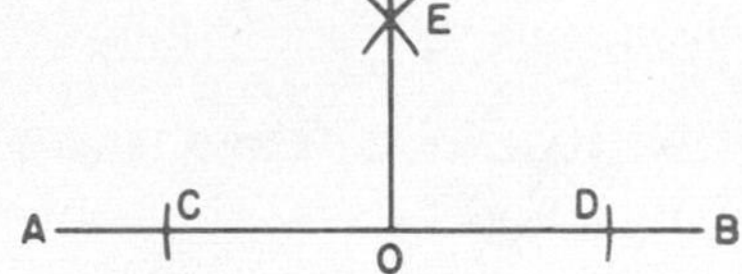

Step 1. Draw line segment AB and locate point O on AB.

Step 2. Place the metal point of the compasses on point O and draw arcs intersecting line segment AB in points C and D.

Step 3. Make the radius of the compasses a little longer than it was in Step 2.

Step 4. Place the metal point of the compasses on point C and draw an arc above segment AB. Then place the metal point on point D and draw an arc which will cross the other arc above segment AB at point E.

Step 5. Connect point E to point O.

Check: See if you have two square corners (right angles). Is EO ____|____ AB?

EXERCISE 2. Draw a horizontal line segment CD and construct a line segment perpendicular to it at point O using compasses and a straight edge.

EXERCISE 3. Draw a vertical line segment EF and construct a line segment perpendicular to it at a point O using compasses and a straight edge.

***EXERCISE 4.** Draw an oblique line segment GH and construct a line segment perpendicular to it at a point O using compasses and straight edge.

Drawing Parallel Line Segments with a Ruler and Right Angle

EXERCISE 1.

Step 1. Place a ruler on your paper.

Step 2. Place the right angle perpendicular to the ruler at about 1 inch and draw line segment AB.

Step 3. Move the right angle down to about $1\frac{1}{2}$ inches and draw line segment CD.

Step 4. Move the right angle down to about 2 inches and draw line segment EF. These appear to be parallel lines.

Could you draw any number of parallel line segments using this method?

EXERCISE 2. Draw two parallel horizontal line segments about 1 inch apart using the above method.

EXERCISE 3. Draw two oblique parallel line segments about $\frac{3}{4}$ inches apart.

Review of . . .
LINES

1. Use each of the following words to describe line segments in your classroom.

   (a) straight line (b) vertical line (c) horizontal line
   (d) oblique line (e) parallel lines (f) perpendicular lines

2. Are parallel lines always horizontal?
3. Is a vertical line always perpendicular to a horizontal line?
4. Name these line segments:

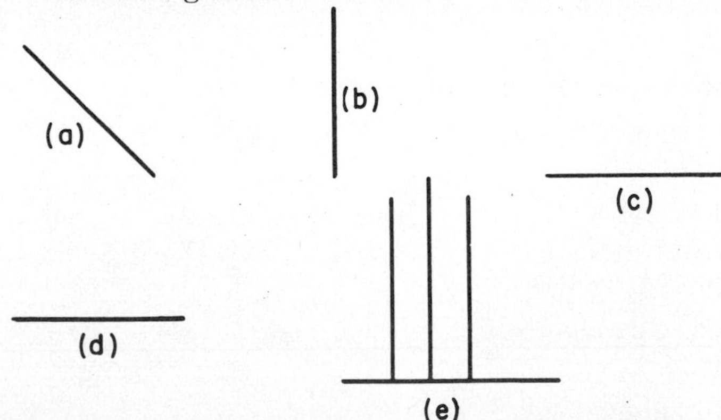

5. Estimate the length of each of the following line segments to the nearest inch. Then measure each to the nearest quarter of an inch.

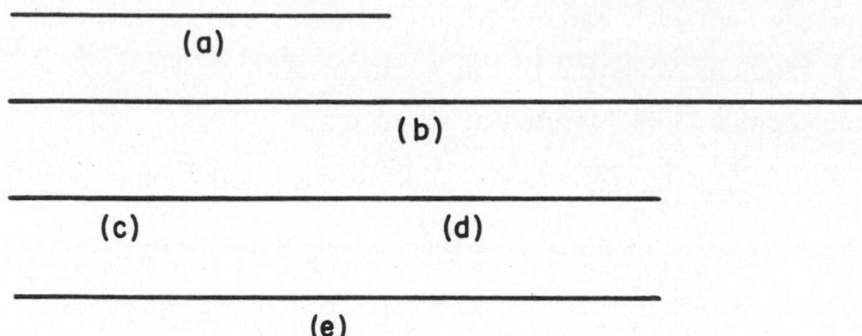

6. Draw a three inch line segment and bisect it using the ruler.
7. Bisect the line segment drawn in Example 6 with compasses.
8. Draw an oblique line segment AB and at point O on the line, draw a perpendicular to AB.
9. Draw a horizontal line segment DE and at point O on the line, construct a perpendicular to line segment DE using compasses.
10. Draw three parallel oblique line segments about $\frac{1}{2}$ inch apart.

Chapter Test

Part I

Tell whether the following are true or false statements.

1. Perpendicular lines form right angles.
2. Parallel lines are always horizontal.
3. To bisect a line segment means to cut the line segment into two equal parts.
4. Parallel lines have the same direction and can meet.
5. A straight line is unlimited in length.
6. Oblique lines can be parallel.
7. A line segment is definite in length and has two end points.
8. Compasses can be used to bisect a line segment.
9. A vertical line which intersects a horizontal line is perpendicular to it.
10. All perpendicular lines are vertical.

Part II

Construct the following:

1. Line segments AB and CD perpendicular to each other.
2. Line segment MN parallel to line segment OP.
3. Line segment RS equal to line segment XY.
4. Line segment VW bisected at point O.

CHAPTER **THREE**    

Exploring Angles

We have used the right angle in drawing lines. Let us see what we can discover about angles. Place a point somewhere near the center of a piece of paper. Lay your pencil flat in a horizontal position on this paper, with one end of the pencil on this point as in Figure 1. Now rotate your pencil on the paper to a vertical position on the paper as in Figure 2.

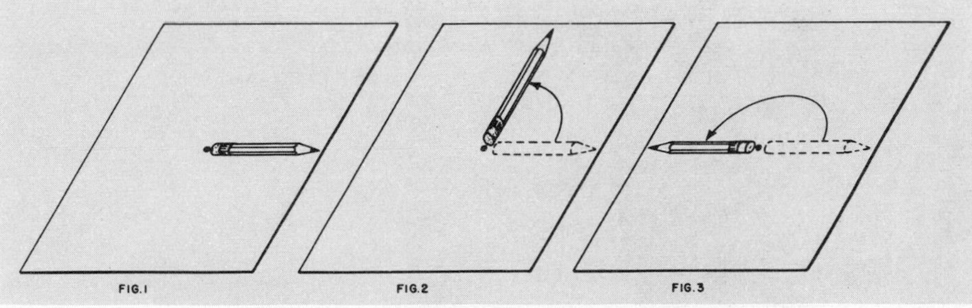

Your pencil has rotated through a right angle. Continue to rotate your pencil until it is again in a horizontal position as in Figure 3.

EXERCISES

1. Through how many right angles have you rotated your pencil?

2. Continue rotating your pencil until it is back in its original position. Through how many right angles have you now rotated your pencil?
3. Now try the same thing with your ruler. Rotate the ruler to a vertical position. Through how many right angles has the ruler been rotated?
4. Continue the rotating in Exercise 3 until the ruler is back in its original position. Through how many right angles has the ruler now been rotated?
5. To make a complete rotation about a point, back to an original position, through how many right angles would an object be rotated?
6. Did the length of the pencil or the length of the ruler affect the amount of rotation?

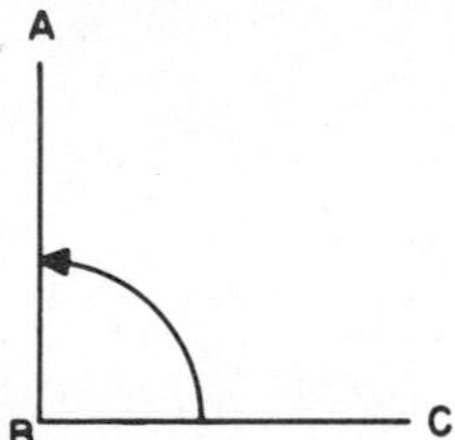

The line segments forming the angle are called the *sides* of the angle. AB and BC are the sides of this angle. The intersection of the line segments forming the angle is called the *vertex* of the angle.

Mechanical drawing devices.

1. An angle between lines may be described in terms of rotation.

2. The size of the angle depends on the amount of rotation. The size does not depend upon the length of the lines that form the angle.

Measuring a Right Angle

The amount of turning that is made in rotating a line is usually measured in degrees. One degree is the measure of $\frac{1}{90}$ of a right angle. The symbol for degree is a small circle placed to the right and above a number. One degree is written 1°.

An instrument for measuring angles is called a protractor. The protractor shown here is half a circle divided into 180 parts. Each part is one degree. Point O is the center of the circle.

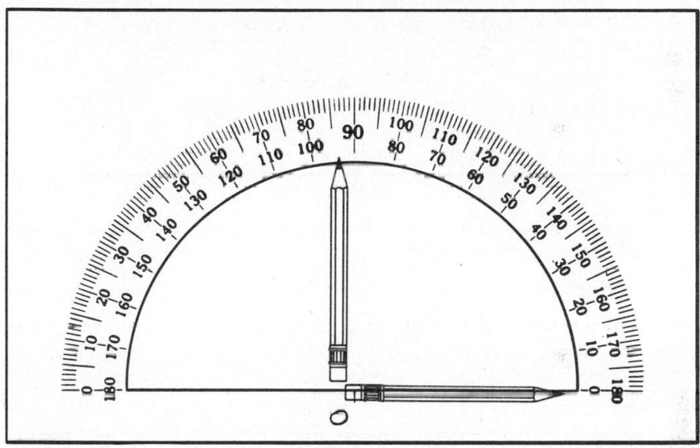

Place your pencil so that the eraser end is at point O or the center of your protractor. Lay your pencil so that the point is to the right and the pencil touches zero on the scale. Now rotate your pencil to a vertical position on the protractor. You have rotated it through a right angle. Your protractor tells you through how many degrees you have rotated the pencil.

EXERCISES

1. Beginning at zero, through how many degrees did you rotate your pencil to reach a vertical position?
2. How many degrees are there in a right angle?
3. One degree is what part of a right angle?

1. **There are ninety degrees (written 90°) in a right angle.**
2. **One degree is $\frac{1}{90}$ of a right angle.**

Why are there two sets of numbers on a protractor? Place the eraser of your pencil at point *O* or the center of your protractor and point your pencil to the left and have it touch zero. Now rotate the pencil to a vertical position on the protractor.

4. Through how many degrees, beginning at zero, have you rotated your pencil? The scale you read depends on which way you rotate the pencil.
5. If there are 90° in one right angle, how many degrees are there in two right angles?
6. How many degrees are there in three right angles?
7. How many degrees are there in four right angles or one complete rotation about a point?

Kinds of Angles

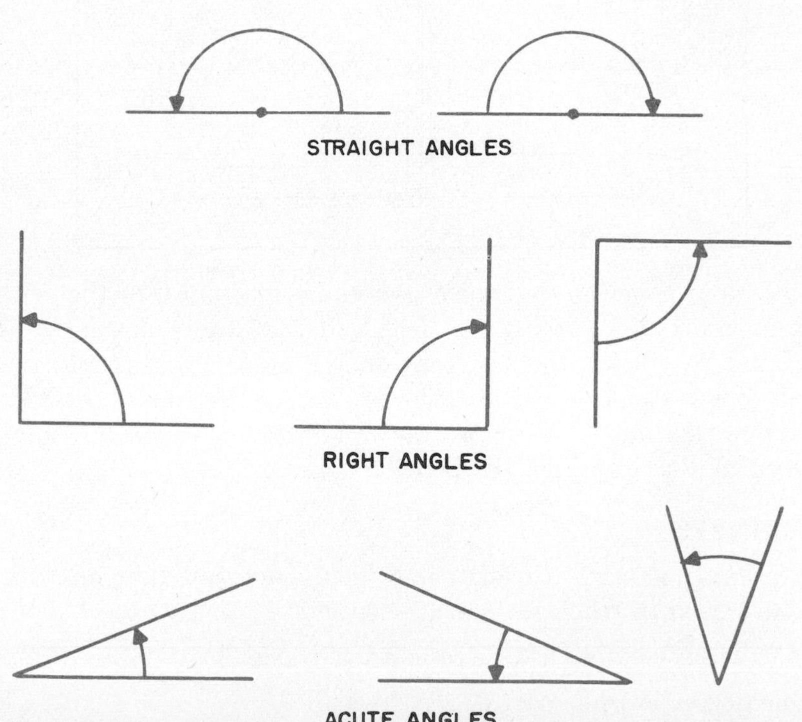

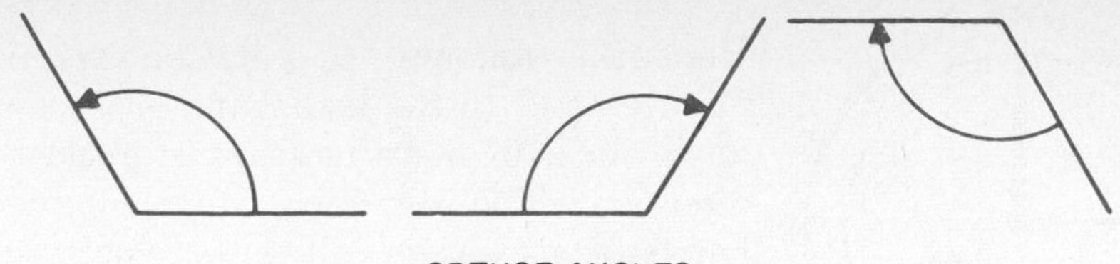

OBTUSE ANGLES

EXERCISES.—Copy these statements and fill in the blanks.

1. A ______ angle is an angle of 90°.
2. An ______ angle is an angle smaller than a right angle or less than 90°.
3. An ______ angle is an angle larger than a right angle or more than 90°, but smaller than two right angles or less than 180°.
4. A ______ angle is an angle of 180°.

FIG. 1 FIG. 2 FIG. 3 FIG. 4

5. Name the kinds of angles formed by the hands of the clock in Figs. 1, 2, 3, and 4.
6. How many minutes are required for the minute hand of a clock to rotate through (a) one right angle? (b) two right angles? (c) three right angles? and (d) four right angles?

Here the amount of rotation from the minute hand to the hour hand is three right angles or 270° if we measure in a clockwise direction. The direction traveled by the hands of a clock is called the clockwise direction. An angle greater than 180° is sometimes called a *reflex* angle.

7. Report your observations of the following angles to the class:
   (a) The angles formed by the rotation of the floor indicator of an elevator.
   (b) The angles formed by the crossing of streets or highways near your home.

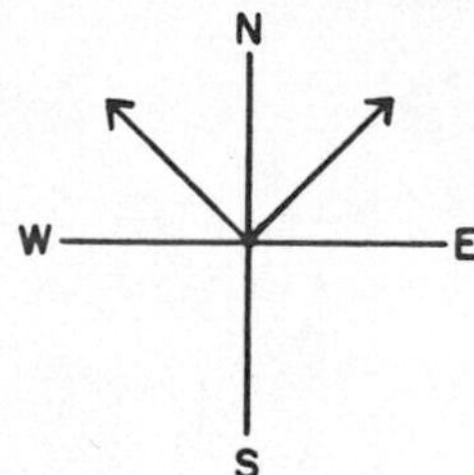

   (c) The angles of direction made by airplanes.
   (d) Angles found in constructing buildings.
   (e) Angles seen in the classroom.
   (f) Angles used in designs.
   (g) Angles around the home.

Angles can be named several ways. The symbol often used for angle is ($\angle$).

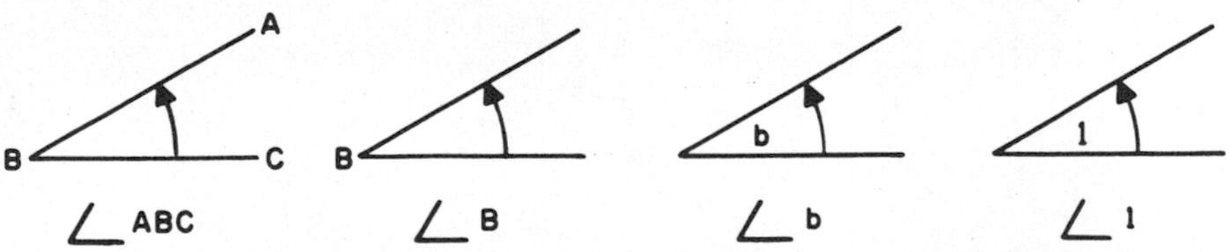

Capital letters, small letters, and numbers can be used to name an angle. When three capital letters are used, the vertex letter is in the middle. When one capital letter is used, it is the letter on the vertex. If small letters or numbers are used, they are placed between the sides of the angle.

8. Draw four angles and name each one a different way.

Drawing and Measuring Angles

EXERCISE 1. Draw an angle of 30°.

Step 1. Draw line segment *MN* (any length).

Step 2. Place center of protractor on *M*, with zero on *MN*.

Step 3. From zero, follow scale until you reach 30°, and mark a point *P* on your paper. Notice which scale you follow.

Step 4. Remove protractor and connect point *P* with *M*. This angle shows a measured counter-clockwise rotation.

EXERCISE 2. Draw an angle of 30° which is measured right or clockwise (the same direction as the hands of the clock).

EXERCISE 3. Draw an angle of 60°. What kind of angle is this?

EXERCISE 4. Draw an angle of 90°. What kind of angle is this?

EXERCISE 5. Draw an angle of 120°. What kind of angle is this?

EXERCISE 6. Draw an angle of 45°. What kind of angle is this?

EXERCISE 7. Draw an angle of 135°. What kind of angle is this?

EXERCISE 8. Measure $\angle RST$.

Step 1. Estimate the size of $\angle RST$.

Step 2. Place center of protractor on *S* with zero on line segment *ST*.

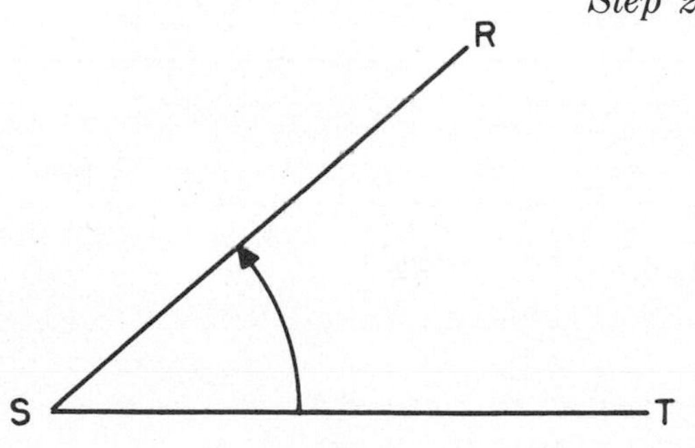

Step 3. Follow the scale from zero until you come to where the line segment *SR* touches the scale. (If line segment is not long enough, extend the line beyond the segment.)

Step 4. Read the scale.

(a) $\angle RST$ measures ______ degrees.
How good was your estimate?

(b) *RST* is an ______ angle.

EXERCISE 9. Measure $\angle MOP$.

Step 1. Estimate the size of $\angle MOP$.

Step 2. Place center of protractor on O with zero on line segment MO.

Step 3. Follow the scale from zero until you come to where line segment OP touches the scale. (Extend line if necessary.)

Step 4. Read the scale.

(a) $\angle MOP$ measures ______ degrees.
How good was your estimate?

(b) $\angle MOP$ is an ______ angle.

EXERCISE 10. Measure the following angles to the nearest degree and tell what kind of angle each is.

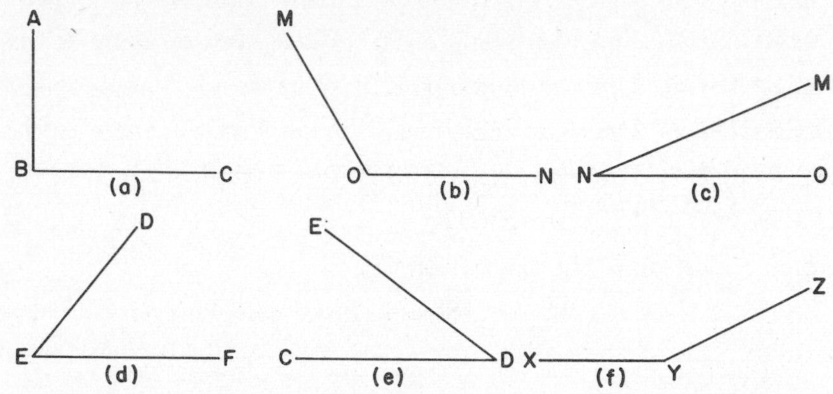

EXERCISE 11. Draw angles that you estimate to be 90°, 45°, 120°, 10°, and 75°. Measure them with your protractor to check your estimate. Find your error for each angle and determine whether the angle was too large or too small. If your error is less than 5°, you have done very well.

Quick Quiz No. 2

1. How many million in a billion?
2. If you know the sum of two numbers and one of the numbers, how do you find the other?
3. How many minutes are there in a day?
4. Which is longer—$2\frac{1}{2}$ feet or 27 inches?
5. $\frac{1}{4}$ of a foot equals how many inches?
6. $\frac{3}{4}$ of a pound equals how many ounces?

7. $\frac{3}{16} + 1\frac{5}{16} = (?)$

8. What are the next three numbers in this series?
   1 10 19 28 37 ____ ____ ____

9. 0.02 is read 2________.

10. What is the sum: 1.9 + 2.1 + 1.4?

More About Angles

EXERCISES

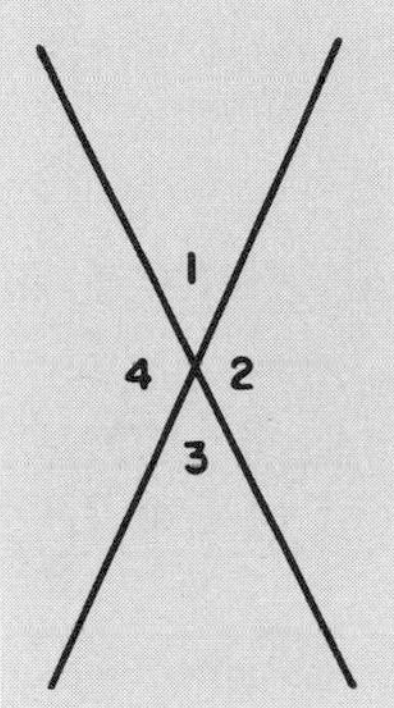

1. In this figure, angles 1 and 3 are called vertical angles. Measure angles 1 and 3 with a protractor. What do you find about their size? Vertical angles appear in pairs, have the same vertex, and their sides extend in opposite directions from the common vertex. Vertical angles are formed in pairs by intersecting lines.
2. Angles 2 and 4 are also vertical angles. Measure angles 2 and 4. What do you find about their size?
3. Draw a pair of vertical angles on your paper and measure them.
4. Draw a different pair of vertical angles and measure them. What do you believe to be true about the size of vertical angles?

Vertical angles are equal in size.

5. In this figure, angles 1 and 2 are adjacent angles because they have the same vertex and a common side between them. Name three other pairs of adjacent angles.
6. Draw two adjacent right angles.
7. Draw two adjacent acute angles.

8. Draw two adjacent obtuse angles.

9. If $\angle CBD = 60°$, draw $\angle DBA$ so that their sum is 90°.

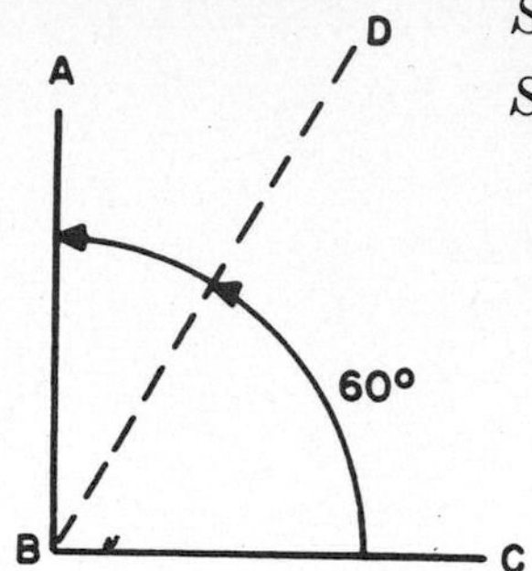

Step 1. Draw $\angle CBD = 60°$.

Step 2. Draw $\angle ABC = 90°$.

The sum of $\angle ABD$ and $\angle DBC$ is 90°. These angles are called *complementary* angles.

$\angle ABD$ is the complement of $\angle DBC$.
$\angle DBC$ is the complement of $\angle ABD$.

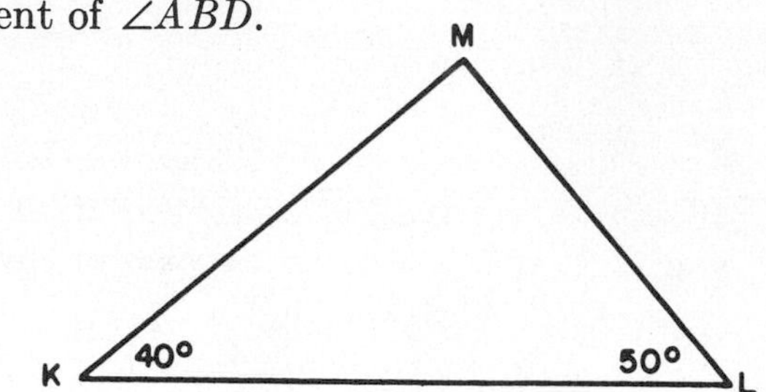

Complementary angles do not have to be adjacent as in the figure above. $\angle K$ and $\angle L$ are also complementary angles.

Complementary angles are two angles whose sum is equal to 90°. Each angle is the complement of the other.

10. Copy and fill in the following blanks.
    (a) The complement of a 60° angle is a ______ angle.
    (b) The complement of an 80° angle is a ______ angle.
    (c) The complement of a 20° angle is a ______ angle.
    (d) The complement of a 16° angle is a ______ angle.
    (e) The complement of an 87° angle is a ______ angle.
    (f) The complement of a 49° angle is a ______ angle.

11. If $\angle CBD = 40°$, draw $\angle DBA$ so that their sum is 180°.
    (a) The sum of $\angle CBD$ and $\angle ABD$ equals 180°. These angles are called *supplementary* angles.

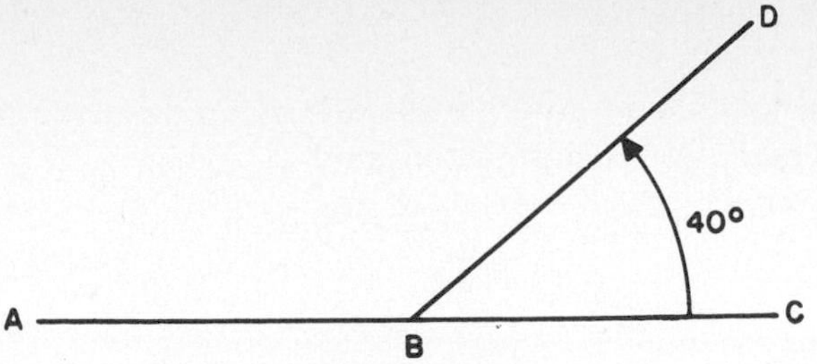

$\angle CBD$ is the supplement of $\angle ABD$.
$\angle ABD$ is the supplement of $\angle CBD$.

Supplementary angles do not have to be adjacent as in the figure above.

Runways at an airport show use of angles.

Supplementary angles are two angles whose sum is equal to 180°. Each angle is the supplement of the other.

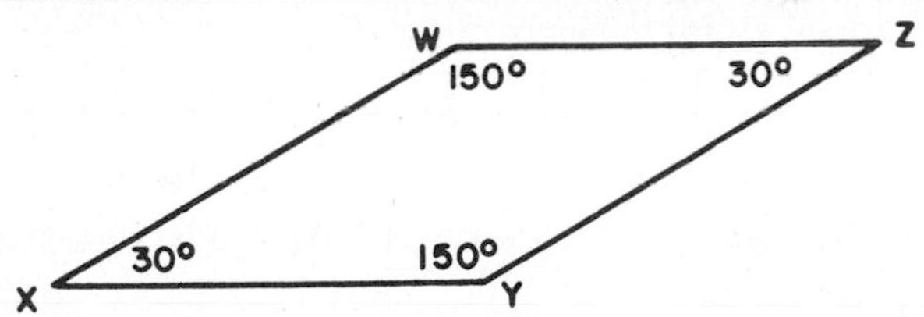

Angles X and Y are supplementary.
Angles Z and W are supplementary.

12. Copy and fill in the following blanks.
    (a) The supplement of an 80° angle is a ______ angle.
    (b) The supplement of a 120° angle is a ______ angle.
    (c) The supplement of a 140° angle is a ______ angle.
    (d) The supplement of a 67° angle is a ______ angle.
    (e) The supplement of a 135° angle is a ______ angle.
    (f) The supplement of a 149° angle is a ______ angle.

13. In the following figure which pair of angles is complementary and which pair is supplementary?

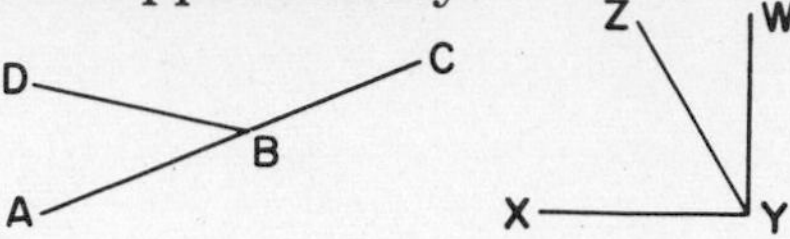

14. Bisect a 60° angle using a protractor.

To bisect an angle means to divide the angle into two equal angles.

15. Draw a 50° angle and bisect it with a protractor.

16. Draw a 90° angle and bisect it with a protractor.

17. Draw a 120° angle and bisect it with a protractor.

*18. Draw any size angle and bisect it with a protractor.

*19. Bisect a 60° angle using compasses and a straight edge.

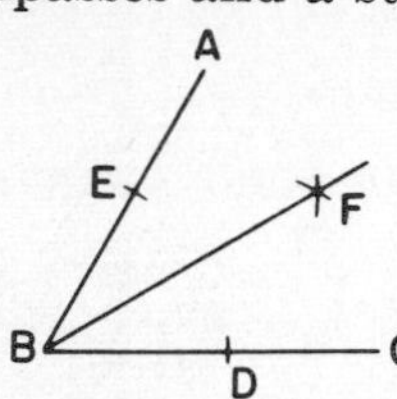

Step 1. Draw $\angle ABC = 60°$.

Step 2. Place metal point of compass on B and draw arcs cutting AB at E and BC at D.

Step 3. Place metal point of compass first at point D and then at point E and draw equal arcs intersecting at point F.

Step 4. Connect point F with point B.

Check: Measure $\angle ABF$ and $\angle CBF$ to see if they are equal.

*20. Draw a 50° angle and bisect it with compasses and a straight edge. Use a protractor to see if the two angles are equal.

*21. Draw a 90° angle and bisect it with compasses and a straight edge. Use a protractor to see if you have bisected it.

*22. Draw a 140° angle and bisect it. Check.

*23. Draw any size angle and bisect it. Check.

Terms you should understand:

1. angle 2. right angle 3. acute angle
4. obtuse angle 5. straight angle
6. complementary angles 7. supplementary angles

Review of . . .
ANGLES

1. Name the different kinds of angles studied in this chapter.
2. At what angle do most city streets intersect?
3. What instrument is used to measure the size of an angle?
4. What unit of measure have we used in measuring angles?
5. How many degrees are there in a right angle?
6. How many degrees are there in a straight angle?
7. What name is given to angles that measure less than 90°?
8. What name is given to angles that measure more than 90° and less than 180°?
9. What name is given to a pair of angles, if the sum of the angles is equal to 180°?
10. The sum of complementary angles is how many degrees?
11. Is the size of an angle increased by extending the sides of the angle?
12. Through how many degrees will a minute hand of a clock turn in:
    (a) 10 minutes? (b) 15 minutes? (c) 30 minutes? (d) 60 minutes?
13. Estimate the number of degrees in each of the following angles. Then measure them with the protractor to the nearest degree.

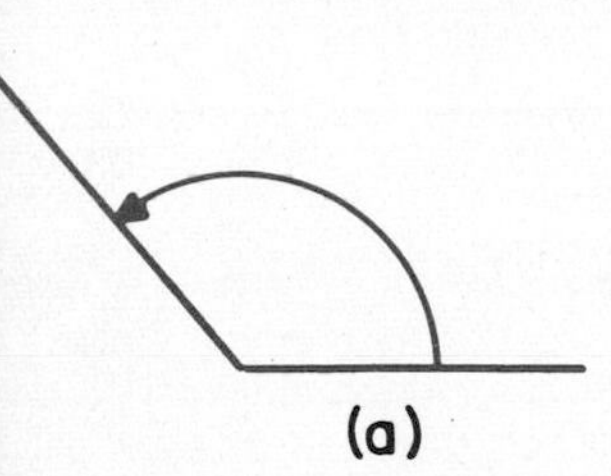
(a)

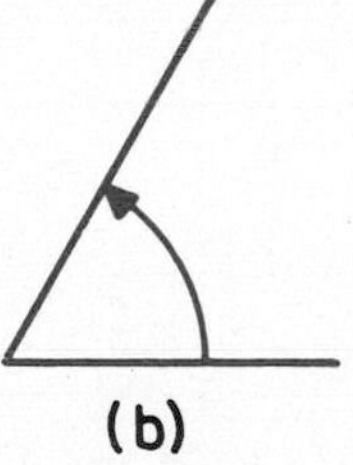
(b)

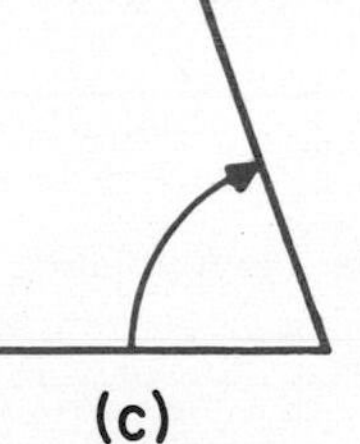
(c)

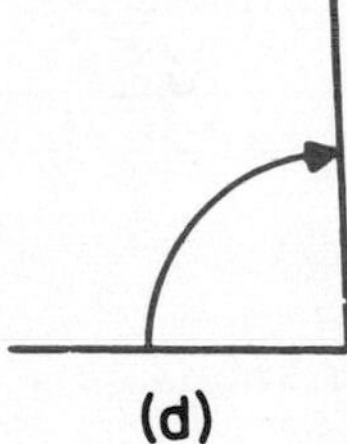
(d)

14. An airplane heading south changed its heading to southwest. Through how many degrees did it turn?
15. Two motorboats left a boat dock at the same time. One headed northeast and the other east. What is the name and size of the angle between the paths of the two boats?
16. John was facing south and he turned directly west. Through how many degrees did he turn?

Chapter Test

1. Draw the following angles using a protractor:
   (a) an angle of 80°. (b) an angle of 110°.
2. How many degrees are there in the following?
   (a) 3 right angles (b) $\frac{1}{2}$ right angle
   (c) $\frac{1}{3}$ right angle (d) $2\frac{1}{2}$ right angles
3. Copy and fill in the names of the angles:
   (a) An angle of 15° is called an ______ angle.
   (b) An angle of 91° is called an ______ angle.
   (c) An angle of 180° is called a ______ angle.
   (d) An angle of 215° is called a ______ angle.
4. The complement of an angle of 60° is an angle of ______.
5. The supplement of an angle of 115° is an angle of ______.
6. John and Bill start from the same point. John walks north and Bill northeast. What is the name and size of the angle between the paths of the two boys?
7. A plane heading south turned right through 135°. In what direction was it then heading?
8. Draw a 90° angle and bisect it with a protractor.
9. Draw a 45° angle and bisect it with straight edge and compasses.
10. Draw a 135° angle and bisect it with straight edge and compasses.

CHAPTER FOUR

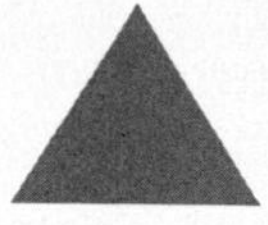

Addition

On the reading shelf of Randall's room at school, there are 75 books of history and science and 23 books of fiction. To find the total number of books on the reading shelf, we would add.

75 + 23 = 98		
or 75	or	23
23	addends	75
98	←sum→	98

To add 75 and 23, we add the 5 ones and the 3 ones. This is 8 ones. We then add the 7 tens and the 2 tens. This is 9 tens. The number of books is 98.

The numbers added are called the addends.
The answer in addition is called the sum.

EXERCISES

1. Find the sums.

(a) 6 + 7 (b) 7 + 6 (c) 12 + 24 (d) 24 + 12 (e) 36 + 25 + 42

(f) 42 + 25 + 36

2. Do the answers to (a) and (b) differ? (c) and (d)? (e) and (f)?

3. Does the order in which the addends are written make a difference in the sum?

You should know the one hundred addition facts. If you are slow in addition, practice with these facts should be helpful to you.

How accurate are you in adding, and how fast can you add? Estimating your answer should increase your accuracy. Perhaps the method of grouping will increase your speed.

Example

4000	estimated sum
1025	
1175	
914	addends
863	
3977	total or sum

First estimate your answer by rounding each addend to the nearest hundred. 1025 rounds to 1000, 1175 rounds to 1200, 914 to 900, and 863 to 900. The estimated sum is 4000.

Next, look for combinations of ten and then for any other combinations.

In the first column 5 + 5 are 10 and 4 + 3 are 7; 10 + 7 = 17, so the sum is 17 ones or 1 ten and 7 ones. In the second column the sum of 1 ten, 2 tens, and 7 tens is 10 tens. With the other numbers the sum of this column is 17 tens or 1 hundred and 7 tens. In the third column, the sum of 1 hundred and 9 hundred is 10 hundred. With the other numbers the sum of this column is 19 hundreds or 1 thousand and 9 hundred. The sum of the fourth column is 3 thousands. Compare your sum with the estimated sum.

"The Mathematician" by Rembrandt.

EXERCISES—Add by finding groups of 10. Check each exercise.

Addition may be checked by using other groupings of the addends than those used in finding the sum. Addition also can be checked by adding downward if the original addition was upward, or if the adding was downward, one can check by adding upward.

1.	2.	3.	4.	5.
9	7	8	5	4
3	8	7	2	4
4	5	9	7	3
2	3	1	1	2
1	1	3	5	6

6.	7.	8.	9.
786	496	567	648
294	827	821	296
381	134	433	384
645	233	875	489

10.	11.	12.	13.
598	796	875	365
284	344	482	848
346	851	958	291
482	962	149	375

*14.	*15.	*16.	*17.
822	265	379	178
468	444	400	454
751	300	382	286
964	906	196	422
872	214	144	181

Words you should understand:

1. addends 2. sum

Test on Addition of Integers

Add on a separate piece of paper. Check each exercise:

1.	2.	3.	4.
9	6	29	74
1	3	46	28
8	2	71	32
2	5	83	96
6	4		

5. 487
292
281
386

6. 4,721
8,764
2,945
3,621
8,721

7. 15,872
46,726
37,854
16,782

8. 48,962
93,428
67,841
47,826

9. 124,567
378,216
457,183
291,475

10. 1,286,427
2,475,872
1,972,654

If you want to increase your speed and accuracy, work on exercises, Appendix page 289.

Practice in Adding

1. The J. B. Green family kept a record of the amount of gasoline they used each week in July. The first week they used 9 gallons, the second week 12 gallons, the third week 18 gallons, and the fourth week 22 gallons. How many gallons did they use in July?

How to solve Problem 1:

Step 1. Read the problem carefully to know what facts the problem deals with and what you are to find.

Step 2. Estimate the answer using round numbers to the nearest 10. This you can do quickly without using your pencil: $10 + 10 + 20 + 20$ or 60 gallons.

Step 3. Write the numbers in a convenient form, letting N be the number you are trying to find. Use the right side of your paper for the computation.

$N = 9 + 12 + 18 + 22 = 61$ 60 gal. estimated answer

Thus 61 gallons of gasoline were used by the J. B. Green family in July.

9
12
18
22
61

Step 4. Check your work. Compare your answer with the estimated answer. Label and explain your answers.

2. The Franklin boys sold apples from their father's orchard. During one week they sold the following number of bushels: Monday, 17 bushels; Tuesday, 37 bushels; Wednesday, 18

bushels; Thursday, 26 bushels; Friday, 52 bushels; and Saturday, 39 bushels. What was the total number of bushels the boys sold during that week?

3. The Bar H Ranch had 225 acres planted in wheat, 107 acres in corn, 19 acres in soybeans, and 14 acres in alfalfa. How many acres were under cultivation at the ranch?
4. Mr. Sam Miller owned four farms containing the following number of acres: 240 acres, 180 acres, 320 acres, and 65 acres. How many acres did he own in all?
5. The Smith family took a five day automobile trip. The first day they drove 462 miles, the second day 465 miles, the third day 440 miles, the fourth day 383 miles, and the last day 375 miles. How many miles did they travel?
6. In a school library there are 490 books of science, 1,242 books of history, 1,364 books of fiction, and 947 books on miscellaneous subjects. How many books are there in the library?

*7. The first day enrollments of five junior high schools were:

Davis Junior High	1,146 pupils
Jefferson Junior High	1,423 pupils
Lincoln Junior High	946 pupils
Roosevelt Junior High	1,464 pupils
Washington Junior High	765 pupils

What was the total junior high enrollment on the first day?

*8. The paid attendance at the Tulsa State Fair was as follows:

Saturday	10,210 people
Sunday	14,165 people
Monday	8,462 people
Tuesday	9,741 people
Wednesday	8,465 people
Thursday	7,456 people
Friday	10,826 people

What was the total paid attendance?

Reading Large Numbers

2
20
200
2000
20000
22222

Hindu-Arabic numerals are made up of the digits 1, 2, 3, 4, 5, 6, 7, 8, 9, and 0. The position a digit occupies in a numeral indicates its value. In the number 22,222 each 2 represents a different value because of the place it occupies.

Place Value Chart

Billions			Millions			Thousands			Units		
Hundred billions	Ten billions	Billions	Hundred millions	Ten millions	Millions	Hundred thousands	Ten thousands	Thousands	Hundreds	Tens	Units (ones)
1	2	3	4	5	6	7	8	9	1	0	2

123, 456, 789, 102 is read 123 billion, 456 million, 789 thousand, 102. So that it can be read easily, the digits are grouped by commas into groups of three, each beginning at the right. In this number, zero was placed in tens place to show there were no tens. Zero is used in this case as a place holder.

8,456 is read eight thousand, four hundred fifty-six. One does not use "and" in reading any of the numerals in the exercises below.

ORAL EXERCISES—Read these numerals.

1. 9,642
2. 8,901
3. 29,415
4. 79,843
5. 121,219
6. 182,471
7. 6,125,041
8. 26,182,004
9. 47,002,000

*10. 9,241,643,182
*11. 12,702,001,000
*12. 462,821,931,002

EXERCISES—Write in Hindu-Arabic notation:

1. One thousand, one hundred seven.
2. Sixteen thousand, five hundred twenty-six.
3. Thirty-nine thousand, fifty-five.
4. Fifty-one thousand, two.
5. Ninety-nine thousand, nine hundred ninety-nine.
6. Six million, one hundred four thousand, sixty-four.
7. Nineteen million, five thousand, five.
8. Thirty-six million, twenty-nine thousand, sixteen.
9. Eleven million, eleven thousand, eleven.
10. One hundred million, one hundred thousand, one hundred.

*11. Two billion, five hundred six million, fifty-four thousand, one hundred nine.

*12. Three hundred two billion, one hundred sixty-nine million, four hundred thirty-two thousand, one hundred ninety-nine.

Fun with Numbers

1. Cross out some of the digits so the sum of the columns will be 1111.

```
111
333
555
777
999
---
```

2. Take any even number like 12 and see how many combinations of two numbers will have the sum, 12. Try this on at least two more even numbers. Now try this on at least three odd integers.

   Begin with the combination of the number and zero as $\begin{array}{r}12\\ \underline{0}\\ 12\end{array}$. See if you can determine by looking at a number how many combinations of two numbers will have this sum.

3. Supply the missing numbers so that the sums will be correct:

(a)	(b)	(c)
6	7	42
9	9	56
5	6	81
?	?	?
28	32	202

(d)	*(e)	*(f)
95	247	756
74	156	843
81	375	721
?	?	?
309	990	2,331

Quick Quiz No. 3

1. $16 + 4 + 2 + 6 = ?$
2. $26 + ? = 44$
3. What date is this? MDCCLXXVI
4. What kinds of quantities can you add?
5. Is 26 an integer?
6. What is the sum of 45 and 37?

7. Add 9 to each of the following: 25, 34, 16, 87, 99.
8. How much did Mary spend if she spent $4.50 for a hat and 15¢ for a ribbon?
9. Write the digits of the Hindu-Arabic number system.
10. If you know the amount you have spent in each of 3 stores, how can you find the total amount you spent?

Rounding Numbers

When Mary Conwell was asked how many pupils were enrolled in her junior high school, she said the enrollment was about 800. The actual count was 812. She said the enrollment in the neighboring junior high was about 900 when the actual count was 860. How did she arrive at these numbers?

The following questions may help you answer this:

1. What number is halfway between 800 and 900?
2. Is 812 more or less than this number?
3. Is 812 nearer 800 than 900?
4. Is 860 nearer 900 than 800?

When we express numbers to the nearest ten, hundred, thousand, ten thousand, hundred thousand, and so forth, we are rounding numbers. Numbers obtained by rounding other numbers are not entirely accurate, but they are often convenient to use.

Example—What is the number halfway between the pair of numbers, 70–80?

The number halfway between 70 and 80 is 75.

EXERCISES—In the following what number is halfway between each pair?

1. 10–20
2. 20–30
3. 30–40
4. 50–60
5. 200–300
6. 700–800
7. 500–600
8. 900–1000
9. 9,000–10,000
10. 10,000–20,000
11. 70,000–80,000
12. 20,000–30,000

*13. 1,700,000–1,800,000

*14. 1,479,600–1,479,700

EXERCISES—If you round the numbers below to the nearest hundred, which numbers will be 900? What will the remaining numbers be? Be sure to compare each number with the halfway number between 800 and 900. We will agree that 850 will be rounded to 900. Round the following numbers to the nearest hundred.

1. 813 2. 890 3. 825 4. 841 5. 806

6. 860 7. 833 8. 865 9. 808 *10. 850

Notice the digit underlined in each number below. This is the first digit to be dropped in rounding the number.

Examples

1. 342 rounded to nearest ten is 340.
2. 345 rounded to nearest ten is 350.
3. 4,432 rounded to nearest hundred is 4,400.
4. 4,462 rounded to nearest hundred is 4,500.
5. 17,365 rounded to nearest thousand is 17,000.
6. 17,875 rounded to nearest thousand is 18,000.

Suggestions for rounding whole numbers:

1. **If the first digit to be dropped is less than five, replace this digit and digits to the right of it with zeros.**
2. **If the first digit to be dropped is 5 or greater than 5, increase the next digit to the left by one and replace digits dropped with zeros.**

EXERCISES

1. Round to the nearest ten.
   (a) 82 (b) 75 (c) 61 (d) 89
2. Round to nearest hundred.
   (a) 542 (b)650 (c) 875 (d) 410
3. Round to nearest thousand.
   (a) 6,251 (b) 12,365 (c) 41,529 (d) 49,750
4. Round to nearest ten thousand.
   (a) 24,267 (b) 35,841 (c) 42,165 (d) 75,872
5. Round to nearest million.
   (a) 2,450,672 (b) 22,875,300
   (c) 12,819,114 (d) 75,162,000

6. Round to the nearest ten thousand:
The land area of each of our five largest states is:

(a) Alaska	586,400 square miles
(b) Texas	267,339 square miles
(c) California	158,693 square miles
(d) Montana	147,138 square miles
(e) New Mexico	121,666 square miles

Meaning of Fractions and Terms Used with Fractions

There are three commonly used meanings of a fraction.

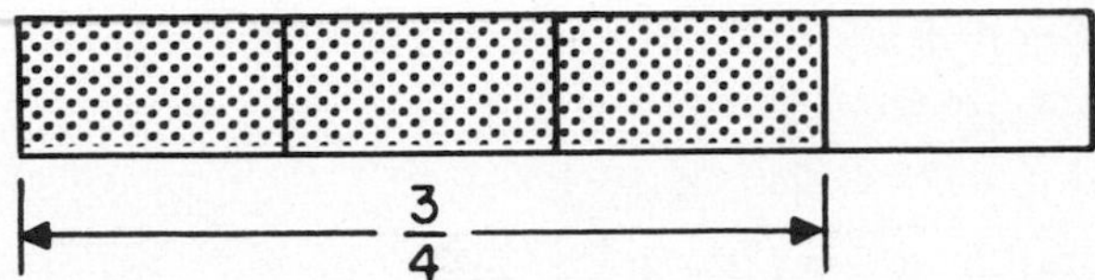

1. In this case the fraction $\frac{3}{4}$ means part of a whole. The denominator 4 tells that the bar has been divided into 4 equal parts. The numerator 3 tells how many of these parts are shaded.

2. Here the fraction $\frac{3}{5}$ means part of a group. The three apples are $\frac{3}{5}$ of the group of five apples.

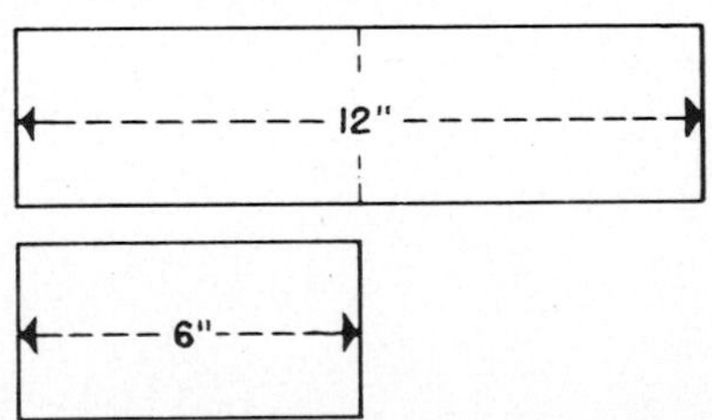

3. Compare 6 inches with 1 foot. Since there are 12 inches in a foot, 6 inches $= \frac{6}{12}$ or $\frac{1}{2}$ of 12 inches. Here the fraction $\frac{1}{2}$ shows the relationship between two quantities.

Common fractions play an important part in our lives today. Besides the three uses of fractions given, you will study other uses of the fractional form which have meanings different from these three.

$\frac{7}{8}$ numerator
denominator

The denominator of a fraction names the equal parts, and the numerator tells how many equal parts are being considered. The fraction $\frac{7}{8}$ means that there are 8 equal parts and 7 of these equal parts are being considered.

ORAL EXERCISES—Explain the meanings of the numerators and denominators in the following:

1. $\frac{1}{2}$ of an apple
2. $\frac{2}{3}$ of a mile
3. $\frac{3}{4}$ of a yard
4. $\frac{5}{6}$ of 6 birds
5. $\frac{4}{5}$ of 5 books
6. one quart is $\frac{1}{4}$ of a gallon

Fractions may be less than one, equal to one, or greater than one.

$\frac{5}{8}$ is less than one and is called a proper fraction. The numerator is less than the denominator.

$\frac{8}{8}$ is equal to one and is called an improper fraction.

$\frac{13}{8}$ is greater than one and is also called an improper fraction. The numerator is greater than the denominator.

ORAL EXERCISES—Tell which of the following are proper or improper fractions:

1. $\frac{5}{6}$
2. $\frac{9}{4}$
3. $\frac{7}{7}$
4. $\frac{6}{6}$
5. $\frac{1}{4}$
6. $\frac{10}{7}$
7. $\frac{1}{5}$
8. $\frac{5}{5}$

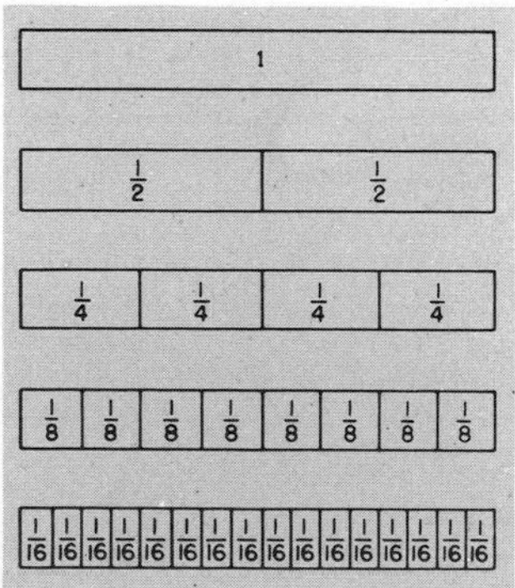

These five bars are equal in length. The second bar is divided into 2 equal parts, the third one into 4 equal parts, the fourth one into 8 equal parts, and the fifth one into 16 equal parts. $\frac{1}{2}$, $\frac{2}{4}$, $\frac{4}{8}$, and $\frac{8}{16}$ represent the same part of the whole. Since these fractions are equal they are called equivalent fractions.

ORAL EXERCISES—Copy and write in the missing number:

1. $\frac{1}{2} = \frac{\ }{4}$	2. $\frac{1}{2} = \frac{\ }{8}$	3. $\frac{1}{2} = \frac{\ }{16}$	4. $\frac{3}{4} = \frac{\ }{8}$
5. $\frac{3}{4} = \frac{\ }{16}$	6. $\frac{7}{8} = \frac{\ }{16}$	7. $\frac{12}{16} = \frac{\ }{4}$	8. $\frac{2}{4} = \frac{\ }{2}$
9. $\frac{12}{16} = \frac{\ }{8}$	10. $\frac{8}{16} = \frac{\ }{2}$	11. $\frac{4}{8} = \frac{\ }{2}$	12. $\frac{14}{16} = \frac{\ }{8}$

13. How many halves are there in one?
14. How many fourths are there in one?
15. How many eighths are there in one?
16. How many sixteenths are there in one?

There are certain principles which we must remember when we use fractions. Proper fractions (less than one) are generally expressed in simplest form. We call this reducing to lowest terms. $\frac{1}{2}$ is the simplest form of all fractions, like $\frac{5}{10}$, $\frac{3}{6}$, and $\frac{2}{4}$, which are equal to $\frac{1}{2}$.

$$\frac{4}{8} = \frac{4 \div 4}{8 \div 4} \text{ or } \frac{1}{2}$$

By what number were the numerator and denominator divided to obtain $\frac{1}{2}$?

Does $\frac{4}{8} = \frac{1}{2}$? Are these fractions equal?

A fraction is in simplest form if there is no whole number other than 1 which divides both the numerator and the denominator evenly.

Both the numerator and denominator of a fraction can be divided by the same number (other than zero) without changing the value of the fraction.

In the fraction $\frac{21}{35}$ both numbers, 21 and 35, are divisible by 7. One number is said to be divisible by another, if, when the first is divided by the second, the quotient is a whole number and the remainder is zero.

In the fraction $\frac{13}{52}$ both numerator and denominator can be divided by 13. In this example we see the denominator can be divided by the number in the numerator. This example suggests one of the first tests to use with a fraction when reducing it to lowest terms.

EXERCISES—Copy and reduce to lowest terms:

1. $\frac{3}{16}$	2. $\frac{8}{16}$	3. $\frac{16}{32}$	4. $\frac{10}{15}$
5. $\frac{12}{14}$	6. $\frac{4}{8}$	7. $\frac{9}{15}$	8. $\frac{5}{15}$
9. $\frac{6}{12}$	10. $\frac{4}{14}$	11. $\frac{24}{36}$	12. $\frac{16}{72}$
13. $\frac{52}{65}$	14. $\frac{98}{154}$	15. $\frac{72}{108}$	16. $\frac{120}{300}$

Rules of Divisibility

1. Numbers like 12, 26, 144, 428 are divisible by 2.
2. Numbers like 5, 20, 25, 710 are divisible by 5.
3. Numbers like 10, 20, 40, 80 are divisible by 10.
4. Numbers like 21, 39, 63, 156 are divisible by 3.

In number 1 above, are the numbers even or odd?

Numbers ending in 0, 2, 4, 6, and 8 are divisible by 2.

In number 2 above, what are the endings of these numbers?

Numbers ending in 5 or 0 are divisible by 5.

Numbers ending in zero are divisible by 10.

In number 4 above, add the digits in each number and see if the sum is divisible by 3. Example: The digits in the number 153 are 1, 5, and 3. The sum of 1, 5, and 3 is 9, and 9 is divisible by 3.

Numbers are divisible by 3 if the sum of the digits of the numbers is divisible by 3.

*Can you determine the rules of divisibility by 4, 6, and 8?

Numbers like *100*, *24*, *116*, and *232* are divisible by 4. (Note the last two digits.)

Numbers like *42*, *126*, *324*, *72*, and *168* are divisible by 6.

Numbers like *128*, *488*, *1208*, and *2432* are divisible by 8. (Note the last three digits.)

EXERCISES—Reduce to lowest terms using the rules of divisibility given above. If you use the largest number by which both numerator and denominator are divisible, you will save time.

1. $\frac{25}{30}$	2. $\frac{16}{18}$	3. $\frac{40}{50}$	4. $\frac{27}{30}$	5. $\frac{14}{35}$

6. $\frac{75}{80}$ 7. $\frac{21}{51}$ 8. $\frac{33}{42}$ 9. $\frac{11}{33}$ 10. $\frac{19}{38}$

11. $\frac{21}{84}$ 12. $\frac{50}{100}$ 13. $\frac{17}{68}$ 14. $\frac{91}{182}$ 15. $\frac{75}{150}$

More practice can be found in Appendix, page 290.

Mixed numbers are usually expressed in simplest form.

$2\frac{6}{8} = 2\frac{3}{4}$

By what number was both the numerator and denominator of the fraction $\frac{6}{8}$ divided to obtain the fraction $\frac{3}{4}$?

Reduce to lowest terms:

1. $3\frac{10}{12}$ 2. $2\frac{9}{15}$ 3. $4\frac{7}{21}$ 4. $6\frac{15}{25}$ 5. $7\frac{10}{20}$

6. $8\frac{15}{18}$ 7. $9\frac{5}{25}$ 8. $6\frac{21}{30}$ 9. $4\frac{18}{21}$ 10. $9\frac{18}{36}$

Simplifying Improper Fractions

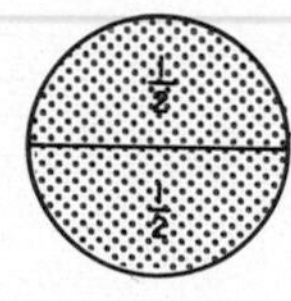

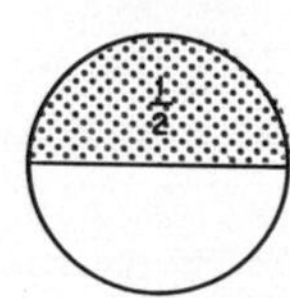

Improper fractions should be expressed in simplest form. In the fraction $\frac{3}{2}$, the denominator tells us we are concerned with halves. Two halves, $\frac{2}{2}$, equal one unit, therefore $\frac{3}{2} = 1$ unit and $\frac{1}{2}$ unit or $1\frac{1}{2}$ units.

In the fraction $\frac{9}{6}$, the denominator tells us we are concerned with sixths. Six-sixths, $\frac{6}{6}$, is one unit, therefore $\frac{9}{6} = 1$ unit and $\frac{3}{6}$ of a unit which is $1\frac{3}{6}$ or $1\frac{1}{2}$. Could you change $\frac{9}{6}$ to $\frac{3}{2}$ first? Would you have $1\frac{1}{2}$ if you did?

EXERCISES—Change these mixed numbers with improper fractions to simplest form:

$6\frac{3}{2} = 7\frac{1}{2}$

$7\frac{6}{4} = 8\frac{2}{4}$ or $8\frac{1}{2}$

1. $4\frac{3}{2}$ 2. $7\frac{6}{5}$ 3. $8\frac{5}{4}$ 4. $9\frac{10}{9}$ 5. $10\frac{7}{8}$

6. $7\frac{10}{8}$ 7. $4\frac{8}{6}$ 8. $9\frac{9}{6}$ 9. $10\frac{25}{15}$ 10. $9\frac{18}{16}$

Adding Fractions

An important principle of addition is that only like terms can be added. In each exercise below the fractions are like terms since they have the same denominator. Fractions which have a common denominator are called *like fractions*.

EXERCISES—Add and reduce to lowest terms:

5 estimated sum

$$\begin{array}{l} 2\frac{3}{4} \\ \underline{1\frac{3}{4}} \\ 3\frac{6}{4} = 4\frac{2}{4} \text{ or } 4\frac{1}{2} \end{array}$$

1. $\frac{1}{2}$ + $\frac{1}{2}$
2. $\frac{1}{4}$ + $\frac{1}{4}$
3. $\frac{2}{3}$ + $\frac{2}{3}$
4. $\frac{3}{4}$ + $\frac{3}{4}$
5. $7\frac{1}{8}$ + $4\frac{3}{8}$
6. $8\frac{1}{12}$ + $9\frac{7}{12}$
7. $4\frac{1}{16}$ + $8\frac{5}{16}$
8. $9\frac{7}{9}$ + $5\frac{3}{9}$

*9. $5\frac{1}{6}$ + $3\frac{2}{6}$ + $8\frac{5}{6}$

*10. $8\frac{7}{8}$ + $2\frac{3}{8}$ + $1\frac{1}{8}$

*11. $2\frac{1}{12}$ + $6\frac{5}{12}$ + $7\frac{3}{12}$

*12. $7\frac{1}{5}$ + $4\frac{3}{5}$ + $8\frac{2}{5}$

Changing to Like Fractions

12 estimated sum

$$\begin{array}{l} 9\frac{3}{4} = 9\frac{3}{4} \\ 1\frac{1}{2} = \underline{1\frac{2}{4}} \\ \quad 10\frac{5}{4} \text{ or } 11\frac{1}{4} \end{array}$$

$$\frac{1}{2} = \frac{1 \times 2}{2 \times 2} \text{ or } \frac{2}{4}$$

The width of a piece of paper to the right of the margin is $9\frac{3}{4}''$, and the margin is $1\frac{1}{2}''$. What is the total width of the paper?
The width is $11\frac{1}{4}''$.

The fractions $\frac{3}{4}$ and $\frac{1}{2}$ are not like fractions since their denominators are not equal. What must you multiply both the numerator and denominator of $\frac{1}{2}$ by to change it to $\frac{2}{4}$?

Does $\frac{1}{2} = \frac{2}{4}$? $\frac{2}{4}$ and $\frac{3}{4}$ are like fractions since their denominators are equal.

Both numerator and denominator of a fraction can be multiplied by the same number (other than 0) without changing the value of the fraction.

The fractions in the above problem could not be added until they are changed to like fractions. Why?

It is a good plan to decide, as the first step, whether one of the denominators given can be used as a common denominator when changing to like fractions.

EXERCISES—Copy and fill in the missing number in Exercises 1 through 4.

$$\frac{3}{4} = \frac{3 \times 3}{4 \times 3} \text{ or } \frac{9}{12}$$

$$\frac{1}{3} = \frac{1 \times 4}{3 \times 4} \text{ or } \frac{4}{12}$$

$$\frac{1}{2} = \frac{1 \times 6}{2 \times 6} \text{ or } \frac{6}{12}$$

1. $\frac{1}{4} = \frac{}{4}$ $\quad \frac{1}{2} = \frac{}{4}$
2. $\frac{1}{3} = \frac{}{6}$ $\quad \frac{5}{6} = \frac{}{6}$
3. $\frac{4}{5} = \frac{}{10}$ $\quad \frac{1}{2} = \frac{}{10}$
4. $\frac{5}{8} = \frac{}{16}$ $\quad \frac{3}{16} = \frac{}{16}$

In Exercises 5 through 20, change to like fractions.

5. $\frac{5}{6}$, $\frac{1}{2}$
6. $\frac{5}{9}$, $\frac{1}{3}$
7. $\frac{3}{4}$, $\frac{1}{3}$
8. $\frac{1}{12}$, $\frac{1}{3}$
9. $\frac{4}{5}$, $\frac{1}{4}$
10. $\frac{1}{6}$, $\frac{1}{12}$
11. $\frac{1}{3}$, $\frac{1}{5}$
12. $\frac{1}{16}$, $\frac{2}{3}$
13. $\frac{2}{3}$, $\frac{3}{5}$
14. $\frac{1}{2}$, $\frac{4}{15}$
15. $\frac{1}{8}$, $\frac{1}{32}$
16. $\frac{1}{9}$, $\frac{1}{3}$

*17. $\frac{1}{2}$, $\frac{1}{3}$, $\frac{1}{12}$

*18. $\frac{5}{8}$, $\frac{3}{4}$, $\frac{1}{2}$

*19. $\frac{1}{15}$, $\frac{1}{5}$, $\frac{1}{3}$

*20. $\frac{1}{12}$, $\frac{1}{2}$, $\frac{1}{3}$

Quick Quiz No. 4

1. Does $\frac{4}{16} = \frac{1}{4}$? Prove your answer.
2. Is $\frac{3}{8}$ larger or smaller than $\frac{1}{2}$?
3. What kind of fraction is $\frac{2}{3}$?
4. What kind of fraction is $\frac{3}{2}$?
5. $2\frac{1}{2} + 2\frac{1}{2} =$
6. Is an odd number ever divisible by 2?
7. Which of these numbers are divisible by 3?
   (a) 136 (b) 96 (c) 423 (d) 42 *(e) 21(base five)
8. Round to the nearest thousand dollars: $4,276,690.
9. Are $\frac{1}{2}$ and $\frac{2}{3}$ like fractions?
10. $1\frac{1}{4} + 2\frac{1}{2}$

More on Adding Fractions

EXERCISES—On a separate piece of paper, add and reduce to lowest terms:

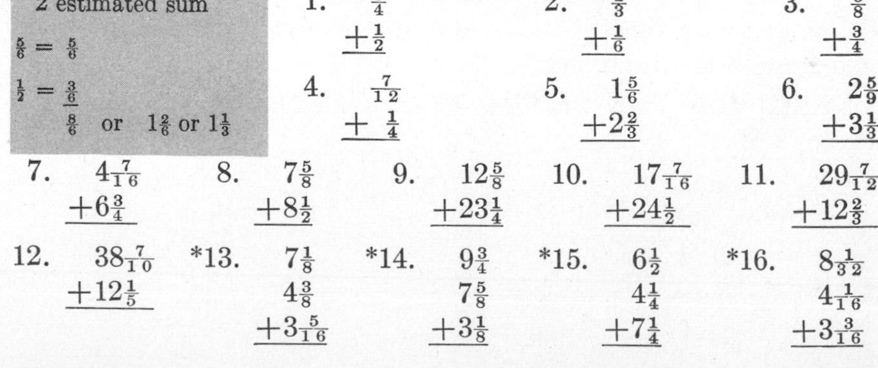

2 estimated sum

$\frac{5}{6} = \frac{5}{6}$

$\frac{1}{2} = \frac{3}{6}$

$\frac{8}{6}$ or $1\frac{2}{6}$ or $1\frac{1}{3}$

1. $\frac{3}{4} + \frac{1}{2}$
2. $\frac{2}{3} + \frac{1}{6}$
3. $\frac{5}{8} + \frac{3}{4}$
4. $\frac{7}{12} + \frac{1}{4}$
5. $1\frac{5}{6} + 2\frac{2}{3}$
6. $2\frac{5}{9} + 3\frac{1}{3}$
7. $4\frac{7}{16} + 6\frac{3}{4}$
8. $7\frac{5}{8} + 8\frac{1}{2}$
9. $12\frac{5}{8} + 23\frac{1}{4}$
10. $17\frac{7}{16} + 24\frac{1}{2}$
11. $29\frac{7}{12} + 12\frac{2}{3}$
12. $38\frac{7}{10} + 12\frac{1}{5}$

*13. $7\frac{1}{8} + 4\frac{3}{8} + 3\frac{5}{16}$

*14. $9\frac{3}{4} + 7\frac{5}{8} + 3\frac{1}{8}$

*15. $6\frac{1}{2} + 4\frac{1}{4} + 7\frac{1}{4}$

*16. $8\frac{1}{32} + 4\frac{1}{16} + 3\frac{3}{16}$

4 is estimated sum

$$
\begin{aligned}
2\tfrac{1}{2} &= 2\tfrac{6}{12} \\
1\tfrac{1}{4} &= 1\tfrac{3}{12} \\
\tfrac{1}{3} &= \underline{\tfrac{4}{12}} \\
& 3\tfrac{13}{12} \text{ or } 4\tfrac{1}{12}
\end{aligned}
$$

The skirt of a dress requires $2\frac{1}{2}$ yards, the blouse $1\frac{1}{4}$ yards, and a detached collar $\frac{1}{3}$ of a yard. How many yards are needed?

Here all the fractions had to be changed in order to make them like fractions so they could be added.

Your work will be simplified if you choose the smallest denominator which can be used.

EXERCISES—Add the fractions and reduce to lowest terms:

6 estimated sum

$$
\begin{aligned}
2\tfrac{7}{8} &= 2\tfrac{21}{24} \\
2\tfrac{5}{6} &= \underline{2\tfrac{20}{24}} \\
& 4\tfrac{41}{24} \text{ or } 5\tfrac{17}{24}
\end{aligned}
$$

1. $\frac{3}{4} + \frac{1}{3}$
2. $\frac{3}{8} + \frac{1}{3}$
3. $\frac{1}{5} + \frac{2}{3}$
4. $\frac{1}{9} + \frac{1}{6}$
5. $2\frac{1}{8} + 3\frac{1}{6}$
6. $5\frac{1}{12} + 6\frac{1}{8}$
7. $7\frac{3}{4} + 2\frac{7}{9}$
8. $8\frac{7}{16} + 6\frac{1}{12}$

*9. $9\frac{1}{2}$, $2\frac{1}{3}$, $+4\frac{1}{8}$

*10. $7\frac{1}{12}$, $3\frac{5}{6}$, $+2\frac{3}{8}$

*11. $3\frac{5}{6}$, $10\frac{3}{5}$, $+\ 4\frac{1}{2}$

*12. $4\frac{5}{6}$, $2\frac{3}{4}$, $+1\frac{2}{3}$

Test

Addition of Fractions. Add the fractions and reduce to lowest terms:

1. $\frac{1}{3} + \frac{1}{3}$
2. $\frac{3}{4} + \frac{3}{4}$
3. $\frac{5}{8} + \frac{3}{8}$
4. $2\frac{5}{6} + 3\frac{1}{6}$
5. $3\frac{3}{4} + 2\frac{1}{2}$
6. $7\frac{5}{8} + 3\frac{1}{2}$
7. $4\frac{1}{16}$, $3\frac{1}{2}$, $+2\frac{1}{4}$
8. $3\frac{15}{16}$, $4\frac{3}{4}$, $+2\frac{3}{8}$
9. $3\frac{1}{3}$, $1\frac{5}{8}$, $+2\frac{1}{4}$
10. $3\frac{1}{5}$, $2\frac{2}{3}$, $+4\frac{1}{2}$
11. $2\frac{5}{6}$, $2\frac{4}{5}$, $+4\frac{1}{2}$
12. $7\frac{7}{8}$, $2\frac{1}{3}$, $+3\frac{5}{6}$

Practice in Adding Fractions

1. Find the total number of yards in three pieces of cloth measuring $2\frac{1}{2}$ yards, $3\frac{1}{2}$ yards, and $5\frac{1}{2}$ yards. Suggested form $N = 2\frac{1}{2} + 3\frac{1}{2} + 5\frac{1}{2}$.
2. Find the length of the perimeter (the sum of the lengths of the sides) of a triangle, if the three sides measure $1\frac{1}{4}$ inches, $1\frac{3}{4}$ inches, and $1\frac{3}{4}$ inches.
3. A board is made of three plies of the following thicknesses $\frac{3}{8}''$, $\frac{7}{16}''$, and $\frac{9}{32}''$. How thick is the board?

4. A sales girl sold the following lengths of cloth, $4\frac{1}{2}$ yards, $3\frac{3}{4}$ yards, and $2\frac{1}{4}$ yards. How many yards did she sell?
5. A boy walked $3\frac{3}{4}$ miles one day, $2\frac{1}{2}$ miles another day, 4 miles the third day, and $6\frac{7}{8}$ miles the fourth. How many miles did he walk on these four days?
6. How long must a piece of cardboard be to mount a picture $6\frac{1}{8}''$ long, if a margin of $2\frac{1}{4}''$ is to be allowed at the top and one of $3\frac{1}{2}''$ at the bottom?
7. What is the total weight of four packages weighing 12 pounds, $6\frac{3}{4}$ pounds, $1\frac{3}{8}$ pounds, and $2\frac{7}{8}$ pounds?

*8. How many feet of molding will be required to go around a room $16\frac{1}{2}$ feet long by $12\frac{3}{4}$ feet wide (remember there are two lengths and two widths).

Words you should understand:

1. numerator 2. denominator 3. proper fraction
4. improper fraction 5. equivalent fractions
6. mixed number.

Review Test

1. Write as Hindu-Arabic numerals:
   (a) XXIV (b) XLII (c) CXII
2. Round to the nearest thousand:
   (a) 4,256 (b) 11,924 (c) 24,500

3. $\begin{array}{r} 6 \\ 2 \\ 4 \\ +1 \\ \hline \end{array}$ 4. $\begin{array}{r} 21 \\ 64 \\ 75 \\ 83 \\ +19 \\ \hline \end{array}$ 5. $\begin{array}{r} 125 \\ 654 \\ 166 \\ 264 \\ +181 \\ \hline \end{array}$ 6. $\begin{array}{r} \$6.25 \\ 1.45 \\ 2.08 \\ +\ 1.75 \\ \hline \end{array}$

7. $7 + 5 + 9 + 2 + 1 =$ 8. $24 + 28 + 10 + 11 =$

9. Reduce to the lowest terms:
   (a) $\frac{4}{8}$ (b) $\frac{15}{20}$ (c) $\frac{6}{9}$
10. Change to mixed numbers:
   (a) $\frac{14}{8}$ (b) $\frac{10}{6}$ (c) $\frac{5}{4}$
11. Change to like fractions:
   (a) $\frac{4}{5}$ (b) $\frac{1}{2}$

In Exercises 12 through 18 add the fractions:

12. $\frac{7}{8}$
 $\frac{7}{8}$

13. $7\frac{1}{3}$
 $8\frac{2}{3}$

14. $8\frac{1}{4}$
 $3\frac{1}{4}$

15. $8\frac{3}{8}$
 $1\frac{1}{2}$

16. $8\frac{1}{16}$
 $3\frac{3}{4}$

17. $2\frac{1}{8}$
 $1\frac{1}{6}$
 $1\frac{1}{4}$

18. $9\frac{2}{3}$
 $1\frac{1}{4}$
 $2\frac{1}{2}$

19. How much did Mary earn baby-sitting in one month if she earned \$3.75 the first week, \$1.25 the second week, \$4.30 the third week, and \$2.80 the fourth week?

20. What is the total weight of three bags weighing $12\frac{1}{2}$ pounds, $8\frac{1}{4}$ pounds, and 7 pounds?

Addition of Decimal Fractions

A decimal fraction is a special kind of fraction whose denominator is a number like 10, 100, 1,000, 10,000, or any other power of 10. In a decimal fraction the position of a digit in reference to the decimal point determines the value it represents.

Place Value in Decimal Fractions													
Millions	Hundred thousands	Ten thousands	Thousands	Hundreds	Tens	Units	.	Tenths	Hundredths	Thousandths	Ten-thousandths	Hundred-thousandths	Millionths
7	6	5	4	3	2	1	.	1	2	3	4	5	6

The decimal point indicates where the fractional part of the number begins. Decimal fractions are commonly called decimals.

$\frac{9}{10}$ is written 0.9

$\frac{21}{100}$ is written 0.21

$\frac{6}{1000}$ is written 0.006

$\frac{14}{10,000}$ is written 0.0014

$\frac{53}{100,000}$ is written 0.00053

$\frac{7}{1,000,000}$ is written 0.000007

0.26 is read "26 hundredths"

0.261 is read "261 thousandths"

2.6 is read "2 and 6 tenths"

14.25 is read "14 and 25 hundredths"

In reading decimals like 2.6 and 14.25, "and" is used for the decimal point. The whole number is associated with the fractional part by the word "and."

ORAL EXERCISES—Read the following decimals:

(1) 0.6	(2) 0.8	(3) 0.24	(4) 3.1	(5) 2.4
(6) 0.54	(7) 0.34	(8) 6.24	(9) 12.02	(10) 1.26
(11) 1.006	(12) 0.174	(13) 0.021	(14) 1.026	(15) 0.007
(16) 0.0007	(17) 0.0024	(18) 0.0212	(19) 6.2746	(20) 0.7684
(21) 6.00002	(22) 0.081	(23) 0.962	*(24) 12.00724	
*(25) 0.001762				

Those in business and industry often do not read the denominators of decimals, but say point-six for 0.6, point-two-four for 0.24, and one-point-zero-one-two for 1.012.

EXERCISES—Write the following in decimal notation:

1. $\frac{7}{10}$	2. $\frac{13}{100}$	3. $\frac{3}{1,000}$	4. $\frac{9}{10,000}$	5. $\frac{11}{10,000}$
6. $\frac{31}{1,000}$	7. $\frac{316}{10,000}$	8. $\frac{3,163}{10,000}$	9. $\frac{2}{100,000}$	10. $\frac{2,002}{10,000}$
11. $\frac{41}{100}$	12. $2\frac{1}{10}$	13. $4\frac{23}{100}$	14. $9\frac{7}{1,000}$	15. $42\frac{63}{10,000}$
16. $9\frac{8}{100}$	17. $\frac{231}{10,000}$			

18. 19 hundredths
19. 3 tenths
20. 6 thousandths
21. 44 ten-thousandths
22. 6 millionths
23. 45 hundred-thousandths
24. 4 and 6 tenths
25. 19 and 1 tenth
26. 7 and 12 thousandths
27. 6 and 125 ten-thousandths
*28. 2 and 45 millionths
*29. 13 and 3 ten-thousandths
*30. 8 and 8 hundred-thousandths

A man drove 96.2 miles on one trip, 142.6 miles on another, and 9.9 miles on the third trip. How many miles did he drive?

250 estimated sum	
96.2 miles	
142.6	addends
9.9	
248.7 miles	sum or total

One of the principles of addition is: "Only like quantities can be added." We must add tenths to tenths, ones to ones, tens to tens, and so on. When we do this, it is convenient to place the decimal points under each other.

Test on Addition of Decimals

Add:

1.	2.	3.	4.
0.6	0.21	2.6	3.26
0.4	0.46	4.7	4.44
0.9	0.09	1.8	1.95
		2.9	2.17

5.	6.	7.	8.
1.002	7.002	12.900	4.270
1.160	1.720	17.210	1.061
4.200	0.009	8.006	8.710
1.210	4.000	1.900	1.250

Copy the remaining exercises in vertical form, add, and check:

9. 0.6 + 1.2 + 4.7
10. 0.220 + 1.6004 + 0.007 + 14
11. 2.11 + 1.5 + 4.75 + 6.10
12. 19 + 2.10 + 17.14 + 0.61

More practice can be found in the Appendix, page 291.

Practice in Adding Decimals

1. A boy earned $14.75 one week, $6.82 the second week, $9.11 the third week, and $12.96 the fourth. What was the total amount earned? Suggested form: N = $14.75 + $6.82 + $9.11 + $12.96.
2. A family drove 296.5 miles the first day of their trip, 481.2 miles the second day, 364.1 miles the third day, and 187.7 miles the fourth day. How many miles did they drive?
3. Three boards measure 16.50 feet, 8.25 feet, and 9.75 feet. What was their total length?
4. A triangle measures 1.75 inches on one side, 1.50 inches on another side, and 2.25 inches on the third side. What is its perimeter?
5. A boy carried four boxes weighing 6 pounds, 4.7 pounds, 8.5 pounds, and 7.9 pounds. What was the total weight?
6. A man deposited in the bank, $121.11, $306.09, and $511.12. What was the total of these deposits?
7. How many yards are in four pieces of goods containing 6.50 yards, 4.25 yards, 8.75 yards, and 2.25 yards?

*8. What is the total thickness of four pieces of paper measuring 0.010 inches thick, 0.020 inches thick, 0.015 inches thick, and 0.021 inches thick?

Quick Quiz No. 5

1. Is $34.85 nearer $30 or $40?
2. What is the total of these amounts: $2.50, $1.50, and $.25?
3. Which numbers are divisible by 5?
   (a) 22 (b) 10 (c) 45 (d) 18 (e) 60
4. Reduce to lowest terms each of the following:
   (a) $\frac{4}{6}$ (b) $2\frac{10}{12}$ (c) $\frac{9}{8}$ (d) $7\frac{6}{5}$
5. Is $\frac{2}{3}$ of a pound greater or less than $\frac{3}{4}$ of a pound?
6. What is the numerator in the fraction $\frac{7}{8}$?
7. Which of these fractions are equivalent in value?
   (a) $\frac{1}{2}$ (b) $\frac{3}{4}$ (c) $\frac{6}{8}$ (d) $\frac{1}{3}$ (e) $\frac{9}{12}$ (f) $\frac{10}{12}$
8. The underlined digit in $0.03\underline{2}$ represents 2 ______.
9. $7\frac{1}{8} + 2\frac{1}{2} = ?$
10. $0.1 + 0.9 + 0.7 = ?$

Adding Denominate Numbers

In adding denominate numbers it is often necessary to change from a smaller unit to a larger unit.

Example—Change 170 minutes to hours and minutes. There are 60 minutes in one hour. 170 is 2 times 60 plus 50. Therefore in 170 minutes there are 2 hours and 50 minutes.

EXERCISES—Copy and complete the following using the tables on pages 312-314.

1. 70 min. = ______ hr. ______ min.
2. 23 in. = ______ ft. ______ in.
3. 7 ft. = ______ yd. ______ ft.
4. 6000 lb. = ______ T.
5. 19 oz. = ______ lb. ______ oz.
6. 244 sq. in. = ______ sq. ft. ______ sq. in.

7. 90 sec. = ______ min. ______ sec.

8. 18 qt. = ______ pk. ______ qt.

9. 18 qt. = ______ gal. ______ qt.

10. 8 cupfuls = ______ pt.

11. 40 in. = ______ yd. ______ in.

12. 15 pk. = ______ bu. ______ pk.

13. 6000 ft. = ______ mi. ______ ft.

14. 11 pt. = ______ qt. ______ pt.

15. 500 rods = ______ mi. ______ rd.

16. 33 ft. = ______ rd.

17. 46 ft. = ______ yd. ______ ft.

18. 192 in. = ______ ft.

19. 45 ft. = ______ yd.

20. 162 oz. = ______ lb. ______ oz.

Additional work on denominate numbers can be found in the Appendix, page 292.

Two boards measure 16 ft. 9 in. and 12 ft. 10 in. What is the total length?

30 ft.	estimated sum
16 ft. 9 in.	addends
12 ft. 10 in.	
28 ft. 19 in.	(sum or total)
29 ft. 7 in.	

What principle of addition must we remember when we add measures?

Why is 28 ft. 19 in. changed to 29 ft. 7 in.?

EXERCISES—Write each sum on a separate piece of paper in simplest form. Label and check each answer.

1. 4 ft. 4 in. 3 ft. 6 in.	2. 6 hr. 12 min. 17 hr. 50 min.	3. 17 ft. 10 in. 18 ft. 9 in.
4. 5 gal. 3 qt. 2 gal. 2 qt. 1 gal. 3 qt.	5. 7 lb. 3 oz. 8 lb. 2 oz. 9 lb. 15 oz.	6. 8 T. 300 lb. 19 T. 1800 lb. 4 T. 200 lb.
7. 3 qt. 1 pt. 2 qt. 1 pt. 4 qt. 1 pt.	8. 6 pk. 3 qt. 9 pk. 3 qt. 4 pk. 5 qt.	9. 6 yd. 2 ft. 3 yd. 1 ft. 9 yd. 2 ft.

10. 3 yd. 1 ft. 4 in.
9 yd. 2 ft. 10 in.
16 yd. 2 ft. 4 in.

Review of . . .
ADDITION

1. Copy and fill in the blanks:
   (a) The answer in an addition problem is called the ______.
   (b) The numbers added are called ______.
   (c) A proper fraction is less than ______.
   (d) An improper fraction is equal to or more than ______.
   (e) Only ______ quantities can be added.
2. Which of the following numbers are divisible by 2?
   (a) 242 (b) 133 (c) 450 (d) 18 (e) 191
3. Which of the following numbers are divisible by 3?
   (a) 192 (b) 63 (c) 120 (d) 49 (e) 61
4. Which of the following numbers are divisible by 5?
   (a) 200 (b) 65 (c) 13 (d) 42 (e) 125
5. Reduce to simplest form:
   (a) $\frac{15}{25}$ (b) $\frac{10}{8}$ (c) $9\frac{10}{12}$ (d) $6\frac{7}{6}$ (e) $18\frac{14}{6}$
6. In the numeral 962.015.
   (a) the digit ______ is in tens place.
   (b) the digit ______ is in units or ones place.
   (c) the digit ______ is in tenths place.
   (d) the digit ______ is in hundredths place.
   (e) the digit ______ is in thousandths place.
7. Add:
   (a) $162 + 25 + 462 + 1728$
   (b) $8\frac{2}{3} + 1\frac{1}{2} + 4\frac{1}{12}$
   (c) $6.5 + 2.25 + 1.125$
   (d) 4 lb. 2 oz. + 6 lb. 10 oz. + 8 lb. 5 oz.
8. Mr. Justice traveled 414.9 miles the first day of a trip, 296.8 miles the second day, and 396.4 miles the third day. What was his total mileage for the three days?

9. Find the total weight of four boxes of books which weigh: $16\frac{1}{2}$ lb., $22\frac{3}{4}$ lb., $17\frac{1}{8}$ lb., and $14\frac{13}{16}$ lb.

10. Which is larger 94″ or 8′?

Chapter Test

1. Write as Roman numerals:

   (a) 39 (b) 125 (c) 960

2. Reduce to lowest terms:

   (a) $\frac{4}{8}$ (b) $3\frac{6}{8}$ (c) $10\,\frac{10}{8}$

3. $\begin{array}{r} 25\\ 46\\ 75\\ 34\\ +21\\ \hline \end{array}$

4. $\begin{array}{r} 4{,}752\\ 1{,}867\\ 1{,}241\\ 6{,}734\\ +1{,}821\\ \hline \end{array}$

5. $\begin{array}{r} 7\frac{1}{2}\\ +3\frac{3}{4}\\ \hline \end{array}$

6. $\begin{array}{r} 6\frac{1}{3}\\ 3\frac{3}{4}\\ +1\frac{1}{2}\\ \hline \end{array}$

7. $\begin{array}{r} \$4.25\\ 1.67\\ 3.33\\ +\ 1.45\\ \hline \end{array}$

8. $\begin{array}{r} 0.641\\ 0.243\\ 1.471\\ +2.121\\ \hline \end{array}$

9. $6 + 2.7 + 3 + 1.6 =$

10. $4 + 1.22 + 6.24 + 7.12 =$

11. Write as decimal fractions:

    (a) $5\frac{6}{10}$ (b) $9\frac{7}{100}$ (c) $12\frac{17}{10{,}000}$

12. Copy and complete:

    14 qt. = ______ gal. ______ qt.

13. $\begin{array}{r} \text{4 ft. 3 in.}\\ \text{6 ft. 2 in.}\\ +\text{8 ft. 7 in.}\\ \hline \end{array}$

14. $\begin{array}{r} \text{6 lb. 5 oz.}\\ \text{7 lb. 10 oz.}\\ +\text{8 lb. 4 oz.}\\ \hline \end{array}$

15. $\begin{array}{r} \text{6 hr. 20 min.}\\ \text{7 hr. 30 min.}\\ +\text{3 hr. 40 min.}\\ \hline \end{array}$

16. $\begin{array}{r} \text{3 qt. 1 pt.}\\ \text{4 qt. 1 pt.}\\ +\text{6 qt. 1 pt.}\\ \hline \end{array}$

17. Mary spent \$.34 on Monday, \$.56 on Tuesday, \$.85 on Wednesday, \$.25 on Thursday, and \$.20 on Friday. Did she stay within her budget of \$2.50?

18. What is the total weight in pounds and ounces of 4 cans weighing 12 ounces, $11\frac{1}{4}$ ounces, $9\frac{3}{4}$ ounces, and $12\frac{1}{2}$ ounces?

19. How many quarts of milk can be filled from 3 vats holding 10 gallons 3 quarts, 5 gallons 2 quarts, and 7 gallons 1 quart?

20. John Bryce was to practice 7 hours a week on his saxophone. His practice chart shows the following record:

Monday	1 hour 10 minutes
Tuesday	1 hour 14 minutes
Wednesday	1 hour 5 minutes
Thursday	1 hour 30 minutes
Friday	50 minutes
Saturday	1 hour 40 minutes

How much more or less than 7 hours did he practice?

CHAPTER **FIVE**  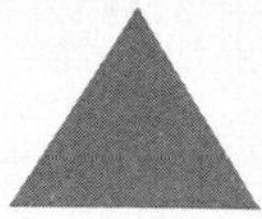  

Subtraction

Read the following statements and decide what question in each can be answered by subtraction.

1. A boy had $5.00 and spent $1.50.

2. There were 41 pupils in one class of the seventh grade during September, but three pupils moved away in October.

3. Each class period is 50 minutes. It usually takes one minute for roll call and announcements.

4. Mary has $9.00 and her sister Sue has $7.50.

5. Bob weighs 97 pounds and Bill weighs 84 pounds.

6. Nancy has saved $7.50 to buy a $12.00 sweater.

7. The citizens of Plainville raised in one week $25,000 for the Community Chest Fund of $47,350.

In 1, 2, and 3, we are interested in what is left or what remains. In 4 and 5, we are interested in the comparison of the two numbers (which is larger or smaller and how much). In 6 and 7, we are interested in how much more is needed.

Engineers made great use of mathematics in building this dam and planning for area to be covered by the river.

A principle of mathematics learned in addition applies to subtraction.

Only like quantities can be subtracted.

There are several ways to subtract. You should know the one hundred subtraction facts for one of the methods. Practice with the facts should be helpful to you.

A man had $4982 and spent $1751. How much was left?

Method I: The Take Away Process

$3,000 (estimated remainder)

$4,982	minuend
1,751	subtrahend
$3,231	remainder
$4,982	check

1. First estimate the remainder.
   $4,982 rounds to $5,000.
   $1,751 rounds to $2,000.
   $5,000 − $2,000 = $3,000 (estimated remainder)
2. In the take away process, start at the right.
   2 ones take away 1 one leaves 1 one
   8 tens take away 5 tens leaves 3 tens
   9 hundreds take away 7 hundreds leaves 2 hundred
   4 thousand take away 1 thousand leaves 3 thousand
3. In the solution illustrated above, a double line has been drawn under the remainder. Compare this answer with the estimated remainder and check by adding the remainder and subtrahend. If this sum equals the minuend, the subtraction is correct.

Method II: The Additive Process

$3,000 (estimated remainder)	
$4,982	minuend
1,751	subtrahend
$3,231	remainder
$4,982	check

1. Estimate remainder by thinking what added to $2,000 gives $5,000. This is $3,000.

2. In the additive process, begin at the right. In this process, we add to the subtrahend to obtain the minuend.

1 one and ? ones = 2 ones. This is 1 one.

5 tens and ? tens = 8 tens. This is 3 tens.

7 hundreds and ? hundreds = 9 hundreds. This is 2 hundreds.

1 thousand and ? thousand = 4 thousand. This is 3 thousand.

3. Check as in Method I.

If you become skillful with both methods, one can serve as a method of checking the other.

In the example $\begin{array}{r}41\\-27\\\hline\end{array}$ one can regroup the number 41 and think of it as 30 + 11. Then we take the 7 from the 11 and the 20 from the 30. In the example $\begin{array}{r}52\\-15\\\hline\end{array}$ one can regroup the 52 and think of it as 40 + 12. Then using the additive process, we think 5 + ? = 12, and 1 + ? = 4.

EXERCISES—Subtract using both methods. Let one method serve as a check on the other. Estimate the answer first.

1. 7946 2534	2. 8967 1641	3. 4129 3117	4. 8754 1513
5. 7637 1514	6. 6962 651	7. 8724 104	8. 7745 7612
9. 5837 4121	10. 8726 14	11. 7628 16	12. 8925 8910

EXERCISES—Using either method, subtract and check:

1. 3,652 1,984	2. 2,975 1,887	3. 3,656 1,689	4. 4,210 3,675
5. 8,534 629	6. 8,112 706	7. 4,561 3,892	8. 7,642 4,785
9. 8,360 2,941	10. 8,112 753	11. 2,121 62	12. 7,678 92

13. 4,890	14. 3,760	15. 8,750	16. 9,140
1,672	1,424	4,368	3,827
17. 6,700	18. 3,500	19. 4,200	20. 4,100
2,198	2,420	730	22
21. 4,000	22. 3,000	23. 44,000	24. 54,000
3,001	464	8,316	961
*25. 56,000	*26. 100,000	*27. 120,000	*28. 750,000
4,721	3,672	16,792	29,996

Test

Subtract and check:

1. 4,726	2. 7,469	3. 8,967	4. 12,641
3,120	1,327	1,437	1,510
5. 3,121	6. 7,220	7. 8,654	8. 13,511
1,946	2,452	3,987	926
9. 6,200	10. 14,300	11. 15,000	12. 20,000
4,775	11,678	3,179	462

Copy in vertical form and subtract:

13. 6,241 − 12
14. 8,290 − 896
15. 10,375 − 292
16. 20,000 − 9,242
17. 8,751 − 296
18. 7,000 − 5,921
19. 41,200 − 396
20. 70,000 − 81

Practice in Subtraction

The following steps should be helpful:

Read each problem carefully.
Decide what process you will use to solve the problem.
Estimate your answer.
Solve and check your solution carefully.
Compare the answer with the estimated one.

1. Jerry made $81 one summer doing odd jobs. He put $35 in the savings bank and kept the rest in a fund for his seventh grade spending money. How much money has he for spending? Suggested form N = $81 − $35.
2. A farmer raised 210 hogs. He decided to keep 31 and sell the rest. How many hogs did he sell?
3. A man sold his house for $10,500 and paid the real estate agent $525 for selling it. How much was left after paying the agent?

4. Center Junior High School has 1,415 pupils and Smith Junior High School has 1,378. What is the difference in the enrollments in these schools?
5. Some passenger planes make one stop from New York City to Los Angeles. The stop is Tulsa, Oklahoma, which is 1,396 miles from New York and 1,561 miles from Los Angeles. How much farther is it from Tulsa to Los Angeles than from Tulsa to New York?
6. Mary's family was driving to the coast which was 1,041 miles away. They drove 410 miles the first day, and 416 miles the second. How many miles were left to be driven the third day? $N = 1041 - (410 + 416)$. The parentheses can be used to show what should be done first. In this case add 410 and 416 and then subtract the sum from 1041.

*7. Mr. Jordan has $15 to pay the utility bills. The gas bill was $2.19, the electricity bill was $4.50, the water bill was $3.50, and the telephone bill was $4.20. After he has paid the bills, how much will he have left?

*8. Philip went to the grocery store for his mother. The groceries came to $3.92 including the sales tax. The checker gave him 3 pennies, 1 nickel, and 1 paper dollar as change from a $5.00 bill. Was the change correct?

Words you should understand:

1. minuend 2. subtrahend
3. remainder 4. difference

Quick Quiz No. 6

1. What name is given to the answer in an addition problem?
2. Which is the subtrahend and which is the minuend in: $\begin{array}{r} 246 \\ -195 \\ \hline 51 \end{array}$
3. $75 - ? = 36$
4. $126 + ? = 387$
5. $300 - 96 = ?$
6. 2 bu. 3 pk. = ______ pk.
7. How much do you have left out of $5 if you spend $3.98?

8. What is the smallest four-digit number that is divisible by 2?
9. Write 152 in Roman numerals.
10. Round each of the following to the nearest hundred:
    862 421 350 697 249

Subtracting Common Fractions

Mary bought $2\frac{3}{4}$ yards of ribbon. She cut off $\frac{1}{4}$ yard for a badge. How many yards were left?

$2\frac{1}{2}$ yards estimated remainder

$$\begin{array}{r} 2\frac{3}{4} \\ -\frac{1}{4} \\ \hline 2\frac{2}{4} \end{array} = 2\frac{1}{2} \text{ yards}$$

Why are these like fractions?

EXERCISES—Copy and subtract. Be sure to reduce answers to lowest terms:

1. $\frac{5}{6} - \frac{3}{6}$
2. $\frac{3}{4} - \frac{1}{4}$
3. $\frac{7}{8} - \frac{7}{8}$
4. $\frac{7}{16} - \frac{5}{16}$
5. $2\frac{2}{3} - \frac{1}{3}$
6. $3\frac{3}{5} - 1\frac{1}{5}$
7. $4\frac{7}{8} - 1\frac{2}{8}$
8. $6\frac{5}{9} - 1\frac{2}{9}$
9. $4\frac{3}{4} - 1\frac{1}{4}$
10. $6\frac{5}{6} - 2\frac{5}{6}$
11. $7\frac{5}{10} - 2\frac{3}{10}$
12. $12\frac{11}{12} - 2\frac{2}{12}$
13. $13\frac{15}{32} - 2\frac{3}{32}$
14. $17\frac{4}{64} - 13\frac{1}{64}$
15. $7\frac{5}{6} - 2\frac{1}{6}$
16. $8\frac{4}{9} - 3\frac{2}{9}$
17. $12\frac{11}{12} - 12\frac{7}{12}$
18. $17\frac{9}{10} - 17\frac{9}{10}$

19. From a board measuring $10\frac{11}{16}$ inches, a piece $4\frac{7}{16}$ inches long was cut. How much was left?
20. Can you cut two pieces of ribbon each measuring $4\frac{7}{8}$ inches from a piece measuring $13\frac{3}{4}$ inches? Will there be enough left over to cut another piece the same length as these?
21. From a ham weighing $14\frac{3}{4}$ pounds, the butcher cut a slice weighing 3 pounds. How many pounds were left?
22. John weighs $78\frac{7}{8}$ pounds. Sam weighs 69 pounds. What is the difference in their weights?
23. Sally lives $15\frac{1}{4}$ blocks from school and Susan lives 11 blocks. How much farther does Sally walk each day coming and going to school than Susan if she walks both ways also?
24. Miss Blue cut two pieces of goods, one $3\frac{7}{8}$ yards and one $4\frac{1}{8}$ yards. How much is left on the bolt if there was $12\frac{1}{2}$ yards on it before she cut off the two pieces?

A boy sawed $1\frac{3}{4}$ feet from a 6-foot board. How many feet were left?

4 estimated remainder

$$\begin{array}{rl} 6 \text{ ft.} = & 5\frac{4}{4} \\ 1\frac{3}{4} = & \underline{1\frac{3}{4}} \\ & 4\frac{1}{4} \text{ ft.} \end{array}$$

In order to subtract $\frac{3}{4}$, one was taken from 5 and changed to $\frac{4}{4}$.

Does $5\frac{4}{4} = 6$? Has the value changed?

EXERCISES—Subtract and check:

1.	$5 \; \underline{-2\frac{1}{2}}$	2.	$3 \; \underline{-1\frac{2}{3}}$	3.	$16 \; \underline{-12\frac{3}{4}}$	4.	$17 \; \underline{-16\frac{4}{5}}$
5.	$9 \; \underline{-4\frac{7}{8}}$	6.	$10 \; \underline{-8\frac{5}{9}}$	7.	$12 \; \underline{-11\frac{7}{12}}$	8.	$17 \; \underline{-9\frac{1}{32}}$

*9. Herman sold $12\frac{3}{4}$ pounds of apples from a basket of apples which weighed 60 pounds. How many pounds were left?

*10. Helenita weighs $78\frac{7}{8}$ pounds and her twin brother, Herbert, 90 pounds. How much more does Herbert weigh?

*11. Joe weighed himself in the morning and found that he weighed $83\frac{3}{4}$ pounds. He weighed himself again before he went to bed and weighed 85 pounds. How much more did he weigh at night than in the morning?

*12. Fred had a stand near his father's orange grove, where he sold oranges. He had 50 pounds to sell one day. He sold the following amounts to customers: $6\frac{1}{2}$ pounds, $5\frac{3}{4}$ pounds, $8\frac{1}{4}$ pounds, and 7 pounds in one hour. How many pounds did he have left to sell?

2 estimated remainder

$$\begin{array}{rl} 9\frac{1}{8} = & 8\frac{9}{8} \\ 6\frac{7}{8} = & \underline{6\frac{7}{8}} \\ & 2\frac{2}{8} \text{ or } 2\frac{1}{4} \end{array}$$

$\frac{7}{8}$ cannot be subtracted from $\frac{1}{8}$, so one unit is taken from 9 leaving 8. The one is changed to $\frac{8}{8}$. Why?

The $\frac{8}{8}$ is added to $\frac{1}{8}$ which makes $\frac{9}{8}$. Does $8\frac{9}{8} = 9\frac{1}{8}$?

13.	$7\frac{1}{3} \; \underline{-2\frac{2}{3}}$	14.	$4\frac{1}{4} \; \underline{-3\frac{3}{4}}$	15.	$6\frac{3}{5} \; \underline{-4\frac{4}{5}}$	16.	$7\frac{1}{6} \; \underline{-6\frac{5}{6}}$	17.	$6\frac{1}{10} \; \underline{-1\frac{7}{10}}$
18.	$9\frac{1}{9} \; \underline{-3\frac{7}{9}}$	19.	$3\frac{1}{12} \; \underline{-1\frac{7}{12}}$	20.	$4\frac{3}{8} \; \underline{-1\frac{5}{8}}$	*21.	$3\frac{1}{16} \; \underline{-1\frac{7}{16}}$	*22.	$9\frac{1}{32} \; \underline{-2\frac{7}{32}}$

*23. If $4\frac{7}{8}''$ is cut from a piece of art paper that measured $11\frac{1}{8}''$, how much is left?

*24. A pupil left a margin of $2\frac{1}{4}''$ at the top of her paper and $1\frac{1}{8}''$ at the bottom. How many inches are left from her poster sheet $15\frac{1}{8}''$ long?

Quick Quiz No. 7

1. What kind of quantities can be subtracted?
2. $9 - \frac{3}{4} = ?$
3. $8\frac{7}{8} - 2\frac{7}{8} = ?$
4. What number is one less than 10,000?
5. Subtract 9 from each of the following:
   16 45 98 109 21
6. Estimate the sum of $770 + 820 + 950$.
7. List all numbers between 25 and 50 that are divisible by 3.
8. Do these mixed numbers have the same value? $2\frac{1}{8}$ and $1\frac{9}{8}$?
9. In which of the following mixed numbers are the fractional parts reduced to lowest terms:
   (a) $7\frac{1}{2}$ (b) $4\frac{4}{6}$ (c) $9\frac{7}{8}$ (d) $12\frac{1}{8}$ (e) $5\frac{7}{12}$
10. From a ham weighing $12\frac{1}{2}$ pounds, a $3\frac{3}{4}$-pound slice was cut. What was the weight of the remaining part of the ham?

9 (estimated remainder)

$$\begin{array}{rcrcr} 12\frac{1}{2} & = & 12\frac{2}{4} & = & 11\frac{6}{4} \\ -\ 3\frac{3}{4} & = & 3\frac{3}{4} & = & \underline{3\frac{3}{4}} \\ & & & & 8\frac{3}{4} \end{array}$$

Why was $12\frac{1}{2}$ changed to $12\frac{2}{4}$?
How was $12\frac{2}{4}$ changed to $11\frac{6}{4}$?

EXERCISES—Copy and subtract:

1. $8\frac{3}{4} - 1\frac{1}{2}$
2. $8\frac{5}{8} - 1\frac{1}{4}$
3. $6\frac{5}{6} - 2\frac{2}{3}$
4. $7\frac{7}{8} - 1\frac{1}{2}$
5. $16\frac{1}{3} - 2\frac{1}{2}$
6. $7\frac{1}{4} - 3\frac{1}{3}$
7. $8\frac{3}{5} - 1\frac{3}{4}$
8. $9\frac{1}{3} - 2\frac{5}{6}$
9. $11\frac{1}{8} - 10\frac{3}{4}$
10. $12\frac{1}{12} - 3\frac{3}{4}$
11. $16\frac{1}{5} - 13\frac{2}{3}$

*12. $7\frac{1}{16} - 2\frac{3}{32}$

*13. A boy weighed $78\frac{3}{4}$ pounds on September 1. On November 1, he weighed $82\frac{1}{2}$ pounds. How much had he gained?

*14. If $2\frac{7}{8}$ yards were cut from a piece of cloth containing $9\frac{1}{4}$ yards, how many yards remain?

Test

Subtract and reduce to lowest terms:

1. $\frac{3}{4} - \frac{1}{4}$
2. $\frac{1}{2} - \frac{1}{2}$
3. $\frac{7}{8} - \frac{3}{8}$
4. $4\frac{5}{6} - 3\frac{1}{6}$
5. $7\frac{1}{2} - 6$

6.	$8\frac{2}{3}$	7.	4	8.	16	9.	$4\frac{1}{4}$	10.	$7\frac{1}{6}$
	-3		$-2\frac{2}{3}$		$-12\frac{4}{5}$		$-3\frac{3}{4}$		$-5\frac{5}{6}$
11.	$\frac{3}{4}$	12.	$\frac{7}{8}$	13.	$6\frac{4}{5}$	14.	$16\frac{1}{16}$	15.	$7\frac{1}{3}$
	$-\frac{1}{2}$		$-\frac{3}{4}$		$-1\frac{1}{3}$		$-2\frac{1}{8}$		$-2\frac{1}{2}$
16.	$18\frac{1}{4}$	17.	$19\frac{1}{2}$	18.	$12\frac{1}{4}$	19.	$11\frac{1}{32}$	20.	$17\frac{1}{10}$
	$-4\frac{2}{3}$		$-17\frac{7}{8}$		$-9\frac{5}{16}$		$-3\frac{7}{8}$		$-3\frac{4}{15}$

Practice in Addition and Subtraction of Fractions

1. Sally's practice schedule on the piano for Saturday is $3\frac{1}{2}$ hours. She practiced $1\frac{1}{4}$ hours before lunch. How long must she practice in the afternoon to meet this schedule? Suggested form: $N = 3\frac{1}{2} - 1\frac{1}{4}$.
2. A live chicken weighed $2\frac{7}{8}$ pounds but when dressed weighed only $2\frac{1}{4}$ pounds. What is the difference between the live and dressed weight?
3. Henry cut $2\frac{1}{4}$ inches from the bottom of a piece of paper 11 inches long. How many inches were left?
4. Sue weighs $69\frac{3}{4}$ pounds and Sara weighs $71\frac{7}{8}$ pounds. What is the difference in their weights?
5. John lives $2\frac{1}{3}$ miles from school and Bill $2\frac{1}{4}$ miles. Who lives the farthest from school and how much farther?
6. Gretchen has $4\frac{3}{4}$ yards of gingham. She needs $1\frac{7}{8}$ yards for an apron. How many yards will be left?
7. One boat traveled 36 miles per hour and another boat traveled $34\frac{7}{8}$ miles per hour. How much faster is the first boat?

*8. A loaded light trailer weighed $1462\frac{1}{2}$ pounds. If the trailer weighed $\frac{1}{2}$ ton, how much did the load weigh?

*9. A carpenter needs two pieces of wood $5\frac{3}{4}$ inches and $6\frac{7}{8}$ inches. How much will he have left when he cuts them from a 13 inch board?

*10. If the top margin of a 12-inch piece of mounting paper is $3\frac{1}{3}$ inches and the bottom margin is $1\frac{1}{2}$ inches, can an 8-inch picture be mounted on it?

Review Test

1. Write as Hindu-Arabic numerals:
   (a) MCMLV (b) DCCLX (c) CCCXCII

2. Round the numbers:
   (a) 6,725 to the nearest ten
   (b) 6,725 to the nearest hundred
   (c) 6,725 to the nearest thousand

3. $\begin{array}{r} 2,721 \\ 1,463 \\ 8,296 \\ +1,421 \\ \hline \end{array}$

4. $\begin{array}{r} 1\frac{1}{2} \\ +3\frac{3}{8} \\ \hline \end{array}$

5. $\begin{array}{r} 6\frac{2}{3} \\ 1\frac{1}{2} \\ +1\frac{1}{4} \\ \hline \end{array}$

6. $\begin{array}{r} 2.23 \\ 1.06 \\ 4.31 \\ +10.02 \\ \hline \end{array}$

7. $\begin{array}{r} 6 \text{ ft. } 2 \text{ in.} \\ 3 \text{ ft. } 9 \text{ in.} \\ 10 \text{ ft. } 12 \text{ in.} \\ + 6 \text{ ft. } 8 \text{ in.} \\ \hline \end{array}$

8. $\begin{array}{r} 6002 \\ -1482 \\ \hline \end{array}$

9. $\begin{array}{r} 12,306 \\ - \quad 492 \\ \hline \end{array}$

10. $\begin{array}{r} \frac{7}{8} \\ -\frac{1}{8} \\ \hline \end{array}$

11. $\begin{array}{r} 2\frac{4}{5} \\ -1 \\ \hline \end{array}$

12. $\begin{array}{r} 7 \\ -3\frac{3}{8} \\ \hline \end{array}$

13. $\begin{array}{r} 6\frac{1}{3} \\ -2\frac{2}{3} \\ \hline \end{array}$

14. $\begin{array}{r} 8\frac{1}{2} \\ -1\frac{1}{4} \\ \hline \end{array}$

15. $\begin{array}{r} 18\frac{1}{3} \\ -12\frac{3}{4} \\ \hline \end{array}$

16. The rainfall for the first 6 months of a year was as follows: 0.56 inches, 1.06 inches, 2.24 inches, 4.96 inches, 3.19 inches, and 6.15 inches. What was the total rainfall for these six months?

17. Four boys went on a hiking trip. George's knapsack weighed 12 pounds 4 ounces, Bill's weighed 13 pounds, Tom's weighed 16 pounds 8 ounces, and Fred's weighed 14 pounds 9 ounces. What was the combined weight of the four knapsacks?

18. Jim measures $63\frac{1}{2}$ inches tall and Sam measures $61\frac{3}{4}$ inches tall. How much taller is Jim?

19. Sue and Sally are twins weighing $61\frac{1}{2}$ pounds and $62\frac{3}{4}$ pounds. Their father weighs 170 pounds. How much more does he weigh than the two girls together?

20. A real estate company bought a 1,260 acre ranch and subdivided it into smaller farms of 80 acres, 160 acres, 240 acres, 320 acres, and 360 acres. The rest of the land was to be used for a park. How many acres were left for the park?

Subtracting Decimal Fractions

Louisiana had 12.00 inches of rainfall in one month. Texas had 1.75

inches of rainfall in the same month. How much greater was the rainfall in Louisiana?

10 estimated difference

$$\begin{array}{r} 12.00 \\ -\ 1.75 \\ \hline 10.25 \end{array}$$

The rainfall in Louisiana was 10.25 in. greater.

The value of twelve has not been changed by adding two zeros.

The same principles apply in subtraction of decimals as apply in subtraction of whole numbers. It is helpful to keep the decimal points in a straight column.

EXERCISES—Subtract and check:

1. $\begin{array}{r} 4.0 \\ -2.5 \\ \hline \end{array}$ 2. $\begin{array}{r} 8.0 \\ -1.75 \\ \hline \end{array}$ 3. $\begin{array}{r} 9.10 \\ -2.13 \\ \hline \end{array}$ 4. $\begin{array}{r} 7.25 \\ -6.00 \\ \hline \end{array}$

5. $\begin{array}{r} 8.36 \\ -1.1 \\ \hline \end{array}$ 6. $\begin{array}{r} 7.21 \\ -1.65 \\ \hline \end{array}$ 7. $\begin{array}{r} 0.008 \\ -0.006 \\ \hline \end{array}$ 8. $\begin{array}{r} 2.001 \\ -0.196 \\ \hline \end{array}$

9. 0.62 − 0.45
10. 2.10 − 0.25
11. 8.0 − 2.06
12. 9.0 − 8.75
13. 0.682 − 0.675
14. 0.941 − 0.883
15. 1.575 − 1.486
16. 19.006 − 12.916

*17. The Zinck Racer won the speedway race with an average of 128.209 miles per hour. The Chapman entry came in second at 127.370 miles per hour. How much faster was the Zinck car?

When we compare decimals by subtraction we should make them alike. To be like fractions, they must have the same denominators. Which is larger and how much—0.8 or 0.08?

Change: 0.8 to 0.80

Are 0.8 and 0.80 the same?

$0.80 = \frac{80}{100}$ or $\frac{8}{10}$ or 0.8

When 0.80 is compared with 0.08, we know that 0.80 is larger than 0.08. Subtracting we find how much.

$$\begin{array}{rl} 0.80 & \text{minuend} \\ -0.08 & \text{subtrahend} \\ \hline 0.72 & \text{difference} \end{array}$$

EXERCISES—Which of the numbers is larger and how much larger is it?

1. 0.6 or 0.8
2. 0.75 or 0.25
3. 0.096 or 0.081
4. 2.009 or 2.018
5. 0.7 or 0.16
6. 7.5 or 7.29
7. 0.52 or 0.6
8. 0.08 or 0.092
9. 1.13 or 0.96
10. 0.1 or 0.001
11. 0.016 or 0.12
12. 4.2 or 4.022
13. 0.12 or 0.1
14. 0.12 or 0.113
15. 0.21 or 0.021
16. 25.2 or 25.72
17. 9.006 or 9.03
18. 18.21 or 18.2
19. 7.075 or 7.69
20. 4.125 or 4.12

Test

1. $\begin{array}{r} 4.2 \\ -1.1 \\ \hline \end{array}$
2. $\begin{array}{r} 3.7 \\ -2.5 \\ \hline \end{array}$
3. $\begin{array}{r} 14.07 \\ -\ 6.24 \\ \hline \end{array}$
4. $\begin{array}{r} 9.02 \\ -7.31 \\ \hline \end{array}$
5. $\begin{array}{r} 0.216 \\ -0.165 \\ \hline \end{array}$
6. $\begin{array}{r} 0.876 \\ -0.841 \\ \hline \end{array}$
7. $\begin{array}{r} 10. \\ -\ 9.006 \\ \hline \end{array}$
8. $\begin{array}{r} 7. \\ -6.15 \\ \hline \end{array}$
9. $\begin{array}{r} 25.002 \\ -16. \\ \hline \end{array}$
10. $\begin{array}{r} 9.036 \\ -2. \\ \hline \end{array}$
11. $\begin{array}{r} 4.002 \\ -3.172 \\ \hline \end{array}$
12. $\begin{array}{r} 6.871 \\ -1.821 \\ \hline \end{array}$

Copy in a vertical column and subtract:

13. 0.6 − 0.4
14. 1.9 − 0.2
15. 0.75 − 0.25
16. 7.5 − 2.25
17. 9 − 0.25
18. 75 − 3.16
19. 200 − 1.75
20. 1750 − 2.35

Practice in Adding and Subtracting Decimals

1. Jack weighs 79.2 pounds. One month ago he weighed 76.8 pounds. How much has he gained? Suggested form: $N = 79.2 - 76.8$.
2. A family was 420 miles from home. By lunch the speedometer showed that they had driven 275.9 miles. How much farther did they have to drive to reach home?
3. Sam is 69.25 inches tall and Bill is 68.5 inches in height. How much taller is Sam than Bill?

4. One plane travels 10.4 miles per minute and the second plane 12.2 miles per minute. How many miles per minute faster is the second plane traveling?

5. Two boxes weigh 69.1 pounds and 69.25 pounds. Which is the heavier and how much?

6. Dewey and Paint, his horse, got on the scales together. They weighed 1072.9 pounds. Dewey weighed 69.4 pounds. How much did Paint weigh?

*7. Maxine made the following amounts baby sitting one week: $0.75, $0.50, $1.10, $0.75, and $0.50. She wants to buy a sweater costing $8.75. How much does she lack in having enough to buy the sweater?

*8. Phil Carter has a half-ton pick-up truck. He has an order to take to Mr. Jack Jones 62.5 pounds of wheat, 375.5 pounds of corn, and 200 pounds of chicken feed. How many pounds of soybeans can he add to take to Mr. Frank Smith and not overload his truck?

Subtracting Denominate Numbers

In solving problems it is often necessary to subtract one measure from another. Common relationships among measures are illustrated in this section.

2 gal. (estimated remainder)

2 gal. 3 qt. −1 gal. 1 qt. 1 gal. 2 qt.	Mary has 2 gallons 3 quarts of water in a can and used 1 gallon and 1 quart. How much was left in the can?
4 15 ~~5~~ ft. ~~3~~ in. −4 ft. 11 in. 4 in.	John is 5 feet 3 inches and Fred is 4 feet 11 inches. How much taller is John?

Since 11 inches cannot be subtracted from 3 inches, 1 foot is taken from 5 feet, changed to 12 inches. The 12 inches are then added to 3 inches to make 15 inches. Does 4′ 15″ = 5′ 3″?

EXERCISES—Subtract the following:

1. 14 ft. 8 in. −11 ft. 4 in.	2. 16 yd. 2 ft. −11 yd. 1 ft.	3. 4 bu. 3 pk. −1 bu. 2 pk.
4. 8 ft. 2 in. −3 ft. 10 in.	5. 14 gal. 1 qt. − 1 gal. 1 qt.	6. 7 lb. 4 oz. −6 lb. 11 oz.

7.	16 hr. 10 min. − 4 hr. 54 min.	8.	26 min. 5 sec. −24 min. 13 sec.	9.	19 qt. − 8 qt. 1 pt.
10.	4 yd. 1 in. −3 yd.	11.	14 T. 100 lb. −13 T. 1800 lb.	12.	6 mi. 40 rd. −1 mi. 96 rd.

Subtracting Measures of Time

The Declaration of Independence was signed on July 4, 1776, and George Washington took the oath of office as the first President of the United States on April 30, 1789. How much time had elapsed between these two dates? (Remember April is the 4th month and July the 7th month.)

Year	Month	Day
1788	16	
~~1789~~	~~4~~	30
1776	7	4
12 yr.	9 mo.	26 da.

Find the difference between these dates:

1. Landing of Columbus on San Salvador, October 12, 1492.
   Landing of Pilgrims at Plymouth, December 21, 1620.
2. Battle of Lexington and Concord, April 19, 1775.
   Signing of the Declaration of Independence, July 4, 1776.
3. First successful air flight by Wright Brothers at Kitty Hawk, North Carolina, December 17, 1903.
   Completion of Charles Lindbergh's Non-stop Solo Flight from New York to Paris, May 21, 1927.
4. Starting of the Pony Express from St. Joseph, Missouri, to Sacramento, California, April 8, 1860.
   Completion of First Transcontinental Railroad, May 10, 1869.
5. Your birth date and today.

Standard Time

In 1883, the United States adopted the system of standard time. The country is divided into four time belts: Eastern Standard Time, Central Standard Time, Mountain Standard Time, and Pacific Standard Time. From one time belt to the next there is a difference of one hour.

In your study of geography, you probably have read about meridians (great circles) that mark the degrees of longitude on the earth. For standard time, the earth is divided into 24 time zones to correspond to the 24 hours in a day. Since $360 \div 24 = 15$, the boundaries of the time zones are 15° longitude apart.

The standard time belts have a central meridian. Theoretically each time belt should be bounded by great circles on the earth, each $7\frac{1}{2}°$ from the central meridian. But, as you see from the map, the time lines are not straight, but often they vary to accommodate railroad schedules or other local conditions. The time belt boundaries in the United States are controlled by the Interstate Commerce Commission.

Since the earth rotates from west to east, we see the sun rise in the east and set in the west. The sun will be overhead at noon in New York much sooner than it will be overhead in San Francisco. The New York clocks will be ahead of the San Francisco clocks.

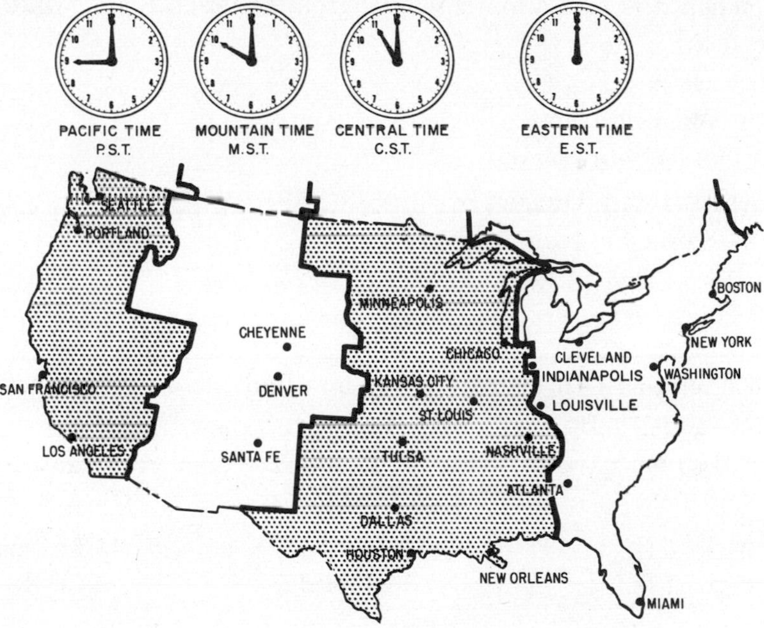

EXERCISES—Use Standard Time in these exercises.

1. When it is 2 p.m. in New York (E.S.T.), what time is it in:
   (a) Chicago, Illinois
   (b) Miami, Florida
   (c) Santa Fe, New Mexico
   (d) Kansas City, Missouri
   (e) Portland, Oregon

2. When it is 4:15 a.m. in Denver (M.S.T.), what time is it in:
   (a) Boston, Massachusetts
   (b) Houston, Texas
   (c) Cheyenne, Wyoming
   (d) Chicago, Illinois
   (e) Los Angeles, California
3. When it is 6:30 p.m. in Seattle (P.S.T.), what time is it in:
   (a) Washington, D. C.
   (b) New Orleans, Louisiana
   (c) St. Louis, Missouri
   (d) San Francisco, California
   (e) Denver, Colorado
4. When it is 7:45 a.m. in Washington, D. C. (E.S.T.), what time is it in:
   (a) Dallas, Texas
   (b) Atlanta, Georgia
   (c) Nashville, Tennessee
   (d) Portland, Oregon
   (e) Santa Fe, New Mexico

Test

In Exercises 1 through 15, copy and find the difference between the given measures:

1. 6 ft. 9 in. 4 ft. 7 in.	2. 12 lb. 14 oz. 12 lb. 11 oz.	3. 16 gal. 3 qt. 12 gal. 2 qt.
4. 3 yd. 1 ft. 2 yd. 2 ft.	5. 6 wk. 1 da. 3 wk. 4 da.	6. 13 hr. 6 min. 4 hr. 48 min.
7. 6 bu. 1 pk. 4 bu. 3 pk.	8. 2 mi. 40 rd. 1 mi. 100 rd.	9. 3 pt. 1 pt. 1 cup
10. 16 min. 16 sec. 10 min. 20 sec.	11. 16 pk. 1 qt. 4 pk. 7 qt.	12. 6 yd. 4 in. 5 yd. 30 in.
13. 4 qt. 1 pt. 3 qt. $\frac{1}{2}$ pt.	14. 9 ft. 1 in. 6 ft. $2\frac{1}{2}$ in.	15. 7 lb. 4 oz. 6 lb. $6\frac{1}{2}$ oz.

16. How many years, months, and days are there from July 1, 1910, to September 9, 1946?

17. How many years, months, and days are there from August 1, 1950, to August 4, 1955?
18. If you are flying from New York to San Francisco, how many hours will you turn your watch back?
19. If you telephone at 6:30 p.m., C.S.T., from Chicago to Denver, what time is it in Denver?
20. If a television program comes on at 4:30 p.m., P.S.T., at Hollywood, what time would it be in Boston?

Practice in Subtraction of Measures

1. Ronnie is 5 feet $4\frac{1}{2}$ inches tall. How much will he have to grow to be as tall as his father who is 6 feet in height? Suggested form: $N = 6$ ft. $-$ 5 ft. $4\frac{1}{2}$ in.
2. The gross weight of a box of cherries is 2 pounds $6\frac{3}{4}$ ounces, and the net weight is 2 pounds. What does the box weigh?
3. If James cut 1 yard 4 inches from a 3-yard piece of rope, how much rope remains?
4. If you use 3 gallons 1 quart of water from a can containing 5 gallons, how much remains?
5. The first telephone message over wires was sent March 10, 1876. The first air mail flew from New York to Washington on May 15, 1918. How much time elapsed between these two dates?
6. Dorothy sold 5 bushels 2 pecks 4 quarts of potatoes from her roadside stand. If she had 7 bushels to start with, how many bushels, pecks, and quarts remain?
7. If the President broadcasts from Washington, D. C., at 10:00 p.m., what time will the broadcast be received in:

   (a) St. Louis (b) Denver (c) San Francisco

*8. If a man left Seattle, Washington, by plane at 11:00 p.m., P.S.T., and arrived at Miami, Florida, at 2:45 p.m., E.S.T., the following day, how many hours was the trip?

The Missing Number

Replace the question mark with a number that will make the answer correct. These are subtraction problems.

1.	2.	3.	4.
65	147	4.216	9.271
− ?	− ?	− ?	− ?
23	96	1.821	8.245

5. $87.2 - ? = 71.1$

6. $125.45 - ? = 65.05$

7. $9.241 - ? = 8.004$

8. $3.821 - ? = 1.752$

Find the Missing Number

If $6 + 5 = 11$
Then $6 = 11 - 5$
and $5 = 11 - 6$

Find the missing number

$6 + N = 11$
$N = 11 - 6$
$N = 5$

1. $8 + N = 21$
2. $N + 6 = 35$
3. $10 + N = 34$
4. $21 + N = 88$
5. $N + 25 = 82$
6. $N + 75 = 140$
7. $N + \frac{1}{2} = \frac{3}{4}$
8. $\frac{1}{3} + N = 2\frac{2}{3}$
9. $\frac{1}{2} + N = 4$
10. $N + \frac{1}{8} = \frac{1}{4}$
11. $0.4 + N = 0.75$
12. $N + 1.2 = 4.6$
13. $N + 0.8 = 0.8$
14. $1.1 + N = 2.2$
15. $N + 1.45 = 2.89$
16. $1.75 + N = 14.83$
17. If you know the sum of two numbers and one of the two numbers, how do you find the other number?

Fun with Subtraction

$791 - 197 = 594$
495

I. Put down any three digit number (791), reverse the digits (197), and subtract one from the other (594). Then reverse the digits of this difference (495) and add to the difference. Try this on at least three examples and see what the results are.

$9{,}876 - 6{,}789 = 3{,}087$

II. Write any number of four digits in descending order and differing by one (9876). Reverse the digits and subtract. Try this on at least three other numbers.

III. Copy and write the next four numbers in the series:

1. 0.9, 0.8, 0.7
2. 1.7, 1.6, 1.5
3. 2, $1\frac{3}{4}$, $1\frac{1}{2}$
4. 3.5, 3, 2.5
5. 7, $6\frac{2}{3}$, $6\frac{1}{3}$
6. 9, $7\frac{1}{2}$, 6
7. $\frac{13}{8}$, $\frac{11}{8}$, $\frac{9}{8}$
8. 4, 3.4, 2.8

Quick Quiz No. 8

1. Which is larger, 0.2 or 0.025?
2. Mary wants a sweater costing $8.25. She has saved $6.75. How much more money does she need in order to buy the sweater?
3. Express as eighths: $\frac{1}{2}$, $\frac{3}{4}$, $\frac{1}{4}$.
4. How many hours are there from 8 a.m. to 3 p.m.?
5. 24 minutes is what fractional part of an hour?
6. How many hundredths are there in the number 6.9?
7. 6 minutes 42 seconds equals how many seconds?
8. What is the largest number you can write with the digits 1, 2, 3, and 4? (Do not use exponents.)
9. 12 ft. + 36 ft. + 9 ft. = ?
10. 9.00 − 2.62 = ?

Review of . . .
SUBTRACTION

1. Copy and fill in the blanks:
   (a) The answer in subtraction is called the ______ or ______.
   (b) The number from which another number is subtracted is called the ______.
   (c) The number subtracted is called the ______.
   (d) Only ______ quantities can be subtracted.
2. Subtraction with zero:
   (a) $\begin{array}{r} 6210 \\ -1476 \\ \hline \end{array}$ (b) $\begin{array}{r} 9200 \\ -2496 \\ \hline \end{array}$ (c) $\begin{array}{r} 7000 \\ -6921 \\ \hline \end{array}$
3. Subtraction of fractions:
   (a) $\begin{array}{r} 22\frac{7}{8} \\ -\ 6 \\ \hline \end{array}$ (b) $\begin{array}{r} 18 \\ -12\frac{7}{8} \\ \hline \end{array}$ (c) $\begin{array}{r} 16\frac{2}{3} \\ -11\frac{1}{2} \\ \hline \end{array}$ (d) $\begin{array}{r} 24\frac{1}{2} \\ -16\frac{7}{8} \\ \hline \end{array}$
4. Subtraction of decimals:
   (a) 16 − 12.25 (b) 19 − 1.2 (c) 29.4 − 16.9
5. When it is 1 p.m. in New York, what time is it in
   (a) Kansas City, Missouri (b) Cheyenne, Wyoming, and (c) Portland, Oregon?

6. How long after the landing of the Pilgrims on December 21, 1620 was the signing of the Declaration of Independence on July 4, 1776?

7. Find N:

   (a) $N + 18 = 121$ (b) $25 + N = 672$

8. Find the difference in the heights of Bob and Bill. Bob is 5′ 2″ tall and Bill is 4′ 11″ tall.

9. How many more pupils has Edison Junior High School with 1004 pupils than Horace Mann Junior High School with 786 pupils?

10. What is the difference in the rainfall during February and March in Green Ridge, Missouri, if 4.2 inches fell in February and 5.1 inches in March?

Chapter Test

1. $\begin{array}{r} 4{,}241 \\ 6{,}892 \\ 1{,}475 \\ +3{,}782 \\ \hline \end{array}$

2. $\begin{array}{r} 7{,}002 \\ -6{,}891 \\ \hline \end{array}$

3. $\begin{array}{r} 3\frac{2}{3} \\ +1\frac{2}{3} \\ \hline \end{array}$

4. $\begin{array}{r} 4\frac{2}{3} \\ -1\frac{2}{3} \\ \hline \end{array}$

5. $\begin{array}{r} 7\frac{2}{3} \\ +6 \\ \hline \end{array}$

6. $\begin{array}{r} 8\frac{4}{5} \\ -4 \\ \hline \end{array}$

7. $\begin{array}{r} 9 \\ +4\frac{4}{5} \\ \hline \end{array}$

8. $\begin{array}{r} 9 \\ -1\frac{7}{8} \\ \hline \end{array}$

9. $\begin{array}{r} 3\frac{1}{2} \\ 1\frac{1}{4} \\ +1\frac{1}{8} \\ \hline \end{array}$

10. $\begin{array}{r} 4\frac{7}{8} \\ -1\frac{3}{4} \\ \hline \end{array}$

11. $\begin{array}{r} 3\frac{1}{5} \\ 2\frac{2}{3} \\ +1\frac{1}{2} \\ \hline \end{array}$

12. $\begin{array}{r} 4\frac{1}{5} \\ -1\frac{2}{3} \\ \hline \end{array}$

13. $\begin{array}{r} 6.2 \\ 1.4 \\ 14.2 \\ +\ 1.6 \\ \hline \end{array}$

14. $\begin{array}{r} 2.010 \\ -1.475 \\ \hline \end{array}$

15. $\begin{array}{r} \text{3 ft. 4 in.} \\ \text{6 ft. 9 in.} \\ +\text{7 ft. 2 in.} \\ \hline \end{array}$

16. $\begin{array}{r} \text{4 yd. 1 ft.} \\ -\text{2 yd. 2 ft.} \\ \hline \end{array}$

17. Which is larger and how much, 0.002 or 0.2?

18. Charles gathered $6\frac{1}{2}$ pounds, $3\frac{1}{4}$ pounds, and $5\frac{1}{2}$ pounds of beans from three rows in the bean field. How many more pounds will he need to gather for the hotel if he promised them 20 pounds?

19. A fisherman brought home fish weighing 1.25 pounds, 1.5 pounds, 1.75 pounds, and 1 pound. How much over 5 pounds did they weigh?

20. A train leaves Kansas City, Missouri, at 5:30 p.m. and arrives in Ponca City, Oklahoma, at 10:58 p.m. How long did it take for the trip?

CHAPTER SIX    

Exploring Triangles and Quadrilaterals

In mathematics, we call a flat smooth surface like a desk top a plane surface, or simply a plane. The name given a figure in a plane depends upon the number or the kind of lines that enclose it. Look about you and notice the planes in the classroom. Notice the number and kind of lines that enclose figures in the planes.

The Triangle

Three line segments enclose this plane figure called a *triangle*. The sides of the triangle form three angles. (In the word *triangle*, *tri* means three.) The three vertices (plural for vertex) of this triangle are A, B, and C. A triangle is named by reading the letters at the vertices, as triangle ABC. We write this as $\triangle ABC$. The sides of this triangle are AB, BC, and AC.

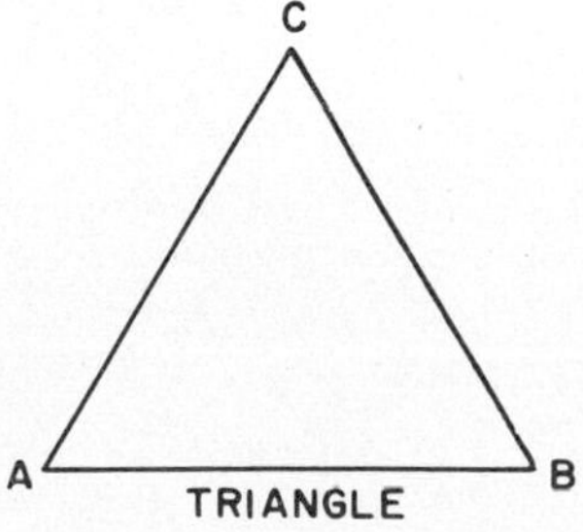

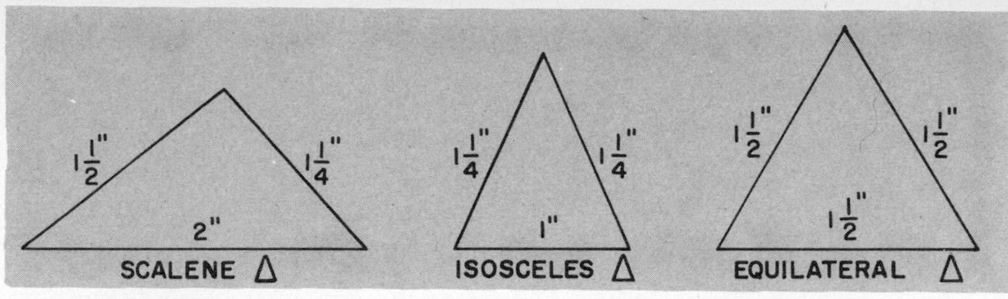

EXERCISES

1. (a) How many sides are equal in length in the *scalene triangle* shown above?

   (b) How would you describe this scalene triangle?

2. (a) How many sides are equal in length in the *isosceles triangle* shown above?

   (b) How would you describe this isosceles triangle?

3. (a) How many sides are equal in length in the *equilateral triangle* shown above?

   (b) How would you describe this equilateral triangle?

4. Draw a triangle with sides 3″ and $1\frac{1}{2}''$ and the angle between the sides equal to 40°.

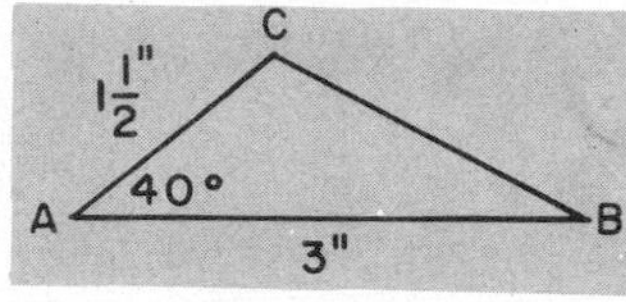

Step 1. Draw a line segment AB 3 inches long.

Step 2. At point A, with a protractor, draw an angle of 40°, making AC $1\frac{1}{2}$ inches long.

Step 3. Connect point C with point B forming $\triangle ABC$.

5. Answer these questions, which refer to Exercise 4:

   (a) How many sides of the triangle are equal in length?

   (b) How many angles are equal?

   (c) What kind of triangle have you drawn?

6. Construct a triangle with two sides each $2\frac{1}{2}''$ and one side 2″.

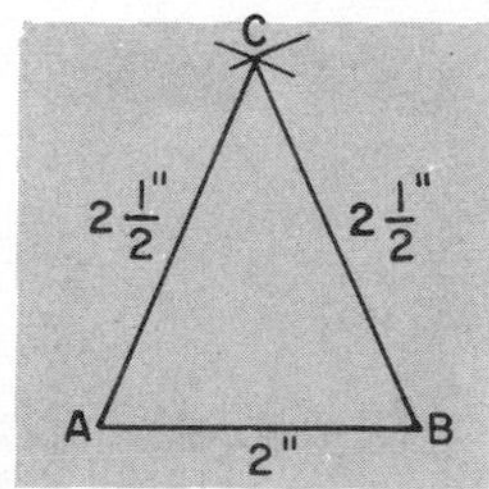

Step 1. Draw line segment AB 2″ long.

Step 2. Set the points of the compasses $2\frac{1}{2}''$ apart.

Step 3. Using points A and B as centers, draw arcs with the compasses intersecting above line segment AB at point C.

Step 4. Draw AC and BC forming $\triangle ABC$.

7. Construct a triangle with each side $2\frac{1}{2}''$.
8. Answer these questions which refer to Exercise 7:
   (a) How many sides of the triangle are equal in length?
   (b) How many angles are equal?
   (c) What kind of triangle have you drawn?
   (d) Why is this triangle also called equiangular?
9. Using other measurements, draw a scalene triangle, an isosceles triangle, and an equilateral triangle.

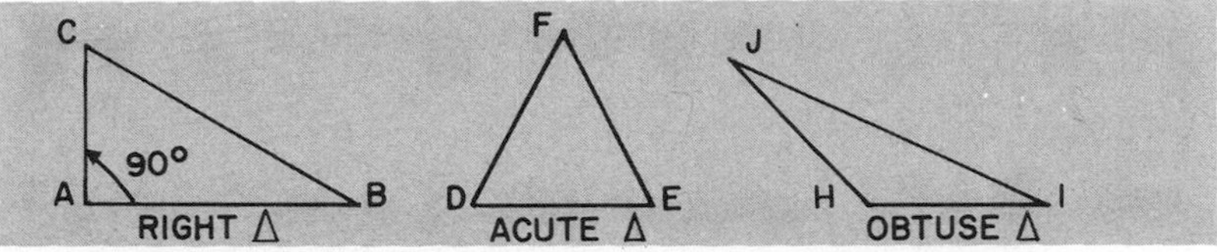

10. (a) What kind of angle does angle A appear to be?
    (b) How would you describe a *right triangle?*
11. (a) What kind of angles do angles D, E, and F appear to be?
    (b) How would you describe an *acute triangle?*
12. (a) What kind of angle does angle H appear to be?
    (b) How would you describe an *obtuse triangle?*
13. What kind of angles do angles B, C, I and J appear to be?
14. What kind of triangles, according to their angles, are these?

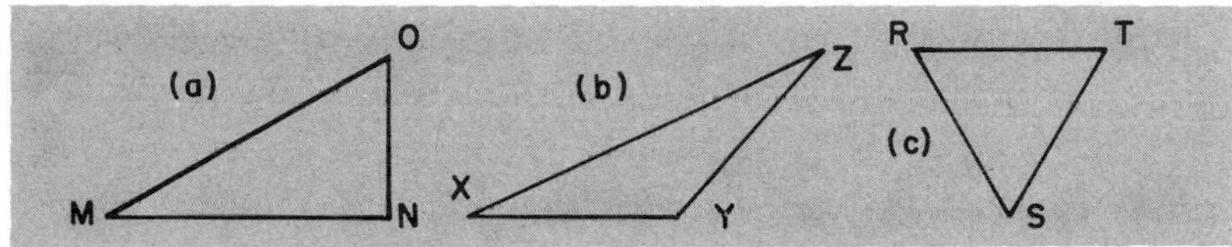

15. Draw a right triangle, an acute triangle, and an obtuse triangle.
16. Draw a triangle on paper like the one in the figure and cut it out. Tear off the angles and fit them together with the vertices at point O.
    (a) $\angle A + \angle B + \angle C$ appear to form what kind of angle at point O?
    (b) $\angle A + \angle B + \angle C$ appear to equal how many degrees?

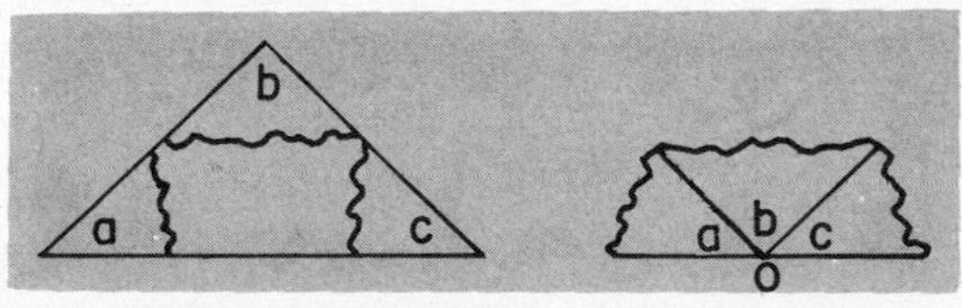

17. Construct an equilateral triangle and measure each angle with a protractor. The sum of the three angles of this equilateral triangle appears to equal how many degrees?
18. Construct an isosceles triangle and measure each angle with a protractor. The sum of the three angles of this isosceles triangle appears to equal how many degrees?
19. Draw a right triangle and find the sum of its three angles.
20. The sum of the angles of any triangle appears to equal how many degrees?
21. Find the size of the third angle of a triangle if two of the angles measure:
    (a) 60° and 40° (b) 50° and 100°
    (c) $10\frac{1}{2}$° and 80° (d) 114° and 61°
22. In a scalene or an equilateral triangle, any side may be called the base. In an isosceles triangle, the side which is not one of the equal sides is usually called the base. The two angles adjacent to the base are called base angles and the third angle is called the vertex angle.
    (a) If the base angles of a triangle are 50° and 70°, how large is the vertex angle?
    (b) In an isosceles triangle, if the vertex angle equals 70°, how large is each of the base angles?
    (c) In $\triangle XYZ$, if $\angle X = 90°$, how many degrees are there in $\angle Y$ and $\angle Z$ if they are equal to each other?
    (d) In an equilateral triangle, how many degrees are there in each angle?
23. Can there be a triangle whose angles measure:
    (a) 50°, 120°, 60°? (b) 90°, 10°, 80°?
    (c) 30°, 80°, 70°? (d) 20°, 140°, 60°?

*24. Draw and name the following triangles with sides:
    (a) 2 in., $2\frac{1}{2}$ in., and 3 in. (b) $1\frac{1}{2}$ in., $2\frac{1}{2}$ in., and $2\frac{1}{2}$ in.
    (c) 3 in., 3 in., and 1 in. (d) 3 in., 4 in., and 5 in.

*25. In the triangles that you have drawn in Exercise 24, is the sum of the lengths of any two sides always greater than the length of the third side?

*26. Can there be triangles whose three sides are:
    (a) 4 in., 3 in., and 7 in.? (b) 9 in., 7 in., and 5 in.?
    (c) 7 in., 2 in., and 9 in.? (d) 11 in., 5 in., and 8 in.?

*27. Draw a triangle with the base $1\frac{1}{2}$ in. and the base angles 40° and 60°.

Step 1. Draw a line segment MN $1\frac{1}{2}$ in. long.

Step 2. Using a protractor draw $\angle M = 40°$ and $\angle N = 60°$.

Step 3. Extend MO and NP to meet at R forming $\triangle MNR$.

$\triangle MNR$ has a base of $1\frac{1}{2}$ in. and base angles 40° and 60°.

*28. Draw and name the following triangles having:

(a) Base $XY = 2$ in. Base angles $X = 30°$ and $Y = 40°$

(b) Base $AB = 1$ in. Base angles $A = 90°$ and $B = 45°$

(c) Base $MN = 2$ in. Base angles $M = 50°$ and $N = 50°$

(d) Base $TW = 1$ in. Base angles $T = 60°$ and $W = 60°$

Words you should understand:

1. triangle 2. scalene triangle 3. isosceles triangle 4. equilateral triangle 5. right triangle 6. acute triangle 7. obtuse triangle

Review of . . .
TRIANGLES

Copy and complete the following statements:

1. A triangle has ______ sides and ______ angles.
2. A triangle with all three sides equal in length is called an ______ triangle.
3. A triangle with two sides equal in length is called an ______ triangle.
4. A triangle with one right angle is called a ______ triangle.
5. A triangle with one obtuse angle is called an ______ triangle.
6. The sum of the three angles of a triangle is ______ degrees.
7. The sum of the lengths of two sides of a triangle is ______ than the length of the third side.
8. The angles adjacent to the base of a triangle are called ______ angles, and the third angle is called the ______ angle.
9. If each of the base angles of an isosceles triangle is 40°, the vertex angle is ______ degrees.
10. If two angles of a triangle measure 90° and 30°, the third angle measures ______.

Draw the following triangles:

11. Given: Base 2 in. and base angles 120° and 40°.
12. Given: Lengths of three sides 1 in., $1\frac{1}{2}$ in., and 2 in.
13. Given: Length of two sides 2 in., $1\frac{1}{2}$ in. and the included angle 20°.
14. Given: Length of one side of an equilateral triangle = $\frac{3}{4}$ in.

The Quadrilateral

A plane figure like *ABCD* is called a *quadrilateral.* In the word quadrilateral, "quad" means four and "lateral" means sides. Name some plane figures in your classroom that are quadrilaterals.

In the quadrilateral *ABCD*, angles *A*, *B*, *C*, and *D* are called interior angles.

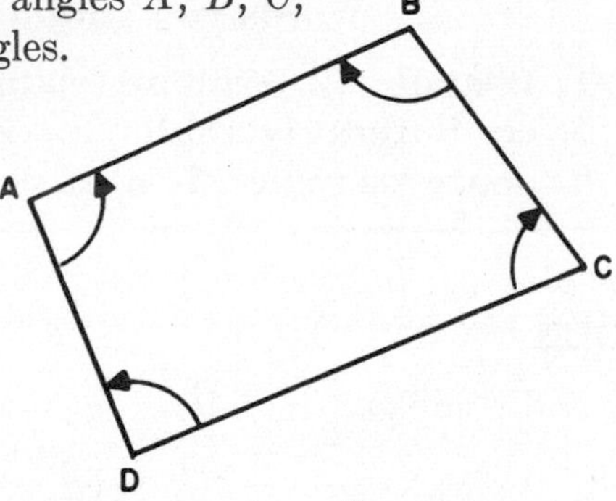

In the quadrilateral *MNOP*, the line drawn from *M* to *O* and the line drawn from *N* to *P* are called diagonals.

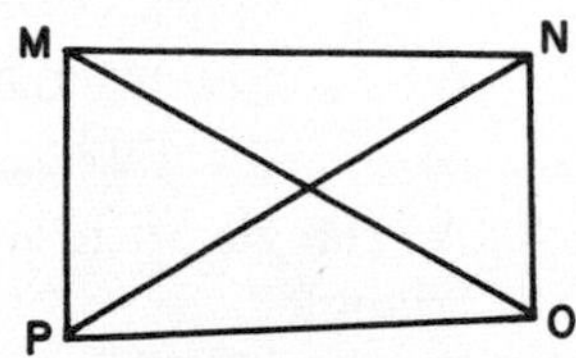

EXERCISES

1. Answer the following questions about quadrilateral *ABCD* above.
   (a) How many sides has the figure *ABCD*?
   (b) How many interior angles has the figure *ABCD*? Name them.
   (c) How many vertices has the figure *ABCD*? Name them.
   (d) How many diagonals has the figure *ABCD*?

If *ABCD* is a parallelogram, side *AB* is parallel to side *DC* and side *AD* is parallel to side *BC*. This is written $AB \parallel DC$
$AD \parallel BC$

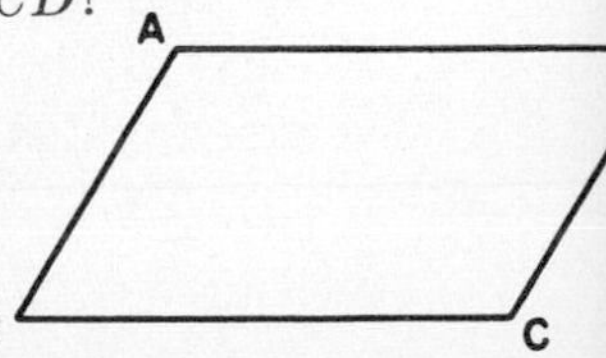

Notice that a parallelogram is a quadrilateral.

2. Answer these questions about parallelogram $ABCD$:
   (a) How do sides AB and DC appear to compare in length?
   (b) How do sides AD and BC appear to compare in length?
   (c) How would you describe a parallelogram?

If $EFGH$ is a trapezoid, side EF is parallel to side HG and the other pair of sides are not parallel.

3. Answer these questions about the trapezoid $EFGH$:
   (a) Does side EF appear to be parallel to side HG?
   (b) How do sides EF and HG appear to compare in length?
   (c) How would you describe a trapezoid?
   (d) Does side EH appear to be parallel to side FG?

1. A parallelogram is a quadrilateral with both pairs of opposite sides parallel.

2. A trapezoid is a quadrilateral with only one pair of opposite sides parallel.

4. Answer these questions about rectangle $ABCD$:
   (a) Do the opposite sides of the rectangle $ABCD$ appear to be parallel?

A B D C RECTANGLE

   (b) Is the rectangle $ABCD$ a parallelogram?
   (c) What kind of angles are angles A, B, C, and D?

Remember that pairs of line segments as AB and BC which meet and form right angles, are called perpendicular line segments.

This is written $AB \perp BC$.

   (d) Name the four pairs of line segments that are perpendicular to each other in rectangle $ABCD$.

Adjoining sides in quadrilaterals are called adjacent sides. Side *BC* is adjacent to *AB*.

(e) What sides are adjacent to *AB*?

(f) What sides are adjacent to *DC*?

(g) What sides are adjacent to *BC*?

(h) What sides are adjacent to *AD*?

(i) How would you describe a rectangle?

A rectangle is a parallelogram with four right angles.

5. Answer these questions about the square *EFGH*:

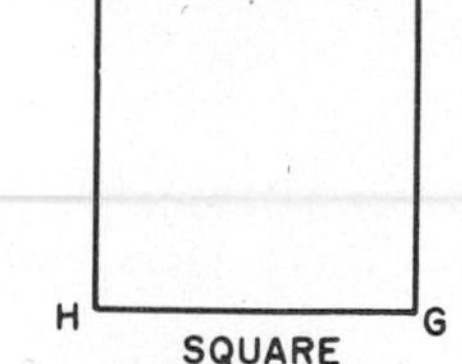

SQUARE

(a) Do the opposite sides of square *EFGH* appear to be parallel?

(b) Is the square *EFGH* a parallelogram?

(c) Are the adjacent sides of the square perpendicular to each other?

(d) Is square *EFGH* a rectangle?

(e) How do the four sides of a square *EFGH* compare in length?

(f) How would you describe a square?

A square is a rectangle with all four sides equal in length.

6. Name these quadrilaterals:

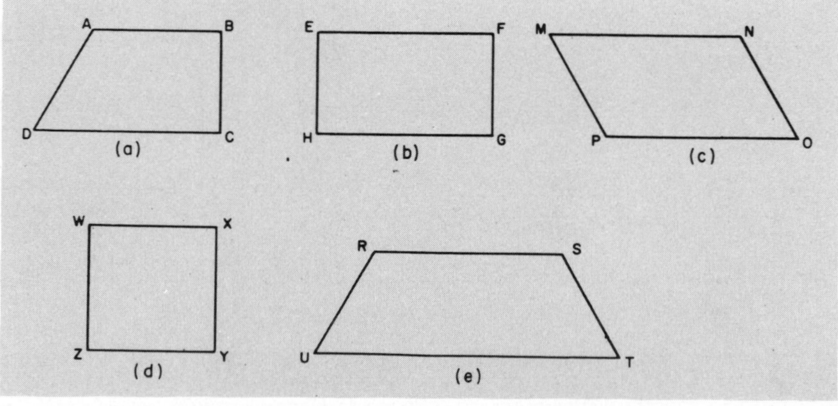

7. Draw a square, a rectangle, a parallelogram (not a square or rectangle), and a trapezoid.

8. Answer these questions about the angles of a quadrilateral:

(a) The sum of the angles of a rectangle equals how many degrees?

(b) Draw a quadrilateral that is not a rectangle. Draw one of the diagonals of the quadrilateral.

(1) Into how many triangles does the diagonal divide the quadrilateral?

(2) What is the sum of the angles of each triangle?

(3) What is the sum of the angles of the quadrilateral?

9. Draw parallelogram $ABCD$ with side $AB = 2$ in., $\angle A = 40°$, and side $AD = 1$ in.

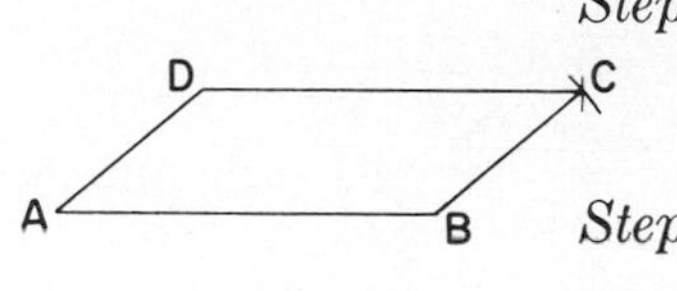

Step 1. Draw side $AB = 2$ in.

Step 2. Draw $\angle A = 40°$ with side $AD = 1$ in.

Step 3. With a 1 in. radius on the compass and B as a center, draw an arc above AB.

Step 4. With a 2 in. radius and D as a center, draw an arc cutting the first arc at C.

Step 5. Draw BC and DC forming parallelogram $ABCD$. Parallelogram $ABCD$ has sides 2 in. and 1 in. and $\angle A = 40°$.

10. Draw parallelogram $MNOP$ with $MN = 3$ in., $\angle M = 90°$, and $MO = 2''$.

11. Draw parallelogram $WXYZ$ with $WX = 1\frac{1}{4}$ in., $\angle X = 60°$, and $XY = 1$ in.

*12. Draw a parallelogram with two adjacent sides each $2\frac{1}{4}$ in. long and the included angle 90°.

*13. Draw a parallelogram with two sides each $1\frac{3}{4}$ in. long and the included angle 75°.

14. (a) The parallelogram in Exercise 10 is called a ______.

(b) The parallelogram in Exercise 12 is called a ______.

Review of . . .

QUADRILATERALS

1. Why is a rectangle a parallelogram?
2. Why is a square a rectangle?

3. Why is a trapezoid not a parallelogram?
4. How large is the fourth angle of a quadrilateral if the other three angles are 90° each?
5. How large is the fourth angle of a trapezoid if the sum of the other three angles is 310°?
6. Can there be quadrilaterals whose angles are:
   (a) 70°, 70°, 60°, 60° (b) 80°, 80°, 100°, 100°
   (c) 140°, 140°, 110°, 110° (d) 75°, 60°, 80°, 40°
7. If one side of a parallelogram is 6 inches long, how long is the opposite side?

Chapter Test

1. Find the third angle of a triangle if two angles measure:
   (a) 70° and 70° (b) 120° and 25°
   (c) 72° and 18° (d) 90° and $22\frac{1}{2}$°
2. If one side of an equilateral triangle is $2\frac{3}{4}$ in., what will be the length of each of the other sides?
3. Can a triangle have angles that measure 60°, 90°, and 40°?
4. Can a triangle have sides that measure 1 in., 2 in. and 3 in.?
5. Draw:
   (a) a right triangle (b) an obtuse triangle (c) an acute triangle
6. Draw an isosceles triangle and name the base, the base angles, and the vertex angle.
7. Draw a right triangle with the sides that include the right angle $1\frac{1}{2}$ in. and $1\frac{1}{4}$ in.
8. Draw a triangle with sides 1 in., $1\frac{1}{4}$ in., and 2 in. What kind of triangle is this?
9. Tell whether the following are true or false statements:
   (a) A parallelogram is a quadrilateral.
   (b) A rectangle is a parallelogram.
   (c) A trapezoid is a parallelogram.
   (d) Only one diagonal can be drawn in a quadrilateral.
   (e) A trapezoid has no two sides parallel.
   (f) The adjacent sides of a rectangle are perpendicular.
   (g) The sum of the angles of a quadrilateral equals 360°.
   (h) A quadrilateral can have angles of 120°, 60°, 120°, and 60°.

CHAPTER SEVEN  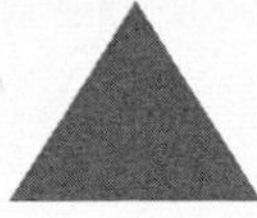  

Multiplication

Read the following problem and study the two solutions and see if you can tell why multiplication was invented.

What will 5 books cost at $2.50 each?

Solution I	Solution II	
$ 2.50	$ 2.50	multiplicand
2.50	× 5	multiplier
2.50	$12.50	product
2.50		
2.50		
$12.50		

In the multiplication method if one book costs $2.50, 5 books will cost how many times as much?

Multiplication is a process of finding the sum of a number of equal groups.

Make a table of multiplication facts through 12 × 12. You can learn many interesting facts about numbers by studying the table.

ORAL EXERCISES—Answer these questions about the table:

1. Can you call this a counting table?
2. By what are you counting in the one's column? In the five's column? In the twelve's column?
3. In which columns are all products divisible by 2?

4. In which columns are all products divisible by 3?
5. In which columns are all products divisible by 5?
6. What is the sum of the digits in each number in the nine's column?
7. $5 \times 9 = ?$
8. $5 \times ? = 45$
9. $? \times 9 = 45$
10. $\frac{1}{5}$ of $45 = ?$
11. $\frac{1}{9}$ of $45 = ?$

The last five questions illustrate number relationships found in each multiplication fact. When you understand these relationships, the multiplication facts will be much more useful to you.

12. 6 and 4 are factors of 24. They are the factors of 24 because their product is 24. We shall restrict the use of the term "factor" to whole numbers. What are other factors of 24? Ans. 1, 2, 3, 8, 12, and 24. The other pairs of factors are (1 and 24) (2 and 12) and (3 and 8).
13. What are the factors of 12? of 25? of 36?

New York World's Fair. General Motors Exhibit.

A fruit man is shipping 4 boxes of fruit, each weighing 42 pounds How much do the 4 boxes weigh?

adding	multiplying	
42 lb.	160 estimated product	
42 lb.		
42 lb.	42 lb.	multiplicand
42 lb.	4	multiplier
168 lb.	168 lb.	product

4 times 2 ones = 8 ones
4 times 4 tens = 16 tens
or
1 hundred and 6 tens

The multiplicand, 42, tells how many pounds in each group. The multiplier, 4, tells how many equal groups.

EXERCISES—Multiply and check by multiplying again:

1. 81	2. 33	3. 41	4. 92	5. 71	6. 61
3	2	9	4	5	6
7. 832	8. 911	9. 721	10. 632	11. 511	12. 422
2	3	4	2	5	4

The average yield of potatoes in a fertile valley is 269 bushels per acre. What yield can a man expect if he has 5 acres planted in potatoes under favorable conditions?

1500 estimated product

269 bu.
5
1345 bu.

$5 \times 9 = 45$. The 5 is placed in ones place and the 4 tens are added onto the 30 tens obtained by multiplying 5×6 tens. (The adding of the four tens is known as carrying in multiplication.) When the 4 tens are added to the 30 tens, there are 34 tens. The four tens are placed in tens place and the 30 tens or 3 hundreds are added to the 10 hundreds obtained by multiplying 5 times 2 hundreds. This makes 13 hundreds which equals 1 thousand and 3 hundreds.

EXERCISES—Multiply and check your products:

1. 89	2. 75	3. 68	4. 97	5. 84
3	4	5	6	7
6. 94	7. 88	8. 73	9. 87	10. 65
9	8	6	7	8

60
3
180

3×0 ones = 0 ones

3×6 tens = 18 tens which equals 1 hundred and 8 tens

2400 estimated product
603
4
2412

4 × 3 = 12. The 2 is written in ones place and the 1 ten is carried. 4 × 0 tens = 0 tens. The 1 ten and zero tens = 1 ten, which is written in tens place. 4 × 6 hundreds = 24 hundreds, or 2 thousand and 4 hundreds.

11. 805 2	12. 706 3	13. 709 4	14. 605 5	15. 502 6
16. 905 7	17. 804 8	18. 405 9	19. 1708 6	20. 1805 5

Example 1

	12,000 estimated product
569	multiplicand
23	multiplier
1707	first partial product
1138	second partial product
13,087	product

Example 2

569	multiplicand
23	multiplier
1707	first partial product
11380	second partial product
13,087	product

21. Answer these questions by studying Example 1 or Example 2:
    (a) What are we multiplying by when we multiply by the digit 3?
    (b) What are we multiplying by when we multiply by the digit 2?
    (c) Why is the 8 in the second partial product of Example 1 placed under the zero?
    (d) What digit is omitted in the second partial product of Example 1?

Notice in Example 1 that the first digit written in each partial product is placed directly under the digit used as a multiplier.

22. 589 45	23. 762 67	24. 845 38	25. 346 59	26. 984 52
27. 846 74	28. 562 89	29. 793 56	30. 1826 27	

Multiplying by 10 and 100 and Multiples of 10 and 100

Examples—1. 40 × 5

40 × 5 is 4 times as much as 10 × 5

10 × 5 = 50   40 × 5 = 4 × 50 = 200

2. 50 × 42

50 × 42 is 5 times as much as 10 × 42

10 × 42 = 420   50 × 42 = 5 × 420 = 2100

3. 600 × 152

600 × 152 is 6 times as much as 100 × 152

100 × 152 = 15,200

600 × 152 = 6 × 15,200 = 91,200

EXERCISES—Copy and fill in the blanks.

1. (a) 12 tens =   (b) 56 tens =   (c) 124 tens =

2. (a) 7 hundreds =   (b) 26 hundreds =   (c) 162 hundreds =

3. (a) 60 × 5 = ______ times as much as 10 × 5 or
______ × 50 or ______.

   (b) 70 × 5 = ______ times as much as 10 × 5 or
______ × 50 or ______.

4. (a) 80 × 42 = ______ times as much as 10 × 42 or
______ × 420 or ______.

   (b) 90 × 42 = ______ times as much as 10 × 42 or
______ × 420 or ______.

5. (a) 500 × 152 = ______ times as much as 100 × 152 or
______ × 15200 or ______.

   (b) 800 × 152 = ______ times as much as 100 × 152 or
______ × 15200 or ______.

<u>12000 Estimated Product</u>

$$\begin{array}{r}256\\ \underline{40}\\ 10{,}240\end{array} \qquad \begin{array}{l}10 \times 265 = 265 \text{ tens or } 2650\\ 40 \times 265 = 4 \times 2650 \text{ or } 10{,}240\end{array}$$

<u>120,000 Estimated Product</u>

$$\begin{array}{r}256\\ \underline{400}\\ 102{,}400\end{array} \qquad \begin{array}{l}100 \times 256 = 256 \text{ hundreds or } 25600\\ 400 \times 256 = 4 \text{ times } 25600 \text{ or } 102{,}400\end{array}$$

In Exercises 6 through 14, multiply and check.

6. $\begin{array}{r}848\\ \underline{20}\end{array}$ 7. $\begin{array}{r}964\\ \underline{40}\end{array}$ 8. $\begin{array}{r}782\\ \underline{50}\end{array}$ 9. $\begin{array}{r}876\\ \underline{60}\end{array}$ 10. $\begin{array}{r}975\\ \underline{90}\end{array}$

11. $\begin{array}{r}463\\ \underline{80}\end{array}$ 12. $\begin{array}{r}875\\ \underline{90}\end{array}$ 13. $\begin{array}{r}324\\ \underline{200}\end{array}$ 14. $\begin{array}{r}486\\ \underline{300}\end{array}$

Example

420,000 estimated product

623	623
701	701
623	623
436100	4361
436,723	436,723

Multiply and check:

15. 576	16. 693	17. 975	18. 742	19. 754
507	608	709	802	903
20. 702	21. 662	22. 475	23. 800	
906	820	760	900	

*24. Is 230×34 the same as 340×23? Multiply them and see.

65	29
29	65
585	145
130	174
1,885	1,885

This is a good way to check multiplying.

Find the products. Check by interchanging the multiplicand and multiplier:

25. 89	26. 75	27. 87	28. 76	29. 123
23	45	93	72	426
30. 456	31. 936	32. 482	33. 835	
821	375	827	672	

Words you should understand:

1. multiplicand 2. multiplier 3. product 4. factor

Test

Multiply and check:

1. 64	2. 223	3. 421	4. 875	5. 600
2	3	4	5	8
6. 700	7. 703	8. 805	9. 1204	10. 1977
9	7	6	7	3
11. 746	12. 475	13. 873	14. 254	15. 8729
23	45	126	337	541

16. 89	17. 635	18. 756	19. 287	20. 793
30	40	80	200	700
21. 725	22. 481	23. 827	24. 807	25. 9006
608	704	509	308	207

Practice in Multiplication

Remember to label the answers after you have checked carefully:

1. The Thompson family average 45 miles per hour on a trip. How many miles can they expect to cover in 8 hours? Suggested form: $N = 8 \times 45$.
2. If there are 24 sheets of paper in a package, how many sheets will there be in 18 packages?
3. Sam King charged 60¢ an hour mowing yards. One month he worked 48 hours in his neighborhood. How much did he make?
4. A farmer shipped 79 crates of fine apples. Each crate weighed 32 pounds. What was the total weight of the shipment?
5. A girl helped her grandfather set out tomato plants. They planted 28 plants in each row. There were 38 rows. How many plants did they set out?
6. Brian Brice sold, for his school, 17 subscriptions to a magazine at $3.50 a subscription. How much money should he turn in?
7. A farmer sold 423 bushels of apples at $2.25 a bushel to a wholesale house. How much should he receive for them?

*8. Mike Marlow bought 16 bunches of flowers at 55¢ a bunch and sold them for 80¢ a bunch. How much did he make?

*9. Miss Sutton sold 15 aprons, which she had made for $1.25 an apron. If the material cost $8.75, how much profit did she make?

*10. Bill Byers' father earns $2.10 an hour for regular time and $3.15 an hour for overtime. Last week he worked 40 hours regular time and 16 hours overtime. How much did he earn in all?

Quick Quiz No. 9

1. Is an even number ever divisible by 3?
2. If it is 8 a.m. in San Francisco, what time is it in New York City?

3. $8 \times N = 24$. What is N?
4. If 3 grapefruit can be bought for 25¢, how many can be bought for $1.00?
5. How many pints of milk are there in $4\frac{1}{2}$ gallons of milk?
6. $8 \times 322 = ?$
7. Round to the nearest thousand miles: 48,721 miles.
8. From the following, select those fractions which are equal to $\frac{2}{3}$:
   $\frac{10}{12}$, $\frac{8}{12}$, $\frac{12}{18}$, $\frac{9}{12}$, $\frac{4}{6}$, $\frac{14}{21}$
9. What is the answer in multiplication called?
10. What is the difference between 102 pounds and 37 pounds?

Multiplication of Common Fractions

As you work with the different types of problems involving multiplication of fractions, it will be helpful to observe relationships among numbers involved in the process.

What is $\frac{1}{2}$ of $\frac{1}{2}$ of this bar?

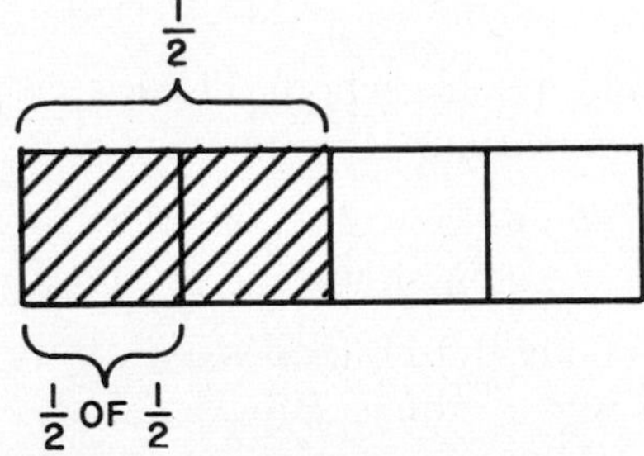

One-half of any quantity means one of the two equal parts of the quantity. Thus $\frac{1}{2}$ of $\frac{1}{2}$ means one of the two equal parts of $\frac{1}{2}$ or $\frac{1}{2}$ of $\frac{1}{2} = \frac{1}{4}$. Also, $\frac{1}{2}$ of $\frac{1}{4}$ means one of the two equal parts of $\frac{1}{4}$ or $\frac{1}{2}$ of $\frac{1}{4} = \frac{1}{8}$.

Example 1: What is $\frac{1}{2}$ of $\frac{3}{4}$?

If $\frac{1}{2}$ of $\frac{1}{4}$ is $\frac{1}{8}$, then $\frac{1}{2}$ of $\frac{3}{4} = 3 \times \frac{1}{8}$ or $\frac{3}{8}$.

($\frac{1}{2}$ of $\frac{3}{4} = \frac{3}{8}$)

Example 2: What is $\frac{1}{4}$ of $\frac{3}{8}$?

$\frac{1}{4}$ of any quantity means one of the four equal parts of the quantity.

If $\frac{1}{4}$ of $\frac{1}{8}$ is $\frac{1}{32}$, then $\frac{1}{4}$ of $\frac{3}{8} = 3 \times \frac{1}{32}$ or $\frac{3}{32}$

($\frac{1}{4}$ of $\frac{3}{8} = \frac{3}{32}$)

Example 3: What is $\frac{7}{8}$ of $\frac{1}{4}$?

$\frac{1}{8}$ of any quantity means one of the eight equal parts of the quantity.

If $\frac{1}{8}$ of $\frac{1}{4} = \frac{1}{32}$, then $\frac{7}{8}$ of $\frac{1}{4} = 7 \times \frac{1}{32}$ or $\frac{7}{32}$

($\frac{7}{8}$ of $\frac{1}{4} = \frac{7}{32}$)

Have you noticed in Examples 1, 2, and 3 the numerator obtained in multiplying the fractions is the product of the numerators of the fractions multiplied and the denominator obtained in multiplying is the product of the denominators of the fractions multiplied.

$\frac{1}{2}$ of $\frac{3}{4}$ can be thought of as $\frac{1}{2} \times \frac{3}{4}$ or $\frac{3}{8}$

$\frac{1}{4}$ of $\frac{3}{8}$ can be thought of as $\frac{1}{4} \times \frac{3}{8}$ or $\frac{3}{32}$

$\frac{7}{8}$ of $\frac{1}{4}$ can be thought of as $\frac{7}{8} \times \frac{1}{4}$ or $\frac{7}{32}$

In multiplying fractions multiply the numerators to obtain the numerator of the product, and the denominators to obtain the denominator of the product.

ORAL EXERCISES—Tell what each exercise means and solve.

1. (a) $\frac{1}{2}$ of $\frac{1}{8}$ (b) $\frac{1}{2}$ of $\frac{3}{8}$
2. (a) $\frac{1}{4}$ of $\frac{1}{3}$ (b) $\frac{1}{4}$ of $\frac{2}{3}$
3. (a) $\frac{1}{8}$ of $\frac{1}{6}$ (b) $\frac{1}{8}$ of $\frac{5}{6}$
4. (a) $\frac{1}{3}$ of $\frac{1}{8}$ (b) $\frac{1}{3}$ of $\frac{5}{8}$

Example 1: $\frac{1}{3}$ of $\frac{3}{4}$

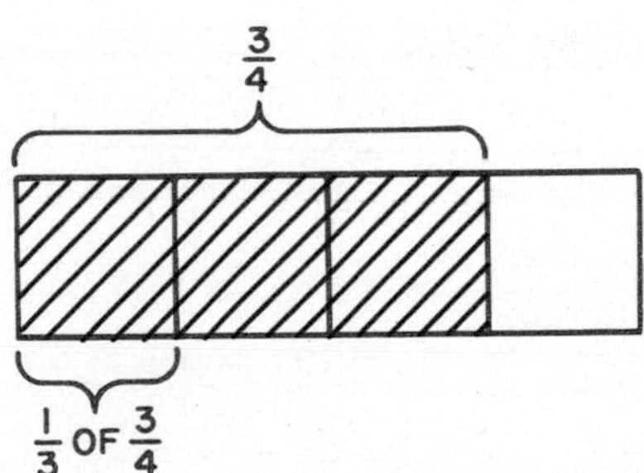

$\frac{1}{3}$ of $\frac{3}{4} = \frac{3}{12}$ or $\frac{1}{4}$ (Reduced to lowest terms)

Sometimes reducing is done in this manner:

$$\frac{\overset{1}{\cancel{3}}}{\underset{4}{\cancel{12}}} = \frac{1}{4}$$

(Both numerator and denominator are divided by 3)

or: $$\frac{1}{3} \times \frac{3}{4} = \frac{\overset{1}{1 \times \cancel{3}}}{\underset{1}{\cancel{3} \times 4}} = \frac{1}{4}$$

(The 3 in the numerator and the 3 in the denominator were both divided by 3)

Which method do you prefer for the solution of this problem and why do you prefer it?

Example 2: $\frac{1}{6} \times \frac{8}{9}$

Method 1: $\frac{1}{6} \times \frac{8}{9} = \frac{8}{54}$ or $\frac{4}{27}$

Here the product was obtained and then reduced to lowest terms.

Method 2:

$$\frac{1}{\underset{3}{\cancel{6}}} \times \frac{\overset{4}{\cancel{8}}}{9} = \frac{4}{27}$$

Here the 8 in the numerator and the 6 in the denominator were both divided by 2 and then the product was obtained.

EXERCISES—Answer the questions in Exercise 1. Find the products in Exercises 2 through 46.

Example 3

Find $\frac{5}{6} \times \frac{9}{25}$

Estimated product is less than $\frac{1}{2}$.

$$\frac{\overset{1}{\cancel{5}}}{\underset{2}{\cancel{6}}} \times \frac{\overset{3}{\cancel{9}}}{\underset{5}{\cancel{25}}} = \frac{3}{10}$$

1. (a) By what were the 5 in the numerator and the 25 in the denominator divided?
(b) By what were the 9 in the numerator and the 6 in the denominator divided?
(c) How was the 3 obtained in the numerator of the answer?
(d) How was the 10 obtained in the denominator of the answer?

2. $\frac{1}{3} \times \frac{6}{7}$
3. $\frac{1}{4} \times \frac{8}{9}$
4. $\frac{1}{5} \times \frac{5}{6}$
5. $\frac{2}{3}$ of $\frac{3}{4}$
6. $\frac{4}{5}$ of $\frac{5}{6}$
7. $\frac{8}{9}$ of $\frac{7}{8}$
8. $\frac{2}{3} \times \frac{6}{11}$
9. $\frac{15}{16} \times \frac{8}{25}$
10. $\frac{10}{11} \times \frac{33}{35}$
11. $\frac{5}{8} \times \frac{1}{3}$
12. $\frac{9}{10} \times \frac{7}{11}$

Example 1: What is $\frac{2}{3}$ of 3?

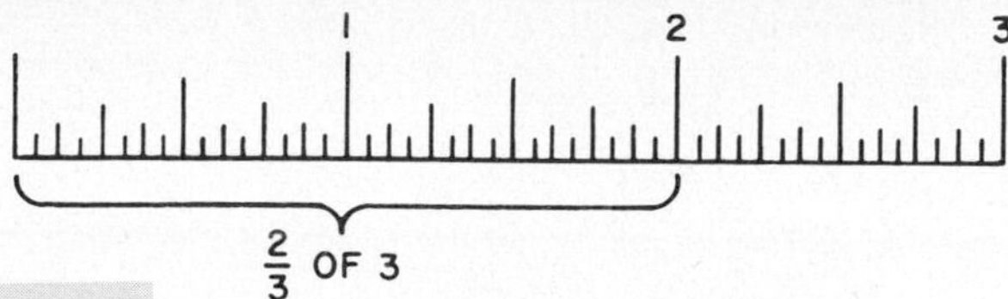

Estimated product is less than 3.

$$\frac{2}{3} \times 3 =$$

$$\frac{2}{\cancel{3}_1} \times \cancel{3}^1 = 2$$

Notice that the position of the whole number 3 is in the numerator.

Example 2: $\frac{2}{3} \times 10$

Estimated product is less than 10.

$\frac{2}{3} \times 10 = \frac{20}{3}$ or $6\frac{2}{3}$

13. $\frac{1}{6} \times 24$ 14. $\frac{3}{8} \times 24$ 15. $\frac{2}{3} \times 10$ 16. $\frac{5}{8} \times 6$ 17. $\frac{4}{9} \times 10$

18. $\frac{7}{8} \times 12$ 19. $\frac{4}{5} \times 9$ 20. $\frac{5}{6} \times 21$ 21. $\frac{9}{10} \times 12$ 22. $\frac{7}{9} \times 24$

Example 1: What is $2\frac{1}{2} \times 2$?

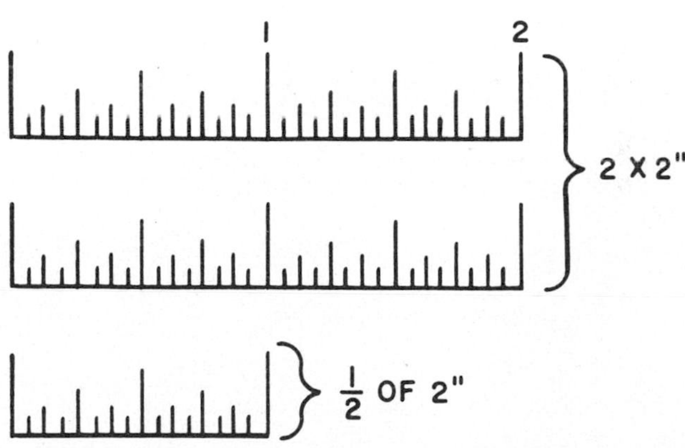

Estimated product is less than 6.

$$2\frac{1}{2} \times 2$$

$$\frac{5}{\cancel{2}_1} \times \cancel{2}^1 = 5$$

Notice $2\frac{1}{2}$ is changed to the improper fraction $\frac{5}{2}$.

Example 2: What is the product of $3\frac{1}{3}$ and 5?

Estimated product is more than 15.

$3\frac{1}{3} \times 5$

$\frac{10}{3} \times 5 = \frac{50}{3}$ or $16\frac{2}{3}$

23. $2\frac{1}{2} \times 4$	24. $3\frac{1}{2} \times 8$	25. $1\frac{1}{3} \times 6$	26. $2\frac{1}{4} \times 8$
27. $4\frac{1}{2} \times 6$	28. $8\frac{2}{3} \times 9$	29. $6\frac{1}{5} \times 15$	30. $5\frac{1}{2} \times 14$
31. $9\frac{1}{3} \times 7$	32. $10\frac{1}{2} \times 12$	33. $7\frac{1}{2} \times 5$	34. $8\frac{1}{3} \times 5$

Example: What is $2\frac{1}{2} \times \frac{2}{3}$ of a bar?

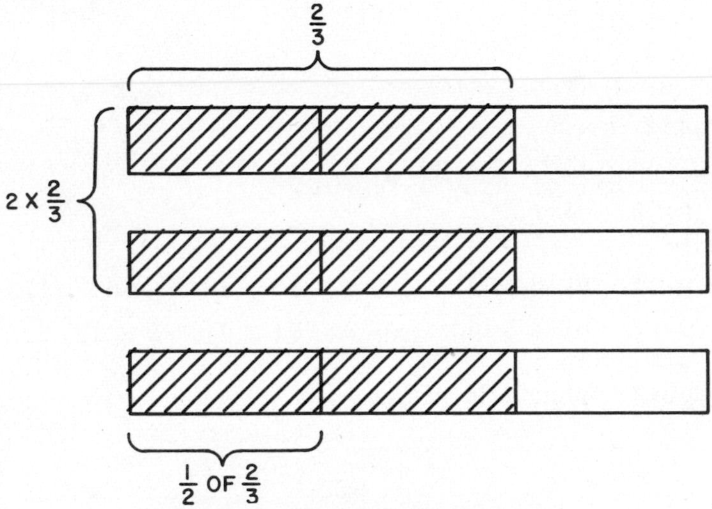

$\frac{2}{3}$

$2 \times \frac{2}{3}$

$\frac{1}{2}$ OF $\frac{2}{3}$

Estimated product is less than $2\frac{1}{2}$

$$2\frac{1}{2} \times \frac{2}{3}$$

$$\frac{5}{2} \times \frac{2}{3} = \frac{5 \times \overset{1}{\cancel{2}}}{\underset{1}{\cancel{2}} \times 3} = \frac{5}{3} \text{ or } 1\frac{2}{3} \text{ bars}$$

35. $1\frac{1}{2} \times \frac{1}{3}$	36. $2\frac{1}{2} \times \frac{1}{5}$	37. $3\frac{1}{3} \times \frac{4}{5}$	38. $7\frac{1}{2} \times \frac{2}{5}$
39. $8\frac{1}{2} \times \frac{4}{5}$	40. $1\frac{4}{5} \times \frac{2}{3}$	41. $6\frac{2}{3} \times \frac{3}{10}$	42. $9\frac{1}{2} \times \frac{4}{5}$
43. $7\frac{1}{2} \times \frac{4}{5}$	44. $8\frac{4}{5} \times \frac{1}{2}$	45. $7\frac{1}{2} \times \frac{2}{3}$	46. $10\frac{2}{3} \times \frac{3}{4}$

Quick Quiz No. 10

1. If you know the cost of one baseball, how would you find the cost of any number of baseballs at the same price?

2. What is the cost of 4 yards of rayon at $2.50 a yard?
3. A girl bought fifteen 5¢ stamps and ten 4¢ stamps. How much change should she receive from $1.50?
4. How many lemons are there in $3\frac{1}{2}$ dozen?
5. Does "of" in the problem $\frac{2}{3}$ *of* 15 mean $+$, $-$, $\times$, or $\div$?
6. What is $\frac{3}{4}$ of 28?
7. What is the cost of $2\frac{1}{2}$ pounds of candy at 80¢ a pound?
8. In the fraction $\frac{7}{8}$ the numerator is ? and the denominator is ?.
9. To reduce a proper fraction to lowest terms, we ______ both numerator and denominator by the same number.
10. What will eight ounces of candy cost if the candy sells for 60¢ a pound?

Multiplication of Mixed Numbers

Example

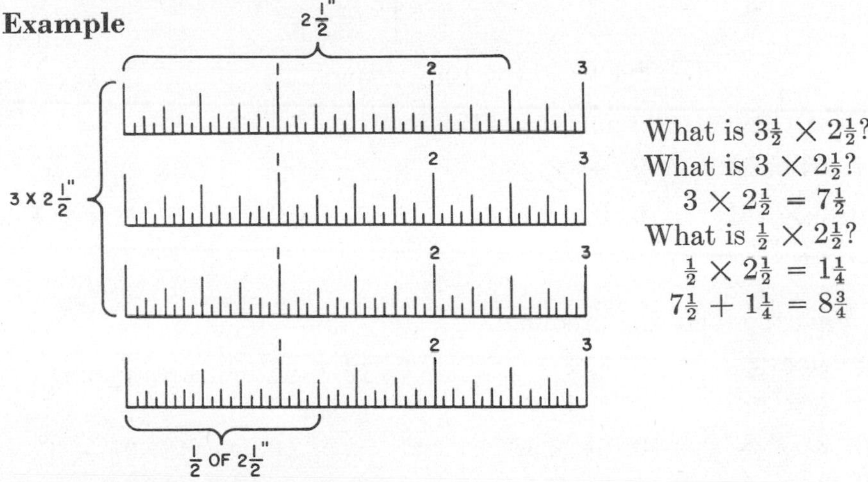

What is $3\frac{1}{2} \times 2\frac{1}{2}$?
What is $3 \times 2\frac{1}{2}$?
$3 \times 2\frac{1}{2} = 7\frac{1}{2}$
What is $\frac{1}{2} \times 2\frac{1}{2}$?
$\frac{1}{2} \times 2\frac{1}{2} = 1\frac{1}{4}$
$7\frac{1}{2} + 1\frac{1}{4} = 8\frac{3}{4}$

Estimated product is less than 9

$3\frac{1}{2} \times 2\frac{1}{2}$

$\frac{7}{2} \times \frac{5}{2} = \frac{35}{4}$ or $8\frac{3}{4}$

The product may be found directly from the diagram.

EXERCISES—Find the following products:

1. $2\frac{1}{2} \times 1\frac{1}{3}$	2. $4\frac{2}{3} \times 1\frac{1}{2}$	3. $7\frac{1}{2} \times 1\frac{2}{3}$	4. $6\frac{2}{3} \times 1\frac{1}{10}$
5. $8\frac{1}{2} \times 1\frac{1}{5}$	6. $2\frac{2}{3} \times 1\frac{1}{2}$	7. $6\frac{1}{2} \times 2\frac{3}{4}$	8. $12\frac{3}{4} \times 2\frac{2}{3}$
9. $7\frac{1}{2} \times 4\frac{1}{2}$	10. $6\frac{2}{3} \times 2\frac{2}{3}$	11. $8\frac{1}{2} \times 3\frac{2}{3}$	12. $24\frac{1}{2} \times 2\frac{1}{7}$

If each box of grapes weighs $6\frac{3}{4}$ pounds, what will 16 boxes weigh?

Method 1	*Method 2*
Estimated product is less than 112	
$16 \times 6\frac{3}{4}$	16
$16 \times \frac{27}{4} = \frac{\overset{4}{\cancel{16}} \times 27}{\underset{1}{\cancel{4}}} = 108$	$6\frac{3}{4}$
	$12 \quad (\frac{3}{4} \times 16)$
	96
	108

The weight is 108 pounds.

What will 7 boxes weigh at $15\frac{2}{3}$ pounds each?

Method 1	*Method 2*
Estimated product is less than 112	
$7 \times 15\frac{2}{3}$	$15\frac{2}{3}$
$7 \times \frac{47}{3} = \frac{329}{3}$ or $109\frac{2}{3}$ lb.	7
	$4\frac{2}{3} \quad (\frac{2}{3} \times 7)$
	105
	$109\frac{2}{3}$ lb.

The weight is $109\frac{2}{3}$ pounds.

EXERCISES—Obtain the products.

1. $6\frac{2}{3} \times 24$ 2. $8\frac{3}{4} \times 32$ 3. $7\frac{1}{2} \times 48$ 4. $9\frac{2}{3} \times 9$

5. $6 \times 15\frac{2}{3}$ 6. $9 \times 18\frac{1}{4}$ 7. $8 \times 10\frac{1}{3}$ 8. $7 \times 15\frac{1}{2}$

Test

Find the following products:

1. $\frac{1}{2} \times \frac{4}{5}$ 2. $\frac{2}{3} \times \frac{5}{6}$ 3. $\frac{15}{16} \times \frac{12}{25}$ 4. $\frac{8}{9} \times \frac{5}{7}$

5. $\frac{3}{4} \times 12$ 6. $\frac{5}{8} \times 16$ 7. $\frac{4}{5} \times 2$ 8. $\frac{8}{9} \times 10$

9. $2\frac{1}{2} \times 8$ 10. $6\frac{2}{3} \times 15$ 11. $5\frac{1}{2} \times 10$ 12. $9\frac{2}{3} \times 6$

13. $3\frac{1}{3} \times \frac{2}{3}$ 14. $8\frac{1}{2} \times \frac{2}{5}$ 15. $7\frac{1}{2} \times \frac{4}{15}$ 16. $2\frac{3}{4} \times 3\frac{1}{3}$

17. $8\frac{2}{3} \times 1\frac{1}{2}$ 18. $\begin{array}{r} 24 \\ \times 8\frac{1}{2} \\ \hline \end{array}$ 19. $\begin{array}{r} 75 \\ \times 9\frac{2}{3} \\ \hline \end{array}$ 20. $\begin{array}{r} 17\frac{2}{3} \\ \times 5 \\ \hline \end{array}$

More Practice in Multiplication of Fractions

1. A recipe calls for $\frac{3}{4}$ of a cup of milk. If you are making only $\frac{1}{2}$ of the recipe, how much milk will you use? Suggested form: $N = \frac{1}{2}$ of $\frac{3}{4}$.
2. If you allow $2\frac{1}{2}$ teaspoons of cocoa for each cup, how many teaspoons will it take for 9 cups?

3. A recipe calls for $2\frac{2}{3}$ cups of milk. How much will you use if you are making $2\frac{1}{2}$ times the recipe?
4. In planning for a camping trip, a group of Boy Scouts decided to provide $1\frac{1}{2}$ dozen oranges for each boy. How many dozen should they buy if 18 boys are going?
5. What will $2\frac{2}{3}$ pounds of candy cost at 75¢ a pound?
6. The girls in an art class were making ribbon awards, allowing $4\frac{3}{4}$ inches for each ribbon. How many inches will they need for 12 ribbons?
7. If it takes $2\frac{3}{4}$ yards of material for each curtain, how many yards are needed for 4 curtains?
8. The 7th grade sewing class offered to make towels for the Red Cross. How many yards of the material must they buy to make 48 towels if they are using $\frac{3}{4}$ of a yard for each towel?

*9. A boy receives $62\frac{1}{2}$¢ per hour for his work. What are his weekly wages if he worked $38\frac{1}{2}$ hours?

*10. Mr. C. A. Burns averages $17\frac{1}{2}$ miles per gallon country driving at the rate of 50 miles per hour. How many miles can he drive at this speed on $12\frac{1}{2}$ gallons of gasoline?

Review Test

1. Write in Roman numerals:
   (a) 520 (b) 1,402 (c) 6,000
2. Round to the nearest hundred:
   (a) 650 (b) 240 (c) 1,360 (d) 1,410

3. $\begin{array}{r} 4216 \\ 1721 \\ 3456 \\ +1824 \\ \hline \end{array}$
4. $\begin{array}{r} 8\frac{1}{2} \\ +3\frac{3}{4} \\ \hline \end{array}$
5. $\begin{array}{r} 7\frac{7}{8} \\ 3\frac{1}{4} \\ +1\frac{1}{16} \\ \hline \end{array}$
6. $\begin{array}{r} 1.216 \\ 3.002 \\ +21.400 \\ \hline \end{array}$

7. $\begin{array}{r} 6 \text{ yd. } 2 \text{ ft.} \\ 7 \text{ yd. } 2 \text{ ft.} \\ +1 \text{ yd. } 1\frac{1}{2} \text{ ft.} \\ \hline \end{array}$
8. $\begin{array}{r} 4002 \\ -1764 \\ \hline \end{array}$
9. $\begin{array}{r} 18 \\ -\ 2\frac{2}{3} \\ \hline \end{array}$
10. $\begin{array}{r} 25\frac{1}{2} \\ -17\frac{3}{4} \\ \hline \end{array}$

11. $\begin{array}{r} 2. \\ -1.75 \\ \hline \end{array}$
12. $\begin{array}{r} 7.25 \\ -2. \\ \hline \end{array}$
13. $\begin{array}{r} 6 \text{ hr. } 2 \text{ min.} \\ -4 \text{ hr. } 58 \text{ min.} \\ \hline \end{array}$
14. $\begin{array}{r} 426 \\ \times 60 \\ \hline \end{array}$

15. $\begin{array}{r} 926 \\ \times 408 \\ \hline \end{array}$
16. $\frac{2}{3} \times \frac{8}{9}$
17. $\frac{3}{4} \times 12$
18. $7\frac{1}{2} \times 3\frac{1}{3}$

19. In a junior high of 960 pupils, $\frac{2}{3}$ were neither tardy nor absent one month. How many were neither tardy nor absent?

20. If $\frac{1}{4}$ pound of meat is allowed for each pupil at lunch, how many pounds must be purchased to feed 250 pupils?

Multiplication of Decimal Fractions

A boy walks 2.8 miles each day going and coming from school. How far will he walk in one week of school?

2.8	(multiplicand)
5	(multiplier)
14.0	(product)

Is the answer reasonable? 2.8 miles is about 3 miles. 5 × 3 = 15 miles (estimated product). Notice there is one decimal place in the product and there is one decimal place in the multiplicand, and none in the multiplier.

If you are driving at the rate of 60 miles per hour, how far can you go in 0.25 of an hour?

```
   60
 0.25
 ----
 3.00
12.0
-----
15.00
```

60 × 0.05 = 3.00
60 × 0.2 = 12.0

Is the answer reasonable? 0.25 of an hour is the same as $\frac{1}{4}$ of an hour.

$$0.25 = \frac{25}{100} \text{ or } \frac{1}{4}$$

$$\frac{1}{\cancel{4}_{1}} \times \cancel{60}^{15} = 15$$

The distance is 15 miles.

Notice there are two decimal places in the product and there are two in the multiplier, and none in the multiplicand.

EXERCISES—Place the decimal points in the following products:

1.	2.	3.	4.	5.
1.25	146	0.476	0.0126	782
6	0.08	2	7	0.002
750	1168	952	882	1564

6.	7.	8.	9.	10.
0.76	8.2	960	0.872	0.0921
12	21	0.17	41	16
152	82	6720	872	5526
76	164	960	3488	921
912	1722	16320	35752	14736

Example 1

```
 0.19
  0.3
-----
0.057
```

What is 0.3 of 0.19?
Is the product a sensible one?
Change the decimals to common fractions and see $\frac{3}{10} \times \frac{19}{100} = \frac{57}{1000}$

Example 2

0.13	(multiplicand)
0.01	(multiplier)
0.0013	(product)

What is 0.01 of 0.13?
Is the product a sensible one?
Prove by using common fractions.

$\frac{1}{100} \times \frac{13}{100} = \frac{13}{10{,}000}$

What do you observe about the number of decimal places in the product when you multiply two decimals?

Notice in Example 1 that a zero was placed in front of the number to make three places or thousandths. How many zeros were placed in front in Example 2 to make four places or ten thousandths?

Multiply and check by reversing the multiplicand and the multiplier or by multiplying again. Estimate the answer before multiplying:

11. 2.6 12	12. 45 0.06	13. 0.006 72	14. 2.1 0.13	15. 0.007 0.02
16. 2.27 64	17. 0.921 0.52	18. 800.1 0.027	19. 0.4216 0.009	20. 2.006 2.01
21. 2.005 0.81	22. 0.0725 0.065	23. 87.52 0.92	24. 7.506 1.21	25. 100.7 2.92

Multiplying by 10, 100, or 1000

EXERCISES—Multiply the following to see if the answers are correct:

1. $10 \times 6 = 60$
2. $10 \times 0.042 = 0.42$
3. $10 \times 1.6 = 16$
4. $10 \times 0.001 = 0.01$
5. $10 \times 0.46 = 4.6$
6. $10 \times 0.2 = 2.$

If a number is multiplied by 10, the decimal point in the product is one place to the right of the decimal point in the original number.

7. $100 \times 6 = 600$
8. $100 \times 0.042 = 4.2$
9. $100 \times 1.6 = 160$
10. $100 \times 0.001 = 0.1$
11. $100 \times 0.46 = 46$
12. $100 \times 0.2 = 20$

If a number is multiplied by 100, the decimal point in the product is two places to the right of the decimal point in the original number.

Find the products in Exercises 13 through 34:

13. 1000×6	14. 1000×0.042	15. 1000×1.6
16. 1000×0.001	17. 1000×0.46	18. 1000×0.2
19. 10×4	20. 10×2.6	21. 10×0.25
22. 10×0.046	23. 10×0.0022	24. 100×42
25. 100×6.1	26. 100×0.25	27. 100×0.275
28. 100×2.002	29. 1000×47	30. 1000×6.2
31. 1000×0.25	32. 1000×0.021	33. 1000×2.0021
34. 1000×8.2		

Test

Find the following products. Show your estimate of the product.

1. 25	2. 0.96	3. 2.1	4. 0.82	5. 4.21
0.7	5	0.6	0.09	0.03
6. 0.87	7. 0.49	8. 7.21	9. 275	10. 0.0021
2.1	0.38	1.6	0.009	1.27
11. 0.272	12. 0.831	13. 8.09	14. 9000	15. 2.278
1.54	1.07	0.608	1.75	0.0027

16. 10×29.6	17. 100×0.128	18. 100×0.02
19. 1000×0.072	20. $1000 \times 71.$	

Practice with Decimals

Always ask yourself when you have finished each problem: (1) Is the answer a sensible one? (2) Is the answer labeled correctly?

1. What is the cost of 10 tons of coal at \$18.50 a ton? Suggested form: $N = 10 \times 18.50$.
2. How much will 1000 sheets of paper cost at \$0.001 a sheet?
3. What will 100 tulip bulbs cost at \$0.075 a bulb?
4. What is the cost of 7.5 yards of cloth at \$1.38 a yard?
5. Sam Stone earns \$1.875 an hour. What will he earn in a 40-hour week?
6. How many ounces are there in 12.6 pounds?
7. A meter is about 39.37 inches. How many inches will 6 meters be?

8. A cubic foot of water weighs approximately 62.5 pounds. How much will 2.5 cubic feet of water weigh?
9. If a cubic foot container will hold approximately 7.5 gallons of water, how many gallons are there in a tank that contains 16.5 cubic feet?
10. There are 16.5 feet in a rod. How many feet are there in 320 rods?
11. Mike averages 18.9 miles per gallon driving in the country. How many miles can he drive with 14.5 gallons of gasoline?
12. What will 14.5 gallons of gasoline cost at 31.3¢ a gallon?

Multiplication of Denominate Numbers

A boy needs four strips of wood, each 2 feet 7 inches long, to make a picture frame. What length of wood will he need?

2 ft. 7 in. 4 8 ft. 28 in. or 10 ft. 4 in.	4×7 in. = 28 in. or 2 ft. 4 in. 4×2 ft. = 8 ft. When 2 ft. 4 in. are added to 8 ft., we have 10 ft. 4 in.

EXERCISES—Find the products in Exercises 1 through 12.

1. 3 hr. 10 min. $\times 7$	2. 3 bu. 2 pk. $\times 8$	3. 3 lb. 8 oz. $\times 3$
4. 13 gal. 1 qt. $\times 6$	5. 17 ft. 3 in. $\times 5$	6. 15 yd. 2 ft. $\times 9$
7. 4 T. 600 lb. $\times 6$	8. 2 pt. 1 cup $\times 3$	9. 16 min. 10 sec. $\times 8$
10. 4 qt. 1 pt. $\times 10$	11. 1 yd. 10 in. $\times 4$	12. 1 mi. 120 rd. $\times 5$

13. How much will 6 cans weigh if each one weighs 4 pounds 6 ounces?
14. A carpenter needs lumber to make 5 shelves, each 4 feet 3 inches long. How much lumber must he buy?
15. It takes 2 yards and 13 inches of binding to go around one scarf. How much will it take to go around 4 scarves?
16. If Mabel practices her music lesson 1 hour and 20 minutes each day, how much will she have practiced in 6 days?

Quick Quiz No. 11

1. What is 0.1×0.01?
2. How many decimal places are there in the product of 3.6 and 0.25?
3. In the following, select the products that equal 12:
   (a) 0.3×0.4 (b) $\frac{1}{2}$ of 24 (c) 0.5×24 (d) 0.1×12
4. When canning peaches, will you need more or fewer jars if you use pint jars rather than quart jars?
5. At 60¢ an hour, what can you earn in 2 hours 20 minutes?
6. Which months have thirty days?
7. If a box weighs 24 ounces, how many pounds does it weigh?
8. Arrange in order of size, beginning with the smallest:
   $\frac{1}{2}$, $\frac{1}{8}$, $\frac{1}{3}$, $\frac{1}{4}$
9. Multiply each number by 10:
   (a) 52 (b) 1.8 (c) $1\frac{1}{2}$ (d) 0.028 (e) 62.2
10. Sally is making only $\frac{1}{2}$ of a recipe which calls for $3\frac{1}{2}$ cups of sugar. How much sugar should she use?

Review of . . .
MULTIPLICATION

1. Copy and fill in the blanks:
   (a) The answer in a multiplication example is called the ______.
   (b) The number that is multiplied and tells how many in each group is called the ______.
   (c) The number by which you multiply and which tells how many groups there are is called the ______.
   (d) To find the product of two numbers you ______.
   (e) To multiply any number by 1000, move the decimal point ______ places to the right.
2. Give the pairs of factors of 30.
3. Show that the product, 24×69, is the same as the product 69×24.
4. Multiply:
   (a) $\frac{2}{3} \times \frac{3}{8}$ (b) $\frac{4}{5} \times 35$ (c) $3\frac{1}{2} \times 7$ (d) $8\frac{1}{2} \times 1\frac{1}{3}$

5. Multiply:

(a) $\begin{array}{r} 46 \\ \times 70 \\ \hline \end{array}$ (b) $\begin{array}{r} 29 \\ \times 300 \\ \hline \end{array}$ (c) $\begin{array}{r} 402 \\ \times 609 \\ \hline \end{array}$ (d) $\begin{array}{r} 8006 \\ \times 4009 \\ \hline \end{array}$

6. Multiply:

(a) $\begin{array}{r} 6.25 \\ \times 16 \\ \hline \end{array}$ (b) $\begin{array}{r} 7.29 \\ \times 0.52 \\ \hline \end{array}$ (c) $\begin{array}{r} 0.0076 \\ \times 0.043 \\ \hline \end{array}$ (d) $\begin{array}{r} 0.029 \\ \times 0.708 \\ \hline \end{array}$

7. Multiply each number first by 10, then by 100, then by 1000:

(a) 6 (b) 0.8 (c) 2.06 (d) 13.124

8. Find the cost to the nearest cent:

(a) 7 erasers @ 3.2¢

(b) 8 tablets @ 4.3¢

(c) 16 gallons of gasoline @ 29.6¢

9. What is the total weight of 4 cans if each can weighs 1 pound 6 ounces?

10. Jess is making a cabinet with 4 shelves each 3′ 7″ long. What is the total length of shelving that he will have in the cabinet?

11. The rainfall in a certain city averages 4.9 inches per month. On this basis, what is the total rainfall per year?

12. Find the number of yards of cloth required to make 8 aprons if $1\frac{1}{3}$ yards of cloth are used in each apron.

13. At the end of the first hour a group of Boy Scouts had hiked $3\frac{2}{3}$ miles. If they keep up this rate, how far will they hike in $2\frac{1}{4}$ hours?

14. If the monthly payments on a house costs the family \$76.80, how much are the yearly payments?

Chapter Test

1. $\begin{array}{r} 6{,}246 \\ 8{,}294 \\ 3{,}165 \\ +1{,}845 \\ \hline \end{array}$ 2. $\begin{array}{r} 6\frac{1}{16} \\ 2\frac{1}{8} \\ +3\frac{1}{4} \\ \hline \end{array}$ 3. $\begin{array}{r} 2.02 \\ 12.06 \\ 14.73 \\ +16.81 \\ \hline \end{array}$ 4. $\begin{array}{r} \text{1 gal. 2 qt.} \\ \text{7 gal. 3 qt.} \\ \text{1 gal. 2 qt.} \\ \text{+4 gal. 3 qt.} \\ \hline \end{array}$

5. $\begin{array}{r} 29801 \\ -\ 6792 \\ \hline \end{array}$ 6. $\begin{array}{r} 85\frac{3}{4} \\ -\ 7\frac{7}{8} \\ \hline \end{array}$ 7. $\begin{array}{r} 200. \\ -\ 4.96 \\ \hline \end{array}$ 8. $\begin{array}{r} \text{1 lb. 10 oz.} \\ -\ \text{14 oz.} \\ \hline \end{array}$

9. $\begin{array}{r} 702 \\ \times 608 \\ \hline \end{array}$ 10. $9\frac{1}{3} \times 1\frac{1}{7} =$ 11. $\begin{array}{r} 6.25 \\ \times 0.45 \\ \hline \end{array}$ 12. $\begin{array}{r} \text{3 hr. 14 min.} \\ \times \quad 8 \\ \hline \end{array}$

13. (a) 4 ft. 2 in. = ______ in.
    (b) 8 lb. 3 oz. = ______ oz.

14. (a) 19 in. = ______ ft. ______ in.
    (b) 214 min. = ______ hr. ______ min.

15. Which is larger and how much?
    (a) 0.12 or 0.6
    (b) 0.004 or 0.04

16. Find the cost of 40 mathematics books at $3.64 each.

17. Find the cost of 6.5 yards of cloth at $1.30 a yard.

18. Find the cost of 12.5 gallons of gasoline at 28.5 cents a gallon.

19. If you buy an $18.75 United States Savings Bond each month for a year, how much will the bonds cost altogether?

20. A recipe calls for $2\frac{3}{4}$ cups of flour. If you plan to make only half of the recipe, how much flour will you use?

CHAPTER EIGHT  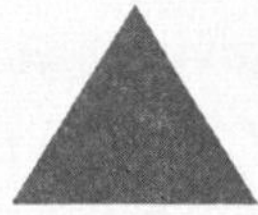  

Division

Read the following problems and see if you know what use of division is involved in each problem.

1. A man has $25 to divide equally among his five sons. How much will each boy receive?

2. If I save $5 a week, how many weeks will it take to save $25?

In Question 1, the $25 is divided into 5 equal parts in order to find the size of the part each boy is to receive.

Division is used to find the size of the equal groups into which some quantity is divided.

In Question 2, it is necessary to find how many groups of $5 each there are in $25.

Division is used to find how many equal groups of a given size there are in a quantity.

There are other uses for division which we will study this year. Be watching for them.

EXERCISES—Show by diagram the size of the equal groups or the number of equal groups in each problem.

1. How many dollars will each child receive if \$8 is divided equally between two children?
2. How many pencils will each child receive if 12 pencils are divided equally between two children?
3. How many marbles will each boy receive if 20 marbles are divided equally among 4 boys?
4. How many books will each girl receive if 10 books are divided equally among 5 girls?
5. How many 5¢ pencils can you buy with 20¢?
6. How many 4¢ stamps can you buy for 20¢?
7. How many groups of 4 pupils each can you make from 12 pupils?
8. How many groups of 6's are there in 18?

Division and the Other Processes

You have learned that multiplication is a short method for addition. Similarly division is a short method in subtraction.

How many \$10 bills can be obtained in exchange for \$50?

Subtraction Method

$$\begin{array}{r} \$50 \\ -10 \\ \hline \$40 \\ -10 \\ \hline \$30 \\ -10 \\ \hline \$20 \\ -10 \\ \hline \$10 \\ -10 \\ \hline 0 \end{array}$$

You have subtracted \$10 five times, so there are 5 \$10 bills in \$50.

Division Method

$$\begin{array}{r} 5 \\ \$10\overline{)\$50} \\ \underline{50} \end{array}$$

Here you say: "How many tens are there in 50?" The answer is 5.

$6 \times 9 = 54$

$$\begin{array}{r} 9 \\ 6\overline{)54} \\ \underline{54} \end{array} \qquad \begin{array}{r} 6 \\ 9\overline{)54} \\ \underline{54} \end{array}$$

Divisor ↓

$$\begin{array}{rl} 9 & \text{quotient} \\ 6\overline{)54} & \text{dividend} \\ \underline{54} & \end{array}$$

$6 \times 9 = 54$

How does multiplication help you in division when you ask how many sixes in 54?

What does the product of the quotient and the divisor equal? We can check division by multiplying.

Test on Division Facts

Divide:

1. $6\overline{)42}$	2. $9\overline{)9}$	3. $4\overline{)0}$	4. $7\overline{)56}$	5. $8\overline{)32}$
6. $3\overline{)24}$	7. $7\overline{)49}$	8. $8\overline{)64}$	9. $9\overline{)45}$	10. $6\overline{)48}$
11. $9\overline{)63}$	12. $6\overline{)54}$	13. $8\overline{)8}$	14. $6\overline{)24}$	15. $9\overline{)81}$
16. $7\overline{)21}$	17. $6\overline{)0}$	18. $8\overline{)48}$	19. $7\overline{)63}$	20. $8\overline{)56}$
21. $4\overline{)32}$	22. $9\overline{)27}$	23. $6\overline{)36}$	24. $8\overline{)72}$	25. $3\overline{)27}$
26. $7\overline{)42}$	27. $3\overline{)21}$	28. $9\overline{)72}$	29. $4\overline{)36}$	30. $4\overline{)20}$
31. $9\overline{)0}$	32. $9\overline{)36}$	33. $4\overline{)28}$	34. $8\overline{)24}$	35. $4\overline{)24}$

Examples

3 oranges
$4\overline{)14}$ oranges
12
2 oranges left over (remainder)

1. If you wish to divide 14 oranges among 4 people, each person will receive 3 oranges. There will be 2 oranges left over.

$3\frac{1}{2}$ oranges
$4\overline{)14}$
12
$\frac{2}{4} = \frac{1}{2}$

2. If these 14 oranges are to be divided equally among the 4 people, each person will receive $3\frac{1}{2}$ oranges. Sometimes we express how much is left over, as in Example 1, as a remainder. Sometimes we express the remainder as a fraction, as in Example 2.

8 tables
$10\overline{)87}$ tables
80
7 people left over which will take another table. The answer is 9 tables.

3. If you wish to seat 87 people with 10 to a table, it will take 9 tables. Sometimes we round the quotient to the next number as in Example 3.

2 shelves
$2\overline{)5}$
4

4. If you have 5 feet of lumber and you are making shelves 2 feet long, you will be able to make 2 shelves from the lumber. Sometimes you drop the remainder, as in Example 4, since you are interested in how many shelves you can make from the lumber.

The nature of the problem should determine what it is reasonable to do with the remainder.

EXERCISES—Decide what to do with the remainders in each of these problems and tell why you decided as you did.

1. Divide 11 books among 5 people.
2. Divide 11 dollars among 5 girls.
3. Divide 9 pounds of candy among 4 boys.
4. Divide 13 roses among 4 women.
5. How many dresses can you make from 7 yards if each dress takes 3 yards?
6. How many rows will you need to seat 26 people if you can seat 9 people in a row?
7. How many pages will it take for 136 lines of poetry if you put 30 lines on a page?
8. How many tables will it take to seat 23 people if you seat 4 at a table?

Estimating Quotients

$6\overline{)426}$ We ask how many sixes in 426. Since there are 7 sixes in 42, there must be more than 70 sixes in 426, as 426 is more than ten times 42. The quotient is between 70 and 80.

$20\overline{)546}$

$20 \times 20 =$
$20 \times 30 =$

The estimated quotient is between 20 and ______.

$43\overline{)8720}$

$43 \times 200 =$
$43 \times 300 =$

The estimated quotient is between ______ and ______.

$212\overline{)4526}$

$212 \times 20 =$
$212 \times 30 =$

The estimated quotient is between ______ and ______.

EXERCISES—Between what two numbers to the nearest tens or hundreds will these quotients fall?

1. $4\overline{)210}$	2. $5\overline{)396}$	3. $6\overline{)459}$	4. $7\overline{)593}$
5. $8\overline{)436}$	6. $9\overline{)757}$	7. $21\overline{)456}$	8. $33\overline{)682}$
9. $44\overline{)902}$	*10. $21\overline{)9750}$	*11. $332\overline{)6920}$	*12. $420\overline{)9780}$

Methods of Division

Divide 546 books among 20 schools:

Example 1

How many 20's are there in 546? Estimated quotient between 20 and 30.

```
 546
-400   (20 × 20)
 146
 140   (20 × 7)
   6
```

27 books with 6 books left over.

Example 2

Estimated quotient between 20 and 30.

```
      7  27
     20
 20)546
    400
    146
    140
      6
```

```
Check:  27  books
        20
       540
         6
       546  books
```

Example 3

Estimated quotient between 20 and 30.

```
     27
 20)546
    40
    146
    140
      6
```

```
Check:  27  books
        20
       540
         6
       546  books
```

In Example 1 we use the subtraction method. Instead of subtracting 20, twenty-seven times, we subtracted groups of twenty. In the first step, 20 groups; in the second step, 7 groups.

In Example 2, we ask how many 20's in 546. Since 20 × 20 = 400 and 20 × 30 = 600, we know the quotient is between 20 and 30. We write 20 in the quotient. 20 × 20 = 400, which we subtract from 546. Now we ask how many 20's in 146. Since 7 × 20 = 140, we write 7 in the quotient. We subtract 140, leaving a remainder of 6 books. The quotient is 27 books with a remainder of 6 books.

In Example 3, we have an abbreviated form of Example 2. We estimate the quotient the same as in Example 2, but we say how many 20's in 54 tens. Since there are 2 tens we write the 2 in tens place and multiply 20 × 2 tens to obtain 40 tens. We subtract 40 tens from 54 tens and have 14 tens. We bring down the 6 ones to make 146. Now we ask how many 20's in 146. Since there are 7, we place the 7 in ones place.

EXERCISES

(a). Estimate quotients.

(b). Express remainders as whole numbers in sets of Exercises A, B, C, and D. Use fractions in Exercises of set E.

(c). Check by seeing if the product of the quotient and divisor, plus the remainder, equals the dividend.

A

1. $20\overline{)620}$ 2. $30\overline{)930}$ 3. $50\overline{)1650}$ 4. $60\overline{)4320}$

5. $40\overline{)14620}$ 6. $70\overline{)97216}$ 7. $90\overline{)12670}$ 8. $80\overline{)17628}$

B

1. $21\overline{)441}$ 2. $32\overline{)508}$ 3. $43\overline{)1075}$ 4. $51\overline{)1836}$

5. $61\overline{)3416}$ 6. $62\overline{)4716}$ 7. $82\overline{)6232}$ 8. $91\overline{)4368}$

9. $21\overline{)2646}$ 10. $33\overline{)8745}$ *11. $44\overline{)15672}$ 12. $53\overline{)49721}$

C

1. $27\overline{)1215}$ 2. $39\overline{)2418}$ 3. $46\overline{)6302}$ 4. $58\overline{)26448}$

5. $67\overline{)61841}$ 6. $75\overline{)63150}$ *7. $89\overline{)51089}$ *8. $99\overline{)86729}$

D

1. $240\overline{)15120}$ 2. $336\overline{)24192}$ 3. $406\overline{)32886}$ 4. $581\overline{)72044}$

5. $686\overline{)497350}$ 6. $772\overline{)257076}$ *7. $819\overline{)444717}$ *8. $926\overline{)105569}$

You will find more practice in the Appendix, page 301.

The 27 boys in Troop 9 picked up pecans for a farmer. For their pay they received part of the pecans they gathered. If their total share was 576 pounds, what was each boy's share?

Estimated quotient between 20 and 30

$$\begin{array}{r} 21\frac{1}{3} \\ 27\overline{)576} \\ \underline{54} \\ 36 \\ \underline{27} \\ \frac{9}{27} = \frac{1}{3} \end{array} \qquad \text{Check:} \quad \begin{array}{rl} 27 & \\ \underline{21\frac{1}{3}} & \\ 9 & (\tfrac{1}{3}\text{ of } 27) \\ 27 & \\ \underline{54} & \\ 576 & \end{array}$$

Each boy's share is $21\frac{1}{3}$ pounds.

E

1. $12\overline{)303}$ 2. $16\overline{)1480}$ 3. $27\overline{)612}$ 4. $60\overline{)1720}$

5. $52\overline{)1222}$ 6. $24\overline{)1348}$ 7. $144\overline{)3384}$ 8. $320\overline{)4080}$

9. $640\overline{)6080}$ 10. $1728\overline{)34704}$

Finding an Average

Estimated quotient between 100 and 200

```
   197
8)1576        Check:
  8
  77            197
  72              8
   56          1576
   56
```

A plane traveled 1576 miles in 8 hours. What is its average rate of speed? When we divide the total number of miles by the number of hours, we obtain an average rate of 197 miles per hour. The plane, no doubt, traveled more than 197 miles during some of those hours and less than 197 miles during other hours; but if it had traveled 197 miles each hour for 8 hours, it would have traveled 1576 miles in that time. This is what we mean by average rate.

EXERCISES

1. Miss Judy Cotton drove 278 miles in 5 hours. What was her average speed?
2. Mr. Scott drove his car 264 miles on 18 gallons of gas. How many miles did he average on one gallon of gasoline?
3. There are 864 pupils in 24 classes in Hillside Junior High School. What is the average class size?
4. A toll road 80 miles long cost $32,000,000 to build. What was the average cost per mile?
5. A city bus transported 276 passengers in 12 trips. What was its average load?
6. A farmer marketed 38 head of cattle, weighing 42,712 pounds. What was the average weight of the cattle?

```
121          128 3/5
142        5)643
135          5
118          14
127          10
643           43
              40
               3
               5
```

The weights of the boys on a high school basketball team are 121 lbs., 142 lbs., 135 lbs., 118 lbs., and 127 lbs. What is their average weight?

Their average weight is $128\frac{3}{5}$ pounds.

To find the average of two or more numbers, divide their sum by the number of addends.

7. The school supply store took in the following amounts one week: Monday, $10.25; Tuesday, $16.85; Wednesday, $14.05; Thursday, $7.80; and Friday, $12.90. What was the average amount taken in each day?

8. The attendance in Room 36 for one week was 38, 36, 38, 37, and 34 by days. What was the average daily attendance?
9. On four consecutive days a company plane flew 364 miles, 562 miles, 756 miles, and 396 miles. What was the average daily mileage?
10. Ken earned $25.40 in June, $16.80 in July, and $34.10 in August. What was his average weekly earning for the 12 weeks, assuming that there are 4 weeks in each month?

More About Division with Whole Numbers

1. Divide 291 pounds of pecans among 14 boys.

```
Estimated quotient
between 20 and 30

     20  remainder 11
 14)291
    28
     11  remainder

Check:  20
        14
        80
       20
       280
        11
       291
```

When we subtract 28 tens from 291 the remainder is 11, which is smaller than 14. The quotient is therefore 20 lbs. and the remainder, 11 lbs.

EXERCISES—Divide and check:

1. 23)2087 2. 35)2831 3. 47)2837 4. 51)3586

5. 64)51219 6. 72)37443 7. 86)61074 8. 921)73697

There is more practice in the Appendix, page 301.

Example—If Charles Smith makes a yearly salary of $6048, what is his monthly salary?

```
Estimated quotient
between 500 and 600

   $ 504        Check:
12)$6048
    6000         $504
      48           12
      48         1008
                 504
                $6048
```

When we subtract 6000 or 60 hundreds from 6048, the remainder is 48. There are 4 twelves in 48. The quotient is 5 hundreds, 0 tens, and 4 or 504.

9. $26\overline{)10472}$ 10. $32\overline{)29024}$ 11. $46\overline{)32568}$ 12. $19\overline{)9538}$

13. $97\overline{)38897}$ 14. $85\overline{)51347}$ 15. $76\overline{)68943}$ 16. $52\overline{)208416}$

Practice in Division

1. A man has 140 pounds of chicken feed. If he uses 4 pounds a day, how long will it last? Suggested form: $N = 140 \div 4$.
2. The cost of food for a class picnic was $21.70. If 35 persons went on the picnic, what was each person's share?
3. The boys in Room 10 were asked to put up the chairs for an assembly in the gymnasium. They were to put 24 chairs to a row. How many rows will they need to seat 720 people?
4. Harold Scott can average 18 miles on a gallon of gasoline. How many gallons will it take to make a trip of 729 miles?
5. The boys on the Eagle baseball team washed windows and mowed yards to earn money to buy uniforms for the team. Each uniform cost $12. They earned $52 in one week. How many uniforms will that amount buy?
6. Mr. Thompson wishes to sell his 80 acre farm for $20,000. How much is he asking per acre?
7. If a steamship travels 28 miles per hour, how long will it take to make a trip of 994 miles?
8. If 1 gallon = 231 cubic inches, how many gallons will an aquarium hold that contains 5,544 cubic inches?

*9. Mrs. Baile bought a crate of 24 cans of peaches for $6.24. How much did she save on each can if this brand of peaches sold regularly for 30¢ a can?

*10. What is the average weight of a basketball team if the boys weigh 121 lbs., 119 lbs., 124 lbs., 118 lbs., and 131 lbs.?

Short Division

You may save time by using short division in which much of the work is done mentally.

Example 1

$$\begin{array}{r} 13 \text{ remainder } 1 \\ 8\overline{)105} \end{array}$$

In Example 1, you may think how many 8's are in 100 or 10 tens, or you may think how many 8's in one 10. Since there is 1, you place the 1 in tens place. There is a remainder of 2 which you then use as 2 tens in ones place. You now have 25 and you think how many 8's in 25. There are 3 with a remainder of 1. See if you can check these mentally, as $8 \times 13 = 104$ and $104 + 1 = 105$.

Example 2

$$6\overline{)630}\quad 105$$

In Example 2, you may think how many 6's are in 6 hundreds, or how many 6's are in 6. Since there is 1, you place the 1 in hundreds place. Since there are no 6's in 3, place 0 in tens place. Then use the 3 tens in ones place as 30. You ask how many 6's in thirty. There are 5. Check: $6 \times 105 = 630$.

EXERCISES—Solve by short division and check:

1. $6\overline{)25}$	2. $8\overline{)34}$	3. $9\overline{)49}$	4. $7\overline{)66}$
5. $3\overline{)369}$	6. $4\overline{)256}$	7. $5\overline{)515}$	8. $2\overline{)618}$
9. $9\overline{)738}$	10. $8\overline{)348}$	11. $7\overline{)294}$	12. $6\overline{)498}$
13. $3\overline{)134}$	14. $4\overline{)875}$	15. $6\overline{)494}$	16. $9\overline{)514}$
17. $8\overline{)756}$	18. $7\overline{)581}$	19. $5\overline{)472}$	20. $4\overline{)179}$
21. $5\overline{)2445}$	22. $4\overline{)2524}$	23. $7\overline{)2814}$	24. $8\overline{)7232}$
25. $6\overline{)1213}$	26. $8\overline{)2604}$	27. $9\overline{)6413}$	28. $7\overline{)8172}$

Words you should understand:

1. dividend 2. divisor 3. quotient 4. remainder

Test

In Exercises 1 through 16, divide:

1. $6\overline{)366}$	2. $7\overline{)284}$	3. $8\overline{)1616}$	4. $9\overline{)3789}$
5. $21\overline{)966}$	6. $42\overline{)3822}$	7. $54\overline{)4590}$	8. $63\overline{)5418}$
9. $37\overline{)8590}$	10. $75\overline{)2182}$	11. $96\overline{)4032}$	12. $89\overline{)2415}$
13. $148\overline{)3996}$	14. $485\overline{)34920}$	15. $512\overline{)25721}$	16. $743\overline{)47216}$

17. Jane entertained her Sunday School class. The refreshments cost $4.80. If 24 were at the party, what did it cost per person?
18. Gene was paid $3.00 for washing the windows on the outside. If there were 20 windows, how much was that per window?
19. Mr. Johnson receives $8,640 a year. What is his monthly salary?
20. The boys in the science class recorded the temperature each morning at 9 o'clock. What was the average temperature for the week if the daily readings were 61°, 58°, 56°, 59°, and 56°?

Review Test

1. Write in decimal notation: six million, six hundred six thousand.
2. Write in decimal notation: two and two hundred two thousandths.
3. Round to the nearest hundred:
   1345 1283 451 726 151
4. Add 621 + 246 + 137 + 1,242.
5. Subtract 395 from 1,200.
6. Find the product of 626 and 409.
7. $7\overline{)1211}$
8. $25\overline{)1175}$
9. Divide 130,356 by 426.
10. $6\frac{2}{3} + 1\frac{3}{4}$
11. $8 - 2\frac{1}{8}$
12. $3\frac{1}{3} \times 2\frac{2}{5}$
13. $1\frac{4}{5} \times \frac{3}{10}$
14. 1.26 + 2.04 + 3.72 + 1.09
15. 20 − 1.9
16. 0.283 × 1000
17. How many yards are there in 420 rods if there are $5\frac{1}{2}$ yards in a rod?
18. Mr. Swift drove 582 miles in 12 hours. How many miles did he average per hour?
19. Judy wants a skirt that costs $8.25. If she saves $0.75 a week, in how many weeks will she have saved enough money to buy the skirt?
20. The yearly subscription to a monthly magazine is $4.75. If this magazine is bought at the newsstand each month, it will cost $0.50 a copy. How much is saved in a year by subscribing for the magazine?

Common Fractions in Division

Don has a 10 foot strip of lumber that he plans to cut into garden markers. Each marker is to be 6 inches or $\frac{1}{2}$ foot in length. How many markers will he be able to make from this strip?

$1 \div \frac{1}{2} = 2$
$10 \div \frac{1}{2} = 20$
10×2 or 20

How many half-foot lengths are there in 1 foot? In 10 feet there will be 10 times as many as in 1 foot or 20.

ORAL EXERCISES

1. How many $\frac{1}{2}''$ are there in $1''$? $1 \div \frac{1}{2} =$
2. How many $\frac{1}{4}''$ are there in $1''$? $1 \div \frac{1}{4} =$
3. How many $\frac{1}{2}''$ are there in $2''$? $2 \div \frac{1}{2} =$
4. How many $\frac{1}{4}''$ are there in $2''$? $2 \div \frac{1}{4} =$
5. How many $\frac{1}{2}''$ are there in $3''$? $3 \div \frac{1}{2} =$
6. How many $\frac{1}{4}''$ are there in $3''$? $3 \div \frac{1}{4} =$
7. How many times is $1\frac{1}{2}$ contained in 3? $3 \div 1\frac{1}{2} =$
8. How many times is $1\frac{1}{4}$ contained in $2\frac{1}{2}$? $2\frac{1}{2} \div 1\frac{1}{4} =$

There are two methods which can be used in dividing fractions. One method may be called the common denominator method. In this method, both the dividend and the divisor are changed to the same denominator.

$4 \div \frac{1}{2}$
$\frac{8}{2} \div \frac{1}{2} = 8$

4 is changed to halves

Now since the denominators are both 2, to find how many one-halves there are in eight-halves we may divide 8 by 1. The quotient is 8.

The second method may be called the reciprocal method.

$5 \div 2 = 2\frac{1}{2}$ $\quad$ $6 \div 4 = 1\frac{1}{2}$

$5 \times \frac{1}{2} = \frac{5}{2}$ or $2\frac{1}{2}$ $\quad$ $6 \times \frac{1}{4} = \frac{6}{4}$ or $1\frac{1}{2}$

Dividing by a number is the same as multiplying by the reciprocal of that number. Where we invert a fraction, we are writing the reciprocal of the fraction. The reciprocal of $\frac{2}{3}$ is $\frac{3}{2}$. The reciprocal of $\frac{1}{2}$ is $\frac{2}{1}$ or 2. The reciprocal of 4 is $\frac{1}{4}$. The reciprocal of N is $1/N$.

EXERCISES—Give the reciprocals of these:

1. $\frac{3}{4}$	2. $\frac{5}{6}$	3. $\frac{8}{9}$	4. $\frac{1}{3}$	5. $\frac{1}{6}$	6. $\frac{1}{8}$
7. $\frac{1}{4}$	8. $\frac{1}{5}$	9. 4	10. 6	11. 8	*12. r

Common Denominator Method	Reciprocal Method
$2 \div \frac{1}{2}$ Change 2 to halves $\frac{4}{2} \div \frac{1}{2} = 4$	$2 \div \frac{1}{2}$ $2 \times 2 = 4$
$1 \div \frac{3}{4}$ Change 1 to fourths $\frac{4}{4} \div \frac{3}{4} = 1\frac{1}{3}$	$1 \div \frac{3}{4}$ $1 \times \frac{4}{3} = \frac{4}{3}$ or $1\frac{1}{3}$
$3 \div 1\frac{1}{2}$ Change 3 to halves $\frac{6}{2} \div \frac{3}{2} = 2$	$3 \div 1\frac{1}{2}$ $\frac{\cancel{3}^{1}}{1} \times \frac{2}{\cancel{3}_{1}} = 2$

EXERCISES—Divide using two methods in each exercise, one a check on the other:

1. $6 \div \frac{1}{2}$
2. $4 \div \frac{1}{8}$
3. $8 \div \frac{1}{3}$
4. $15 \div \frac{1}{2}$
5. $7 \div \frac{1}{4}$
6. $12 \div \frac{1}{8}$
7. $10 \div \frac{1}{16}$
8. $9 \div \frac{1}{5}$
9. $8 \div \frac{2}{3}$
10. $9 \div \frac{3}{4}$
11. $6 \div 1\frac{1}{2}$
12. $7 \div 1\frac{3}{4}$
13. How many $\frac{1}{4}$ lb. packages of candy can you make from 8 lb. of candy?
14. How many $\frac{1}{10}$ miles are there in 7 miles?

*15. How many $\frac{1}{2}$ pint cartons of milk can be filled from 4 quarts of milk?

Example

If $\frac{3}{4}$ lb. of cheese is to be divided equally among 6 people, how much cheese will each person receive?

Method 1

$\frac{3}{4} \div 6 =$

$\frac{3}{4} \div \frac{24}{4} = \frac{3}{24}$ or $\frac{1}{8}$ lb.

In this solution, after you have changed 6 to $\frac{24}{4}$, you may think $3 \div 24$, which is expressed as a fraction $\frac{3}{24}$ and is reduced to $\frac{1}{8}$.

Method 2

$\frac{3}{4} \div 6 =$

$\frac{3}{4} \times \frac{1}{6} = \frac{\cancel{3}^{1} \times 1}{4 \times \cancel{6}_{2}} = \frac{1}{8}$ lb.

You can often reduce as you solve a problem by dividing a number in the numerator and a number in the denominator by the same number. Here we divided 3 in the numerator and 6 in the denominator by 3.

Divide:

16. $\frac{1}{3} \div 2$ 17. $\frac{1}{2} \div 4$ 18. $\frac{2}{3} \div 3$ 19. $\frac{7}{8} \div 4$ 20. $\frac{15}{16} \div 5$

21. $\frac{9}{16} \div 3$ 22. $\frac{5}{6} \div 10$ 23. $\frac{2}{3} \div 3$ 24. $\frac{5}{12} \div 4$ 25. $7\frac{1}{2} \div 2$

26. $3\frac{1}{3} \div 5$ 27. $4\frac{2}{3} \div 2$ 28. $4\frac{1}{2} \div 2$

29. A recipe is to be cut in half. How much milk will be required if the recipe calls for $\frac{3}{4}$ cup of milk?

*30. If $8\frac{1}{3}$ lb. of candy is to be packaged in 10 packages, how much should be placed in each package?

31. How many $\frac{1}{8}''$ are there in $\frac{3}{4}''$? How many $\frac{1}{8}''$ are there in $1''$?

$\frac{3}{4} \div \frac{1}{8}$

$\frac{6}{8} \div \frac{1}{8} = 6$

or

$\frac{3}{4} \div \frac{1}{8}$

$$\frac{3}{4} \times \frac{8}{1} = \frac{3 \times \overset{2}{\cancel{8}}}{\underset{1}{\cancel{4}} \times 1} = 6$$

32. $\frac{7}{8} \div \frac{3}{4}$ 33. $\frac{9}{16} \div \frac{7}{8}$ 34. $\frac{1}{32} \div \frac{1}{4}$

35. $2\frac{1}{2} \div \frac{1}{4}$ 36. $4\frac{1}{8} \div \frac{3}{4}$ 37. $7\frac{1}{2} \div \frac{3}{4}$

38. $6\frac{2}{3} \div \frac{5}{6}$ 39. $1\frac{1}{2} \div 1\frac{1}{4}$ 40. $4\frac{2}{5} \div 2\frac{1}{10}$

41. $6\frac{7}{10} \div 1\frac{1}{10}$ 42. $7\frac{1}{2} \div 1\frac{3}{4}$ 43. $\frac{1}{2} \div 1\frac{1}{3}$

44. $\frac{3}{4} \div 1\frac{1}{2}$ 45. $\frac{7}{8} \div 2\frac{1}{2}$ 46. $\frac{9}{10} \div 1\frac{4}{5}$

47. $\frac{4}{5} \div 1\frac{1}{10}$ 48. $\frac{3}{8} \div 1\frac{1}{2}$

*49. How many $\frac{3}{4}$-hour periods are there in $4\frac{1}{2}$ hours?

*50. How many pieces of rope $3\frac{3}{4}$ yards in length can be cut from 15 yards of rope?

Test on Dividing Fractions

1. $18 \div \frac{1}{2}$ 2. $27 \div \frac{2}{3}$ 3. $\frac{4}{5} \div 8$ 4. $\frac{7}{8} \div 2$

5. $\frac{2}{3} \div \frac{2}{3}$ 6. $\frac{15}{16} \div \frac{3}{4}$ 7. $4\frac{1}{2} \div \frac{1}{2}$ 8. $7\frac{2}{3} \div \frac{2}{3}$

9. $16\frac{2}{3} \div 2$ 10. $12\frac{1}{2} \div 3$ 11. $2\frac{2}{3} \div 1\frac{1}{3}$ 12. $5\frac{1}{2} \div 1\frac{1}{2}$

13. $\frac{1}{8} \div 1\frac{1}{4}$ 14. $\frac{1}{5} \div 1\frac{3}{10}$ 15. $4\frac{1}{2} \div 1\frac{3}{4}$ 16. $6\frac{2}{3} \div 10$

17. How many bags of peanuts, each containing $\frac{3}{8}$ lbs., can be sacked from $26\frac{5}{8}$ lbs.?

18. How many blocks $2\frac{1}{2}$ inches long can you cut from 30 inches of wood?

19. The hiking club hiked $8\frac{1}{4}$ miles in $2\frac{3}{4}$ hours. What was the club's average number of miles per hour?

20. If $12\frac{1}{2}$ pounds of apples are divided among 4 people, how many pounds will each receive?

More Practice with Fractions

Examples

1 lb. = $\frac{2}{2}$ lb.	
$\frac{1}{2}$ lb.	$\frac{1}{2}$ lb.

1. If $\frac{1}{2}$ lb. of candy costs 35c, what will a pound cost at this rate?

If $\frac{1}{2}$ lb. costs 35¢

$\frac{2}{2}$ or 1 lb. will cost 2 × 35¢ or 70¢

Check: $\frac{1}{2} \times 70¢ = 35¢$

1 lb. = $\frac{3}{3}$ lb.

2. If $\frac{2}{3}$ of a pound of candy costs 40¢, what will one pound cost at this rate?

If $\frac{2}{3}$ of a lb. costs 40¢

$\frac{1}{3}$ of a lb. will cost $\frac{1}{2}$ of 40¢ or 20¢

$\frac{3}{3}$ or a lb. will cost 3 × 20¢ or 60¢

Check: $\frac{2}{\cancel{3}_1} \times \cancel{60}^{20}¢ = 40¢$

EXERCISES—Solve and check:

1. If $\frac{1}{2}$ of a number is 16, what is the number?
2. If $\frac{1}{8}$ of a number is 8, what is the number?
3. Nancy pays 20¢ for $\frac{1}{4}$ lb. of nuts. How much at this rate would a pound cost?
4. If 4 boys were absent one day and they are $\frac{1}{4}$ of the boys in the class, how many boys are there in the class?
5. Jack saves 25¢ a week, which is $\frac{1}{5}$ of his allowance. What is his allowance?
6. If 24 pupils made a perfect score on a mathematics test and they were $\frac{2}{3}$ of the pupils in the class, how many were in the class?
7. If $\frac{3}{4}$ of the distance to Britt is 60 miles, how far is it to Britt?
8. If 28 pupils in one class entered an essay contest and this was $\frac{7}{8}$ of the pupils in the class, how many were in the class?
9. If $\frac{1}{16}''$ represents 25 miles on a map, what will a whole inch represent?
10. If Tom sold 30 chickens, which were $\frac{2}{5}$ of his flock, how many chickens did he have?
11. If $\frac{5}{6}$ of a yard of material costs $.80, what will a whole yard cost?

12. If a family saves \$50 a month and that is $\frac{1}{10}$ of its income, what is its monthly income?

Quick Quiz No. 12

1. If a whole number is multiplied by a proper fraction, is the product larger or smaller than the whole number?
2. How many 50's are there in 800?
3. What is the answer in division called?
4. Find the product of 90 and 20.
5. Divide each number by 6:
   (a) 24 (b) 6 (c) 50 (d) 82 (e) 1.26
6. Mr. Smith drove 487 miles in 10 hours; what was his average speed?
7. If $\frac{3}{4}$ of a pound of seed costs 75¢, what will a pound cost?
8. A certain whole number rounded to the nearest hundred is 2500. What is the greatest value a whole number could have had which would be rounded to this? What is the least value it could have had?
9. What is the difference between 1200 miles and 975 miles?
10. If you put a dozen pencils in a box, how many boxes will it take to hold 168 pencils?

Division of Decimal Fractions

Examples

1. $0.6 \div 2$ $\quad \frac{6}{10} \div 2 = \frac{3}{10}$ $\quad 2\overline{)0.6} = 0.3$

2. $0.12 \div 2$ $\quad \frac{12}{100} \div 2 = \frac{6}{100}$ $\quad 2\overline{)0.12} = 0.06$

3. $0.036 \div 2$ $\quad \frac{36}{1000} \div 2 = \frac{18}{1000}$ $\quad 2\overline{)0.036} = 0.018$

4. $0.0812 \div 2$ $\quad \frac{812}{10000} \div 2 = \frac{406}{10000}$ $\quad 2\overline{)0.0812} = 0.0406$

In Example 1, we were dividing tenths, so the quotient is in tenths. In Example 2, we were dividing hundredths, so the quotient is in hundredths.

EXERCISES—Copy and fill in the blanks.

1. (a) In Example 3, we are dividing thousandths, so the quotient is in ______.
   (b) In Example 4, we are dividing ten-thousandths, so quotient is in ______.
   (c) When we are dividing a decimal by a whole number, there are as many decimal places in the quotient as there are in the ______.

2. Jim drove 241.5 miles in 5 hours.

   48.3 mi.
   5)241.5 mi.
   Check: 48.3 mi. × 5 = 241.5 mi.

   (a) How many miles did he average per hour?
   (b) How many decimal places are there in the dividend?
   (c) How many decimal places are there in the quotient?

3. Copy and place the decimal points in the quotients:

(a) 2)4.48, quotient 2 24	(b) 3)9.03, quotient 3 01	(c) 8)64.8, quotient 8 1	(d) 12)1.728, quotient 144
(e) 25)0.625, quotient 025	(f) 21)1.286, quotient 061	(g) 15)30.15, quotient 2 01	(h) 121)229.9, quotient 1 9

Examples

1. 6)0.36 = 0.06 — Check 0.06 × 6 = 0.36
2. 6)0.012 = 0.002 — Check 0.002 × 6 = 0.012
3. 6)12.24 = 2.04 — Check 2.04 × 6 = 12.24

4. Divide and check:
   Suggestion: Before you begin to divide a decimal by a whole number, it may be desirable to place the decimal point in the quotient directly above the decimal point in the dividend.

(a) 9)0.369	(b) 8)16.88	(c) 6)0.126
(d) 16)2.56	(e) 24)53.04	(f) 37)140.6
(g) 49)318.5	(h) 53)3.233	(i) 74)6.882
(j) 96)451.2	(k) 125)975.0	(l) 364)101.92

*5. The Smith family spent $22.75 for a week's supply of groceries. What was the daily average cost for food?

*6. If 18.75 lbs. of nuts were divided among 15 boys, how many pounds would each boy receive?

Dividing by a Decimal

In the example $2\overline{)4}$ (quotient 2), if we multiply both the divisor 2 and the dividend 4 by 10 and divide, we have $20\overline{)40}$ (quotient 2). The quotient is 2.

If we multiply both the divisor 2 and the dividend 4 by 100 and divide, we have $200\overline{)400}$ (quotient 2). The quotient is 2.

EXERCISES

1. (a) Divide 12 by 6 or $6\overline{)12}$.
   (b) Multiply both the divisor and the dividend by 10 and divide. The quotient is ______.
   (c) Multiply both the divisor and the dividend by 100 and divide. The quotient is ______.

If the divisor and the dividend are multiplied by the same number, the quotient remains unchanged.

2. If Mike can save \$0.75 a week, how long will it take him to save \$6.75?

$\$0.75\overline{)\$6.75}$ (quotient 9)

It will take Mike 9 weeks to save \$6.75.

Check: 0.75
× 9
\$6.75

When you express the division as a fraction, you obtain

$$\frac{\$6.75}{\$0.75} = \frac{\$6.75 \times 100}{\$0.75 \times 100} \quad \text{or} \quad \frac{\$675}{\$75} \quad \text{or} \quad 9$$

(a) By what was \$0.75 multiplied to obtain \$75?

(b) Was \$6.75 multiplied by the same number to obtain \$675?

This division may also be performed using common fractions.

Change \$0.75 to $\frac{3}{4}$ of a dollar and \$6.75 to $\$6\frac{3}{4}$

$$6\tfrac{3}{4} \div \tfrac{3}{4} = \frac{\overset{9}{\cancel{27}}}{\underset{1}{\cancel{4}}} \times \frac{\overset{1}{\cancel{4}}}{\underset{1}{\cancel{3}}} \quad \text{or} \quad 9$$

A caret ($\wedge$) is placed in a number to show that we are thinking as if the number were multiplied by 10, 100, or 1000 and the decimal point is now where the caret is.

3. Study these examples and answer the questions below.

1.	2.	3.
$\begin{array}{r} 2. \\ 0.8_\wedge\overline{)1.6_\wedge} \end{array}$	$\begin{array}{r} 3.\,1 \\ 0.08_\wedge\overline{)0.24_\wedge 8} \end{array}$	$\begin{array}{r} 750. \\ 0.008_\wedge\overline{)6.000_\wedge} \end{array}$
Check $\begin{array}{r} 0.8 \\ \times\ 2 \\ \hline 1.6 \end{array}$	Check $\begin{array}{r} 3.1 \\ \times\ 0.08 \\ \hline 0.248 \end{array}$	Check $\begin{array}{r} 750 \\ \times\ 0.008 \\ \hline 6.000 \end{array}$

By what were the divisor and the dividend multiplied when the carets were placed in the numbers?

(a) in Example 1? (b) in Example 2? (c) in Example 3?

It may help you to follow these steps in dividing by a decimal:

1. Multiply the divisor by 10, 100, and 1000 to make it a whole number.
2. Multiply the dividend by the same number. Annex zeros to the dividend if necessary.
3. Place the decimal point in the quotient directly above the new position of the decimal point in the dividend and proceed to divide.

EXERCISES—Divide and check:

1. $0.5\overline{)1.25}$ 2. $1.2\overline{).192}$ 3. $0.75\overline{)6.}$
4. $2.4\overline{)19.68}$ 5. $3.9\overline{).2808}$ 6. $0.42\overline{)0.6552}$
7. $5.6\overline{)29.344}$ 8. $0.65\overline{)13.}$ 9. $7.21\overline{)40.376}$
10. $0.831\overline{)166.2}$ 11. $9.06\overline{)41.676}$ 12. $603\overline{)180.9}$

*13. How many books costing $2.75 each can be purchased by a Student Council for a school library if the waste paper sale netted them $74.25 which was to be used for the purchase of books?

*14. A steel plant needs pipes measuring 6.5″ in length. How many of these pipes can be cut from a pipe 13 feet long?

Rounding Decimals

We round decimals to the nearest tenth, hundredth, or thousandth just as we round whole numbers to the nearest ten, hundred, or thousand.

Rounding to the nearest tenth:

Round 0.32 to the nearest tenth. It may help to think what decimal is halfway between 0.30 and 0.40. The decimal halfway between is 0.35. Is 0.32 nearer 0.30 or 0.40? Copy and fill in blanks.

0.32 rounded to nearest tenth is 0.3
0.36 rounded to nearest tenth is 0.4
0.33 rounded to nearest tenth is ______
0.37 rounded to nearest tenth is ______
0.39 rounded to nearest tenth is ______
0.361 rounded to nearest tenth is ______
0.378 rounded to nearest tenth is ______

We will use these agreements in rounding to the nearest tenth:

1. **If the digit in hundredths place is less than 5, drop all digits to the right of tenths place.**
2. **If the digit in hundredths place is 5 or more, increase the digit in tenths place by one and drop all digits to the right of tenths place.**

EXERCISES—Round the following decimals to the nearest tenth:

1. 46.21	2. 84.29	3. 65.33	4. 71.39
5. 6.52	6. 8.49	7. 296.216	8. 793.285
9. 4.217	10. 8.655	11. 746.752	*12. 247.96

In rounding to hundredths, we use agreements like those used for rounding to tenths. 2.676 rounds to 2.68 and 5.223 rounds to 5.22.

Round the following decimals to the nearest hundredth:

13. 4.216	14. 7.259	15. 8.372	16. 12.356
17. 121.513	18. 17.861	19. 9.375	20. 24.877
21. 456.788	22. 452.326	23. 28.945	24. 82.896

In rounding to the thousandths, we use agreements like those used in rounding to tenths and hundredths. 8.7256 rounds to 8.726 and 4.2932 rounds to 4.293.

Round the following decimals to the nearest thousandth:

25. 9.2461	26. 5.7282	27. 85.9676	28. 91.2371
29. 12.5683	30. 14.8219	31. 75.6125	32. 803.4729

Some divisions have remainders even though the quotients are carried to many decimal places. We can express these quotients to the nearest tenth, hundredth, or thousandth, depending on the problem.

Example

$$3\overline{)181.00} = 60.33$$

60.3

A man drove 181 miles in 3 hours. What was his average speed per hour expressed to the nearest tenth of a mile?

To express a quotient to the nearest tenth, find the quotient to the nearest hundredth, and then round the quotient to the nearest tenth.

EXERCISES—In Exercises 1–8 divide and express quotients to the nearest tenth:

1. $6\overline{)125}$	2. $9\overline{)32.1}$	3. $12\overline{)1033}$	4. $0.15\overline{)2.81}$
5. $7.5\overline{)824.9}$	6. $92\overline{)725}$	7. $35\overline{)10.296}$	8. $341\overline{)756}$

*9. A plane flew 2392 miles in 6 hours. What was its average speed per hour to the nearest tenth of a mile?

*10. A student's average on ten tests was 84.3. What is the sum of the 10 test grades?

Example

```
   2.455 = 2.46
12)29.460
   24
    54
    48
     66
     60
      60
      60
```

If 12 people in a club have a bill of $29.46 for a party, how much will each have to pay to the nearest cent?

Each pays $2.46.

To express a quotient to the nearest hundredth, find the quotient to the nearest thousandth and then round it to the nearest hundredth.

In Exercises 11–18 divide and express quotients to the nearest hundredth:

11. $8\overline{)121}$	12. $7\overline{)62.1}$	13. $13\overline{)451}$	14. $0.24\overline{)8.26}$
15. $3.2\overline{)141.3}$	16. $48\overline{)221}$	17. $125\overline{)722}$	18. $26.1\overline{)755}$

*19. Sixteen scouts shared $29.10 expenses of a camping trip. What was each person's share to the nearest cent?

*20. The total yearly rainfall was 49 inches in Brown County. What was the average monthly rainfall to the nearest hundredth of an inch?

21. Give a rule for expressing a quotient to the nearest thousandth.

In Exercises 22–26 divide and express quotient to the nearest thousandth:

22. $7\overline{)1.2}$	23. $0.21\overline{)7.21}$	24. $8.5\overline{)16}$	25. $450\overline{)161}$

*26. Find to the nearest tenth of a cent the cost of each egg if eggs are selling for 69¢ a dozen.

You will find more practice in the Appendix, page 303.

IBM's System 360 computer can produce over 64,000 characters of information in 2.5 millionths of a second.

Dividing by 10, 100, or 1000

1. $460 \div 10 = 46$

$$10\overline{)460}\quad = 46$$

Check: $10 \times 46 = 460$

2. $46 \div 10 = 4.6$

$$10\overline{)46.0}\quad = 4.6$$

Check: $10 \times 4.6 = 46$

3. $4.6 \div 10 = 0.46$

$$10\overline{)4.60}\quad = 0.46$$

Check: $10 \times 0.46 = 4.6$

4. $0.46 \div 10 = 0.046$

$$10\overline{)0.460}\quad = 0.046$$

Check: $10 \times 0.046 = 0.46$

EXERCISES

1. Copy and fill in the blanks:
   To divide a number by 10, move the decimal point ______ place to the ______.

1. $460 \div 100 = 4.6$

```
    4.6
100)460.0
    400
     600
     600
```

Check: $100 \times 4.6 = 460$

2. $46 \div 100 = 0.46$

```
    0.46
100)46.00
    400
     600
     600
```

Check: $100 \times 0.46 = 46.$

3. $4.6 \div 100 = 0.046$

```
    0.046
100)4.600
    400
     600
     600
```

Check: $100 \times 0.046 = 4.6$

4. $0.46 \div 100 = 0.0046$

```
    0.0046
100)0.4600
      400
       600
       600
```

Check: $100 \times 0.0046 = 0.46$

2. Copy and fill in the blanks:
   To divide a number by 100, move the decimal point ______ places to the ______.

1. $460 \div 1000 = 0.46$

```
      0.46
1000)460.00
     4000
      6000
      6000
```

Check: $1000 \times 0.46 = 460$

2. $46 \div 1000 = 0.046$

```
      0.046
1000)46.000
     4000
      6000
      6000
```

Check: $1000 \times 0.046 = 46.$

3. $4.6 \div 1000 = 0.0046$

$$\begin{array}{r} .0046 \\ 1000\overline{)4.6000} \\ \underline{4000} \\ 6000 \\ \underline{6000} \end{array}$$

Check: $1000 \times 0.0046 = 4.6$

4. $0.46 \div 1000 = 0.00046$

$$\begin{array}{r} 0.00046 \\ 1000\overline{)0.46000} \\ \underline{4000} \\ 6000 \\ \underline{6000} \end{array}$$

Check: $1000 \times 0.00046 = 0.46$

3. Copy and fill in the blanks:

   To divide a number by 1000, move the decimal point ______ places to the ______.

In Exercises 4 through 18 copy the problem.
If the answer is correct, write: $32 \div 10 = 3.2$ ✓
If the answer is not correct, write: $32 \div 100 \neq 3.2$ and write correctly: $32 \div 100 = 0.32$

4. $0.021 \div 10 = 0.21$
5. $650 \div 1000 = 0.65$
6. $8260 \div 1000 = 8.26$
7. $0.25 \div 100 = 0.0025$
8. $4.6 \div 10 = 46$
9. $360 \div 100 = 03.6$
10. $75 \div 100 = 0.75$
11. $256 \div 1000 = 256$
12. $7.21 \div 10 = 0.721$
13. $0.86 \div 100 = 86.$
14. $756 \div 10 = 7.56$
15. $8729 \div 1000 = 87.29$
16. $0.421 \div 100 = 42.1$
17. $830 \div 10 = 0.83$
18. $275 \div 1000 = 0.0275$

Solve and check:

1. If 10 pounds of sugar sell for 95¢, what is the price per pound?
2. A hundred-acre farm in Texas sold for $10,250. How much was that per acre?
3. A man bought 1000 feet of lumber for $120. How much did he pay per foot?
4. Rex Jordan produced 457 bushels of corn from a 10-acre field. What was the average number of bushels per acre?
5. A 10-pound bag of potatoes sold for 45¢. How much would be charged for six pounds at the same rate?
6. The Brook Nursery advertised 100 celery plants for $3.50. How much are they per plant?
7. If a roof is measured by squares of 100 square feet, how many squares will a roof have that contains 2400 square feet?

*8. Mr. Jack Warner will need 1350 bricks for a wall. The bricks cost \$2.80 a hundred. How much will the bricks cost him?

*9. Fertilizer for the yard is sold in 100 lb. sacks for \$2.90 or in 10 lb. sacks for \$.35. How much cheaper per pound is the fertilizer when bought in the larger sack?

*10. The Alcorn family has 2950 square feet of lawn. They will plant winter grass using $1\frac{1}{4}$ lb. of seed for every hundred square feet. How many pounds of grass seed will they need?

You will find more practice in the Appendix, page 304.

Quick Quiz No. 13

1. What is the meaning of the 0 in 902?
2. $14 \div \frac{1}{2} = ?$
3. Write the reciprocals of these numbers:
   (a) $\frac{2}{3}$ (b) $\frac{1}{2}$ (c) 2 (d) $\frac{8}{9}$ (e) $\frac{1}{4}$ (f) 6
4. Is $\frac{2}{3}$ of 30 the same as $30 \div 1\frac{1}{2}$?
5. Divide each number by 100:
   (a) 400 (b) 40 (c) 22.1 (d) 0.225 (e) 625
6. What is the product:
   $9 \times 6 \times 2 \times 0 = ?$
7. $96 = ? \times 12$
8. If you know the product of two numbers and one of the numbers, how do you find the other number?
9. Round to the nearest thousandth:
   (a) 0.4672 (b) 1.8756 (c) 2.3009 (d) 0.5734
10. Divide 1000 by 0.01.

Changing Fractions to Decimals and Decimals to Fractions

One-half represents one of two equal parts of a unit, and $\frac{1}{4}$ represents one of the four equal parts of a unit. We can also think of fractions as indicating a division. We know

$\frac{1}{2}$ of a dollar = \$0.50

$\frac{1}{4}$ of a dollar = \$0.25

$\frac{3}{4}$ of a dollar = \$0.75

These results could have been obtained by division.

$$2\overline{)1.0}\ = 0.5 \qquad 4\overline{)1.00}\ = 0.25 \qquad 4\overline{)3.00}\ = 0.75$$

```
    0.5         0.25        0.75
 2)1.0       4)1.00      4)3.00
   1.0         8           2 8
              20            20
              20            20
              20            20
```

$\frac{1}{2} = 0.5 = 0.50 \qquad \frac{1}{4} = 0.25 \qquad \frac{3}{4} = 0.75$

$\frac{5}{8}$ of a dollar, is $\frac{5}{8}$ of 100 cents, or $62\frac{1}{2}$ cents.

$\frac{5}{8} \times \frac{100}{1} = \frac{500}{8} = 62\frac{1}{2}$

```
   0.62
 8)5.00
   4 8
    20
    16
     4
```

$\frac{5}{8} = 0.62\frac{1}{2}$

To change a fraction to a decimal, divide the numerator by the denominator.

EXERCISE 1. Complete this fraction-decimal equivalent table:

$\frac{1}{2}$ = 0.5 or 0.50	$\frac{1}{5}$ = 0.2 or 0.20	$\frac{1}{10}$ = 0.1 or 0.10	$\frac{1}{8} = 0.12\frac{1}{2}$	$\frac{1}{6} = 0.16\frac{2}{3}$
$\frac{1}{4}$ = 0.25	$\frac{2}{5}$ =	$\frac{3}{10}$ =	$\frac{3}{8}$ =	$\frac{5}{6}$ =
$\frac{3}{4}$ =	$\frac{3}{5}$ =	$\frac{7}{10}$ =	$\frac{5}{8}$ =	$\frac{1}{12}$ =
$\frac{1}{3} = 0.33\frac{1}{3}$	$\frac{4}{5}$ =	$\frac{9}{10}$ =	$\frac{7}{8}$ =	$\frac{1}{16}$ =
$\frac{2}{3}$ =				

The decimal equivalents of fourths and eighths are used so much it will be helpful to know them. Spend some time on them each day until you have memorized them.

In Exercises 2 through 6, change to decimals expressed to nearest hundredth:

2. $\frac{3}{7}$ 3. $\frac{21}{25}$ 4. $\frac{1}{11}$ 5. $\frac{8}{9}$ 6. $\frac{6}{7}$

*7. Margaret thought she had $\frac{7}{8}$ of the problems correct on a test, and Peter thought he had 0.90 of the exercises correct. Which one has a higher standing on the test, on this basis?

*8. The Claremore football team won $\frac{5}{8}$ of their games played, and the Mounds team won 0.55. Which team has a higher standing?

You will find more practice in Appendix, page 304.

Example

$0.50 = \frac{50}{100}$ or $\frac{1}{2}$

$0.37\frac{1}{2} = 0.375$ or $\frac{375}{1000}$ or $\frac{3}{8}$

How do you change a decimal to a fraction?

In Exercises 9 through 20 change the decimals to common fractions: (Remember to reduce to lowest terms)

9. 0.15 10. 0.75 11. 0.06 12. 0.36 13. 0.85 14. 0.38
15. 0.95 16. 0.09 17. 0.42 18. $0.12\frac{1}{2}$ 19. 0.825 20. $0.333\frac{1}{3}$

Sometimes it is easier to use the fractional equivalent than the decimal form when solving a problem.

Decide which is easier, and use the easier form in Exercises 21 through 32:

21. 0.50×90 or $\frac{1}{2}$ of 90
22. 0.25×60 or $\frac{1}{4}$ of 60
23. 0.75×100 or $\frac{3}{4}$ of 100
24. $0.33\frac{1}{3} \times 60$ or $\frac{1}{3}$ of 60
25. $0.12\frac{1}{2} \times 32$ or $\frac{1}{8}$ of 32
26. $0.06\frac{1}{4} \times 16$ or $\frac{1}{16}$ of 16
27. $0.66\frac{2}{3} \times 90$ or $\frac{2}{3}$ of 90
28. 0.875×80 or $\frac{7}{8}$ of 80
29. 0.90×90 or $\frac{9}{10}$ of 90
30. 0.80×150 or $\frac{4}{5}$ of 150
31. 0.60×60 or $\frac{3}{5}$ of 60
32. 0.625×40 or $\frac{5}{8}$ of 40

*33. Jacob wants to save 0.25 of what he earns. If he earns $16, how much will he save if he saves 0.25 of it?

*34. Mrs. Landry thought that $0.62\frac{1}{2}$ of her class of 40 pupils knew the table of fraction-decimal equivalents. According to her estimate how many knew the table?

*35. Katy has paid $0.33\frac{1}{3}$ of her pledge of $12 to her church. How much has she paid?

*36. Roger sold 160 boxes of seed at $0.25 a box. How much money did he take in?

Practice in Dividing Fractions

a. Read the problem carefully.

b. Estimate the answer.

c. Solve and check.

d. Label the answer carefully.

1. If $\frac{1}{16}''$ represents 1 mile on a map, how many miles apart are two towns which are $2\frac{1}{8}''$ apart on the map? Suggested form: $N = 2\frac{1}{8} \div \frac{1}{16}$

2. Soap is 15¢ a bar or 4 bars for 50¢. How much is saved on each bar if bought in 4-bar amounts?

3. A piece of rope remaining from a bolt was marked $2\frac{1}{4}$ yards for 54¢. How much was that a yard?

4. A package of meat was marked 2 lb. 12 oz. for $1.10. What was the price per lb.?

5. Jim's father paid him $2.00 each time he mowed and trimmed the yard. He worked $2\frac{1}{2}$ hours on the yard one Saturday. How much did Jim receive per hour?

6. The sewing class bought 18 yards of material to make towels. If each towel requires $\frac{3}{4}$ of a yard, how many towels can they make from the material purchased?

7. The total rainfall one year at Piermont was 36.4 in. The next year the total rainfall was two-thirds as great. How much was this?

8. There are 16.5 feet in a rod. How many rods are there in 330 feet?

9. Mr. Henry's cow gave 1085 pounds of milk during the month of November. What is the average milk production to the nearest tenth of a pound per day from the cow?

10. Carl Bates drove 246 miles on 15 gallons of gas. How many miles to the nearest tenth of a mile per gallon did he average?

11. Bill Boyd picked up pecans on shares. If he was to receive a fourth of all he picked up, what is his share to the nearest tenth of a pound if he picked up the following amounts: 10.6 lb., 21.2 lb., 5.8 lb., 9.7 lb., and 12 lb.?

Quick Quiz No. 14

1. $400 - ? = 40$
2. $? + 45 = 70$
3. $9 \times ? = 180$
4. $640 \div ? = 160$
5. Does $\frac{2}{3} \times \frac{1}{9} = \frac{1}{3} \times \frac{2}{9}$?
6. The total weight of 12 boys used on the seventh grade basketball team is 1060 pounds. The average weight of the players is ______ pounds.
7. 1,000,000 is how many times 100?

8. If 1″ on a map represents 50 miles, what will $5\frac{1}{2}$″ represent?
9. Multiply each number by 7:
   (a) 21 (b) 45 (c) 60 (d) 208 (e) 3500
10. What number multiplied by 0.05 will give 4 for the product?

Division of Denominate Numbers

```
  2′1″
4)8′4″
```

Mike has a board 8′4″ long to be cut into 4 equal parts. How long will each part be? 8′ ÷ 4 = 2′, 4″ ÷ 4 = 1″? We can see that each piece will be 2′ 1″ long.

```
  1 yd. 14 in.
3)4 yd.  6 in.
  3
  1 yd. = 36 in.
          42 in.
```

A boy has 4 yards 6 inches of wire to divide among 3 classmates. How much wire will each classmate receive?
4 yd. ÷ 3 = 1 yd. with a remainder of 1 yd. The remainder of 1 yd. is changed to 36″ which is added to 6″ to make 42″. 42″ ÷ 3 = 14″. Each one will receive 1 yd. 14 in.

EXERCISES

1. 5)20 ft. 10 in.	2. 6)6 yd. 30 in.	3. 2)4 gal. 2 qt.
4. 4)20 lb. 12 oz.	5. 3)6 gal. 3 qt.	6. 2)5 bu. 2 pk.
7. 5)16 min. 10 sec.	8. 12)20 qt. 1 pt.	9. 9)12 hr. 9 min.

10. Tom Barker has a board 10′3″ which he is going to cut into 3 equal pieces to make a set of shelves for his room. How long will each piece measure?
11. If Peg Classen is to practice 7 hr. 30 min. in 5 days, how long will each day's practice be?
12. Bill Camp has 6 quarts 1 pint of feed which must last his chickens 4 days. How much can he feed them each day?
13. Mr. Scott lives 6 miles from town. He drove the distance in 9 minutes 30 seconds. What was his average time per mile for this trip?
14. Dewey Davis has 5 lb. 14 oz. of nuts to divide among 3 boys. How much will each receive?
15. Mrs. Little bought three chickens weighing 2 lb. 3 oz., 3 lb. 1 oz., and 3 lb. 10 oz. What was the average weight of the three chickens?
16. The heights of the five boys on the Warrensburg basketball team

were 6′4″, 6′2″, 6′1″, 6′, and 5′11″. What was the average height of the boys?

Fun with Numbers

Find the missing number:

Examples

1. $3 \times N = 75$
   $N = 75 \div 3$
   $N = 25$
2. $0.04 \times N = 18$
   $N = 18 \div 0.04$
   $N = 450$

$$0.04\overline{)18.00}\ \ 450$$

1. $2 \times N = 150$
2. $N \times 4 = 60$
3. $10 \times N = 900$
4. $N \times 16 = 48$
5. $1\frac{1}{2} \times N = 6$
6. $2\frac{1}{2} \times N = 50$
7. $0.08 \times N = 16$
8. $0.25 \times N = 100$
9. $0.9 \times N = 27$
10. $0.7 \times N = 14$
11. Find a number that when you divide it by 2, 3, 4, 5, and 6 you will have a remainder of 1, but when you divide it by 7 the remainder is zero.
12. 6 is a perfect number because the sum of all the integers (except 6) by which 6 is divisible is 6. These factors are 1, 2, and 3, the sum of which is 6. Can you find another perfect number?

Review of . . . DIVISION

1. Copy and fill in the blanks:
   (a) The answer in a division problem is called the ______.
   (b) In division, the number which is divided is called the ______.
   (c) In division, the number by which you divide is called the ______.
   (d) To divide by 10 move the decimal point ______ place to the ______.
2. Divide:
   (a) $7\overline{)1421}$ (b) $25\overline{)5150}$ (c) $326\overline{)6194}$
3. Divide:
   (a) $4 \div \frac{2}{3}$ (b) $\frac{4}{5} \div 3$ (c) $\frac{7}{8} \div \frac{3}{4}$ (d) $6\frac{2}{3} \div 1\frac{1}{4}$
4. Divide:
   (a) $12\overline{)0.1728}$ (b) $6.5\overline{)559.}$ (c) $0.93\overline{)0.26004}$ (d) $8.7\overline{)4.089}$
5. Rose spent for lunches one week \$0.30, \$0.28, \$0.35, \$0.32, and \$0.25. What was the average daily expenditure for lunch?

6. Write the reciprocals of these numbers:

(a) $\frac{1}{4}$ (b) $\frac{2}{3}$ (c) 6 (d) $\frac{8}{7}$

7. Divide to the nearest thousandths:

$6.2\overline{)0.17}$

8. If $\frac{2}{3}$ of a number is 42, what is the number?

9. Divide each number first by 10, then by 100, and then by 1000:

(a) 621 (b) 8.2 (c) 14.216 (d) 0.816

10. Four persons are to share equally some candy weighing 5 lb. 4 oz. How much should each person receive?

11. An airplane flies 3850 miles in 12 hours of flying time. What is its average speed in miles per hour?

12. The 34 pupils in Room 3 agreed to make the favors for the school party. How many favors should each pupil make if the work is to be equally divided and 646 favors are needed?

13. A 320-acre farm was sold for $40,160. What was the price per acre?

Chapter Test

1. $\begin{array}{r} 2645 \\ 1829 \\ 1675 \\ +1846 \\ \hline \end{array}$

2. $\begin{array}{r} 60{,}000 \\ -49{,}612 \\ \hline \end{array}$

3. $\begin{array}{r} 702 \\ \times\ 604 \\ \hline \end{array}$

4. $26\overline{)18434}$

5. $\begin{array}{r} 7\frac{2}{3} \\ +1\frac{1}{6} \\ \hline \end{array}$

6. $\begin{array}{r} 14\frac{1}{2} \\ -\ 6\frac{9}{16} \\ \hline \end{array}$

7. $3\frac{2}{3} \times 6$

8. $8\frac{2}{3} \div 6$

9. $8 - 2.25$

10. $1.21 + 2.30 + 6.45 + 7.$

11. 4.5×0.75

12. Express the quotient to the nearest hundredth:

$7.2\overline{)12.1}$

13. $\begin{array}{r} 6\text{ lb. } 3\text{ oz.} \\ 4\text{ lb. } 10\text{ oz.} \\ +13\text{ lb. } 12\text{ oz.} \\ \hline \end{array}$

14. $\begin{array}{r} 8\text{ gal. } 1\text{ qt.} \\ -4\text{ gal. } 2\text{ qt.} \\ \hline \end{array}$

15. $\begin{array}{r} 4\text{ yd. } 2\text{ ft.} \\ \times\ 9 \\ \hline \end{array}$

16. $8\overline{)12\text{ bu. } 2\text{ pk.}}$

17. Multiply 3.5 by:

(a) 10 (b) 100 (c) 1000

18. Divide 3.5 by:

 (a) 10 (b) 100 (c) 1000

19. If $\frac{7}{8}$ of my money is \$350, how much money do I have?

20. If Sara can save \$1.75 a week, how long will it take her to save \$33.25?

CHAPTER NINE  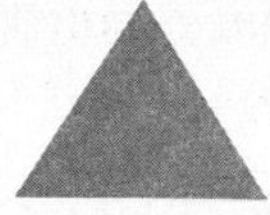  

Comparing Quantities

Comparing Quantities by Subtraction

96 lb.
−84 lb.
12 lb.

Betty weighs 84 pounds and George weighs 96 pounds. We can compare their weights by subtraction. When we do this we can make two statements of comparison:

1. George weighs 12 pounds more than Betty.
2. Betty weighs 12 pounds less than George.

A wise buyer compares the size of food containers with the price.

EXERCISES

Compare the following quantities by subtraction and make two statements of comparison about each:

1. James' allowance is \$2.00 a week and Henry's allowance is \$1.75 a week.
2. Sara is 5′ 2″ tall and Helen is 5′ $3\frac{1}{2}$″ tall.
3. Hilda worked 33 problems and Freda worked 18 problems.
4. Harry spent \$0.75 at the fair and Sam spent \$1.10.
5. Kansas City is 505 miles from Chicago and St. Louis is 295 miles from Chicago.
6. The Empire State Building in New York City is 1250 feet high and the Eiffel Tower in Paris is 984 feet high.
7. Lake Superior has a surface elevation of 602 feet above sea level and Lake Ontario has an elevation of 246 feet above sea level.
8. The Mississippi River flows a distance of 2,555 miles and the Amazon River flows 3,900 miles.
9. The area of California is 158,693 square miles and the area of Texas is 267,339 square miles.
10. The area of the Pacific Ocean is estimated to be 63,801,668 square miles and the area of the Atlantic Ocean is estimated at 41,400,000 square miles.

Comparing Quantities by Division

\$2 is $\frac{2}{5}$ of \$5

\$5 is $\frac{5}{2}$ or $2\frac{1}{2}$ times \$2

Ronnie has \$2 and Vicki has \$5. When we compare by division we may use a fraction to express the division and say:

1. Ronnie has $\frac{2}{5}$ as much money as Vicki.
2. Vicki has $2\frac{1}{2}$ times as much money as Ronnie.

EXERCISES—Compare the following quantities by division. For each pair make two statements, answering these questions:

(a) The smaller quantity is what part of the larger quantity?

(b) The larger quantity is how many times the smaller quantity?

4″; 2′ $\quad$ 2′ = 24″
4″ is $\frac{4}{24}$ or $\frac{1}{6}$ of 2′
2′ is $\frac{24}{4}$ or 6 times 4″

1. \$25; \$15	2. 24 in.; 18 in.	3. 3 ft.; 6 ft.
4. 10 oz.; 1 lb.	5. 3 qt.; 1 gal.	6. 5 days; 30 days
7. 6 yd.; 4 ft.	8. 30¢; \$1.00	9. 8 eggs; 1 doz. eggs
10. 45 min.; 60 min.	11. 6 in.; $1\frac{1}{2}$ ft.	12. 4 oz.; $1\frac{1}{4}$ lb.

Ratio

A ratio expresses a comparison of two quantities by division.

The ratio of 6 inches to 1 foot or 12 inches is $\frac{6}{12}$ or $\frac{1}{2}$ which is a ratio of 1:2. (We read this as a ratio of 1 to 2. The ratio sign may be thought of as an abbreviation of the division sign ÷)

The first named quantity becomes the numerator and the second named quantity becomes the denominator, if the ratio is expressed as a fraction.

When we say the ratio of 6 inches to 1 foot is $\frac{6}{12}$ or $\frac{1}{2}$ or 1 to 2, we mean 6 inches is $\frac{1}{2}$ of one foot.

What is the ratio of 1 foot to 6 inches?

Building models involves measurement, proportion, and imagination.

The ratio of 1 foot or 12 inches to 6 inches is

$\frac{12}{6}$ or $\frac{2}{1}$ which is a ratio of 2:1.

When we say the ratio of 1 foot to 6 inches is 2:1, we mean 1 foot is 2 times as large as 6 inches.

EXERCISES—What is the ratio of the numbers in each Exercise, 1 through 15?

1. 10 to 100	2. 16 to 32	3. 12 to 18
4. 75 to 100	5. 24 to 16	6. 200 to 20
7. 27 to 36	8. 5 to 45	9. 90 to 80
10. 12 to 5	11. 80 to 30	12. 55 to 44
13. 300 to 150	14. 75 to 300	15. 500 to 125

16. What is the ratio of 9″ to 12″?
17. What is the ratio of 6 lb. to 30 lb.?
18. What is the ratio of 14 problems to 12 problems?
19. Sam is 15 years old, and his father is 45 years old. What is the ratio of the father's age to Sam's age?
20. 5″ 3″
(a) What is the ratio of the width of the rectangle to the length?
(b) What is the ratio of the length of the rectangle to the width?

Practice Using Ratios

Example 1. John and Bill cleaned the weeds out of the city park. They received \$15 for the work. John worked 3 days, and Bill worked 2 days. How shall they divide the money?

> 3 days work + 2 days work = 5 days work
> John should receive $\frac{3}{5}$ of \$15, or \$9
> Bill should receive $\frac{2}{5}$ of \$15, or \$6

John worked 3 days out of the 5 days of work and should receive $\frac{3}{5}$ of the pay. Why should Bill receive only $\frac{2}{5}$ of the pay? The ratio of John's share to Bill's share is $\frac{3}{2}$ or 3:2.

Example 2. Mike invests \$5 in a peanut stand near the zoo and George invests \$3 in the stand. They make a profit of \$6. What is each boy's share of the profit?

$\$5 + \$3 = \$8$ invested

Mike should receive $\frac{5}{8}$ of \$6

$$\frac{5}{8} \text{ of } \$6 = \frac{5 \times \overset{3}{\cancel{6}}}{\underset{4}{\cancel{8}}} = \frac{\$15}{4} \text{ or } \$3.75$$

George should receive $\frac{3}{8}$ of \$6

$$\frac{3}{8} \text{ of } \$6 = \frac{3 \times \overset{3}{\cancel{6}}}{\underset{4}{\cancel{8}}} = \frac{\$9}{4} \text{ or } \$2.25$$

1. What is each boy's share of the total amount invested?
2. Why should Mike receive more than George out of the profits?
3. Does \$3.75 + \$2.25 = \$6?

EXERCISES

1. Kent agreed to clean the basement of his home for \$2.50. He had worked a while when his friend, Edward, came along and wanted him to go fishing. Edward offered to help him finish and Kent agreed to share the pay with Edward. Kent worked 4 hours and Edward 1 hour. What is each boy's share of the money?
2. Suzanne and Sharon had a flower stand. Suzanne invested \$10 and Sharon \$6. They cleared \$8. What was each girl's share of the profit?
3. Charles and Frank helped Mr. Brown pick up his potatoes when he harvested them. Charles worked 6 hours and Frank became ill and worked only 4 hours. Mr. Brown paid them \$8. What was each boy's share?
4. The Kirkpatrick and Childs families rented a large cabin at the lake for a weekend. The rent was \$30. If there are 5 in the Kirkpatrick family and 3 in the Childs family, what is each family's portion of the rent?
5. Mr. Bradshaw and Mr. Parker went into business. Mr. Bradshaw invested \$8,000 and Mr. Parker \$7,000. How will they share \$6,000 profit?
6. The ratio of frozen juice to water used in making punch is 1 : 3. How many quarts of frozen juice will you need if you want 2 gallons of punch? How much water will you add to the juice? (Hint: The ratio 1 : 3 means 1 part juice and 3 parts water, which added together make 4 parts.)
7. Clyde and LaVon helped their grandfather replant corn. Clyde worked 3 days and LaVon 2 days, and their grandfather paid them \$6. What was each boy's share?

8. In making syrup for fruit drinks, one part sugar is used for two parts water. How much sugar will be used with two quarts of water?
9. In setting stakes it was agreed the ratio of the part of a stake in the ground to the part above the ground should be 1 to 4. How deep into the ground should a 1-foot stake be set?
10. The teams playing the championship basketball game were to share the gate receipts in the ratio of 3 to 2, the winners to the losers. What is each team's share of the $750 gate receipts if Maplewood won and Claremont lost?
11. Write ten pairs of numbers whose ratio is 1:2.
12. Write five pairs of numbers whose ratio is 3:4.
13. Write five pairs of numbers whose ratio is 3:2.
14. Draw 2 line segments illustrating each of the following ratios:
    (a) 1:2 (b) 5:6 (c) 3:2 (d) 5:4
15. Write *True* if the statement is true, and *False* if the statement is false:
    (a) The ratio of 9 feet to 27 feet is $\frac{1}{3}$ or 1:3.
    (b) The ratio of 150 lb. to 90 lb. is $\frac{5}{3}$ or 5:3.
    (c) The ratio of 16 inches to 12 inches is $\frac{3}{4}$ or 3:4.
    (d) The ratio of 14 ounces to 1 pound is $\frac{14}{1}$ or 14:1.
    (e) The ratio of $\frac{1}{2}$ inch to $1\frac{1}{2}$ inches is $\frac{1}{3}$ or 1:3.
    (f) The ratio of $\frac{1}{2}$ pint to 1 quart is $\frac{1}{2}$ or 1:2.
    (g) The ratio of $25 to $15 is $\frac{5}{3}$ or 5:3.
    (h) The ratio of 32 pupils to 40 pupils is $\frac{5}{4}$ or 5:4.

Quick Quiz No. 15

1. The yearly subscription to a monthly magazine is $5.50. How much do you save a year by subscribing for the magazine instead of buying it each month for 50¢ a copy?
2. If the product of two fractions is $\frac{1}{12}$, and one of the fractions is $\frac{3}{4}$, what is the other fraction?
3. One foot is what part of one yard?
4. If you divide 5 lb. 1 oz. of candy evenly among 3 boys, how much will each boy receive?
5. $60 \times ? = 720$

6. Select the numbers that will divide 1200 exactly:

   (a) 15 (b) 16 (c) 20 (d) 25 (e) 65 (f) 82

7. What part of a bushel is 1 peck?
8. When a car travels 13 miles in 12 minutes, what is its speed in miles per hour?
9. Name the months that have 31 days.
10. Are $\frac{65}{90}$ and $\frac{13}{18}$ equivalent fractions?

Using Bar Graphs to Make Comparisons

The bar graph is a drawing or picture used to show comparisons.

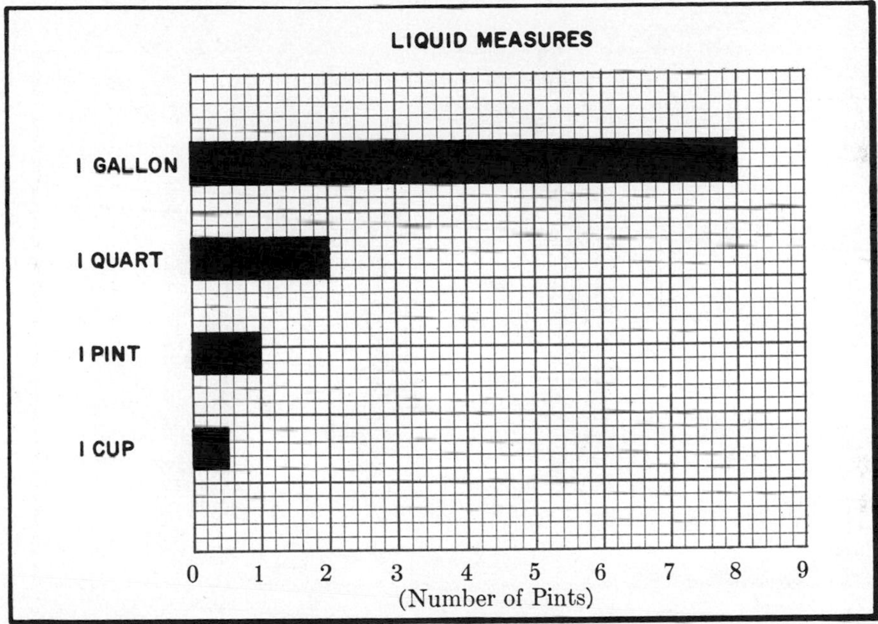

This is a horizontal bar graph showing a comparison of various liquid measures.

Answer the following questions from the graph:

1. 1 cup is what part of a pint?
2. 1 pint is what part of a quart?
3. 1 quart is what part of a gallon?
4. 1 cup is what part of a gallon?
5. 1 pint is what part of a gallon?

6. 1 cup is what part of a quart?
7. 1 gallon is how many times as much as a quart?
8. 1 quart is how many times as much as a pint?
9. 1 quart is how many times as much as a cup?
10. 1 pint is how many times as much as a cup?
11. 1 gallon is how many times as much as a cup?
*12. What unit is used in drawing the bars of the graph?

EXERCISES

1. This vertical bar graph shows the enrollment in the Park Junior High School by grades.

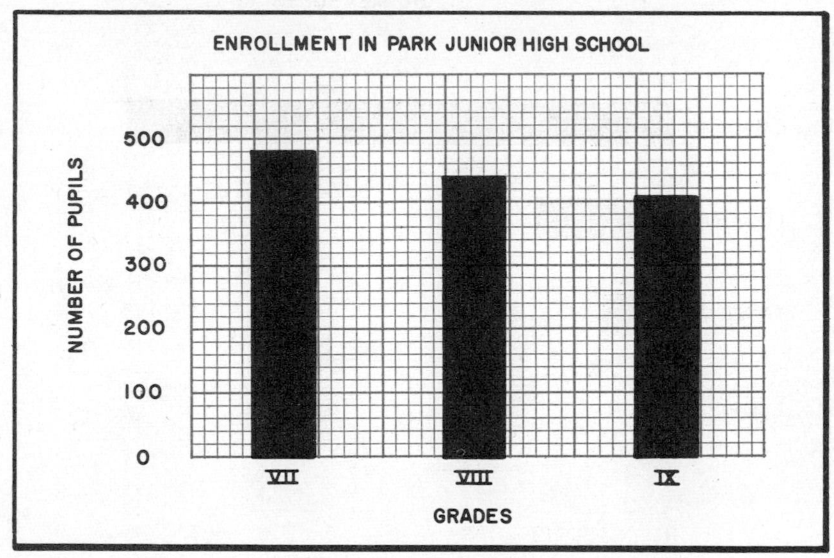

(a) The height of each small square represents how many pupils?
(b) The height of each half of a small square represents how many pupils?
(c) Which grade has the largest enrollment?
(d) Which grade has the smallest enrollment?
(e) The 8th grade has how many more pupils than the 9th grade?
(f) The 7th grade has how many more pupils than the 9th grade?
(g) The 7th grade has how many more pupils than the 8th grade?
(h) Compare by ratio the enrollment in the 8th grade with the enrollment in the 7th grade.

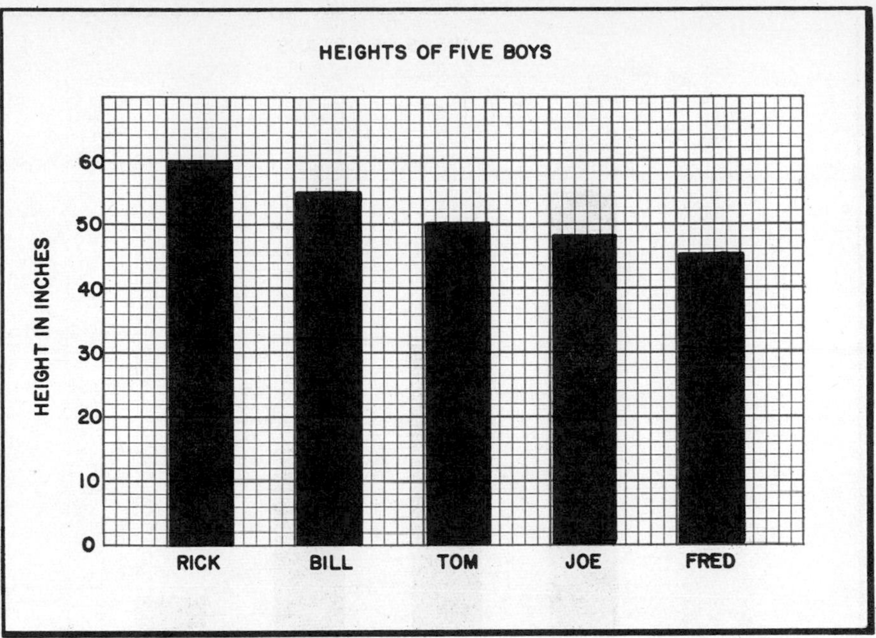

2. This vertical bar graph shows a comparison of heights of five boys.
   (a) The height of each small square represents how many inches?
   (b) The height of each half of a small square represents how many inches?
   (c) How tall is each boy?
   (d) How much taller is Rick than each of the other boys?
   (e) Each of the other boys is how much shorter than Rick?
   *(f) Compare by ratio the heights of each boy with Rick.

   Example: The ratio of Bill's height to Rick's is

   $\frac{55}{60}$ or $\frac{11}{12}$ or 11:12.

3. In graphing large numbers, we round them to the nearest million or hundred thousand. Since the areas of oceans are in millions of square miles, these areas were rounded to the nearest million. When we round areas, we call them approximate areas.
   (a) Each small square represents how many million square miles?
   (b) Each half of a small square represents how many million square miles?
   (c) What is the approximate area of each ocean?

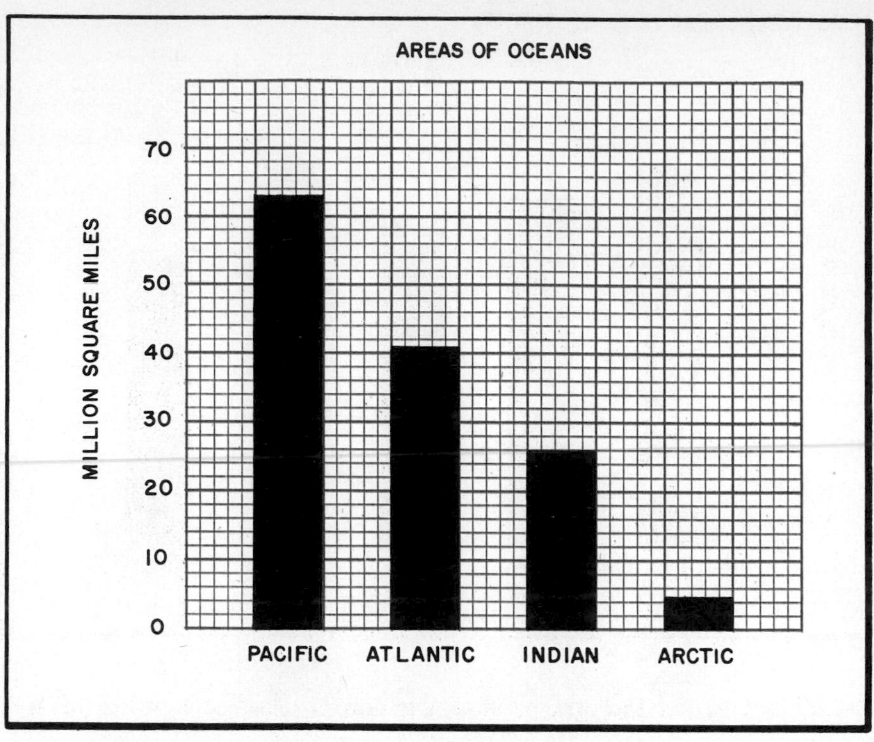

(d) Which ocean is approximately $\frac{1}{3}$ as large as the Pacific Ocean?

(e) Which ocean is approximately $\frac{2}{3}$ as large as the Pacific Ocean?

*(f) Compare by ratio the area of the Arctic Ocean with each of the other oceans. Give as an approximate ratio, as:

(a) The Arctic Ocean is approximately $\frac{1}{14}$ as large as the Pacific Ocean.

Review of . . .
COMPARING QUANTITIES

1. What are two ways of comparing like quantities?
2. Compare James' weight of 90 pounds with his father's weight of 180 pounds in two ways.
3. What is the ratio of:

   (a) 18′ to 54′? (b) 14″ to 2″?

   (c) 64 bu. to 40 bu.? (d) 1 pt. to 3 qt.?
4. Express the ratio of 1″ to 4″ in three ways.

5. What part of a yard is:

   (a) 1 in.? (b) 1 ft.?

6. If 1″ represents 50 miles on a map, what is the approximate distance between two cities that measure $3\frac{1}{4}$ inches apart on the map?

7. Jerry makes \$6 a week delivering the evening paper. If he saves \$2 a week and spends the rest, what is the ratio of the amount he saves to the amount he spends?

8. Mildred solved 28 problems correctly out of 30 problems assigned. What fractional part of the assigned problems did she solve correctly?

9. Pete and Bob sold peanuts at the Old Time Picnic. If Pete had invested \$3 and Bob \$2 in peanuts, what was each boy's share of the \$4.80 profit?

10. If you are using the ratio of 2 cups of sugar to 3 cups of water to make a syrup, how many cups of water will you use with 5 cups of sugar?

Chapter Test

1. Compare by subtraction and make two statements of comparison about each:

   (a) Howard weighs 87 pounds and Fred weighs $92\frac{1}{2}$ pounds.

   (b) Jean lives 12 blocks from school and Judy lives $6\frac{1}{2}$ blocks from school.

2. Compare by division or ratio and make two statements of comparison about each:

   (a) Barbara solved 12 problems during a 30-minute study period and Donna solved 16 problems during the same time.

   (b) Tom read 70 books from the school library during one year and Alan read 20 books during the same time.

3. Give two pairs of numbers that have the ratio of $\frac{4}{5}$ or 4:5.

4. Select from the following, the pairs of numbers that have a ratio of $\frac{3}{2}$ or 3:2:

   (a) 15, 10 (b) 6, 5 (c) 36, 24 (d) 9, 4

5. A baseball team won 15 games and lost 10 games.

   (a) What part of the games played did the team win?

   (b) What part of the games played did the team lose?

6. What part of a class of 36 pupils received each of the following ratings:

(a) Excellent	9 pupils	(b) Good	12 pupils
(c) Fair	10 pupils	(d) Poor	5 pupils

7. Helen needed 30 inches of velvet ribbon to trim a dress. What part of a yard did she need?

8. If the ratio of the amount of money Mr. Rickman has invested to the amount of money Mr. Thornton has invested in a business which they operate together is 3 to 2, how will they share a profit of $4500?

CHAPTER TEN

Perimeters and Areas

It is often desirable to know the distance around figures like a square, a rectangle, a triangle, and a trapezoid.

The sum of the lengths of the sides of a polygon is called the perimeter of the polygon. (The word *perimeter* is made up of *peri*, which means around and *meter* which means measure.)

Perimeters of Squares and Rectangles

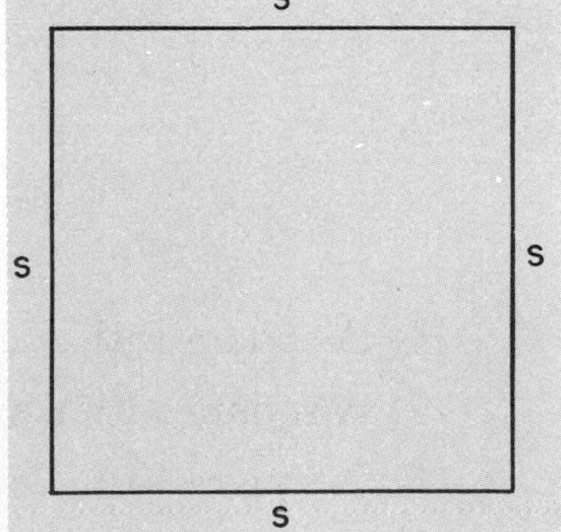

EXERCISE—With your ruler measure the sides of this square. What is its perimeter? If you know the length of the side of a square, how would you find its perimeter?

A formula is a short statement of a relationship in which letters are used to represent numbers.

The formula for the perimeter of a square could be written:

$$p = s + s + s + s$$

or

$$p = 4s$$

In this formula "p" represents the number of units in the perimeter and "s" represents the number of units on a side. The number which represents the length of the perimeter and number which represents the length of a side, can be substituted for p and s.

Using the formulas for the figure on page 167.

$s = 1\frac{1}{2}$ $\quad p = s + s + s + s$

$p = 1\frac{1}{2} + 1\frac{1}{2} + 1\frac{1}{2} + 1\frac{1}{2}$

$p = 6$

The perimeter is 6 inches.

or

$s = 1\frac{1}{2}$ $\quad p = 4s$

$p = 4 \times 1\frac{1}{2}$

$p = 6$

The perimeter is 6 inches.

$$\begin{array}{r} 1\frac{1}{2} \\ \underline{4} \\ 2 \\ \underline{4} \\ 6 \end{array}$$

EXERCISES

1. Which formula do you prefer in the example above? Why?

Using the formula, find the perimeters of the squares in Exercises 2 through 8. Illustrate each problem by drawing a square and writing the length of a side on the square as in Exercise 3.

2. 3. 4. 5.

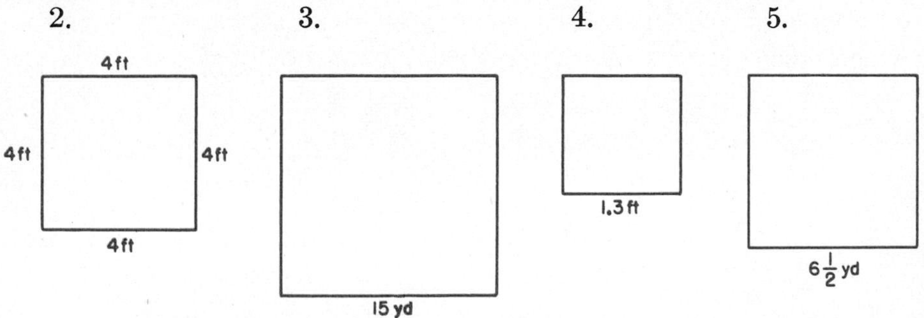

6. A square with a side of $4\frac{2}{3}''$.
7. A square with a side of 8.4 yd.
8. A square with a side of $\frac{3}{4}''$.

*9. How many feet of baseboard will be needed for a bedroom 12 feet on a side, allowing for two doors, each 3 feet wide?

*10. If the perimeter of a square is 64 inches, what is the length of one side?

*11. If a square garden plot measures $43\frac{3}{4}$ feet around, what is the length of one side?

Rectangular lots in Tulsa, Oklahoma.

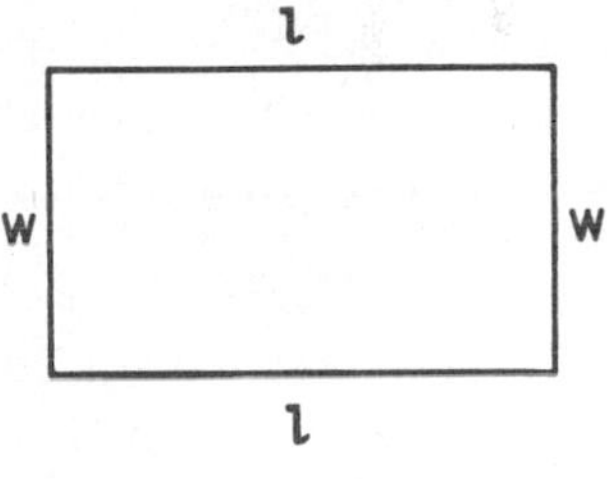

A rectangle has two dimensions, the length and the width. With your ruler measure the length and width of this rectangle. If you know the length and width of a rectangle, you can find its perimeter. The formula for finding the perimeter of a rectangle could be written:

$p = l + w + l + w$

or

$p = 2l + 2w$

l is used to represent the number of units in the length.

w is used to represent the number of units in the width.

p is used to represent the number of units in the perimeter.

Using the formula for the above figure:

$l = 2$ $\quad p = l + w + l + w$

$w = 1\frac{1}{2}$ $\quad p = 2 + 1\frac{1}{2} + 2 + 1\frac{1}{2}$

$p = 7$

The perimeter is 7 inches.

or

$l = 2$ $\quad p = 2l + 2w$

$w = 1\frac{1}{2}$ $\quad p = (2 \times 2) + (2 \times 1\frac{1}{2})$

$p = 4 + 3$

$p = 7$

The perimeter is 7 inches.

The dimensions must be in the same unit of measure to find the perimeter; for example, each side must be in yards, in feet, or in inches.

EXERCISES—Use the formula to find the perimeters of the rectangles in Exercises 1 through 7. Illustrate each problem by drawing a rectangle and writing the dimensions on it.

1. 2. 3.

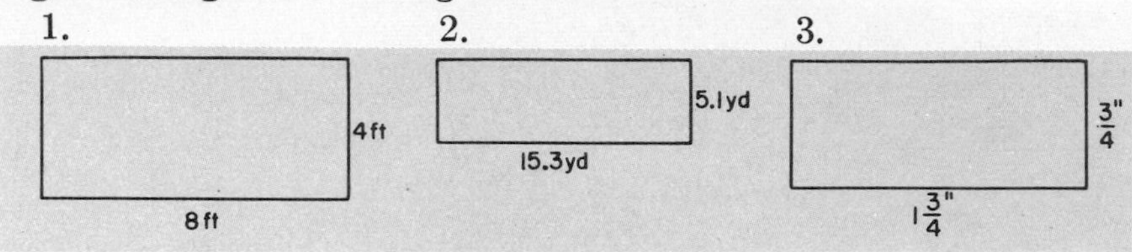

4. A rectangle $4\frac{1}{2}'$ by $6\frac{1}{2}'$.
5. A rectangle 3.5 yd. by 10.5 yd.
6. A rectangle 16 rd. × 27 rd. 7. A rectangle 4′ by $6\frac{1}{2}'$.
8. Find the perimeter in feet of a rectangle 6 inches by 2 feet.

*9. How many feet of picture framing will be needed to frame a picture 2 feet 9 inches by 3 feet?

*10. How much molding will be needed to go around a schoolroom 32 feet by 28 feet?

*11. How many feet of fencing will be needed to enclose a yard 90 feet by 110 feet?

*12. How many feet of baseboard will be needed in a room $12\frac{1}{2}$ feet by 15 feet allowing for two doors, each 3 feet wide?

Perimeters of Triangles

EXERCISES—1. With your ruler measure the sides of this triangle. What is its perimeter? If you know the lengths of the three sides of a triangle, how will you find its perimeter?

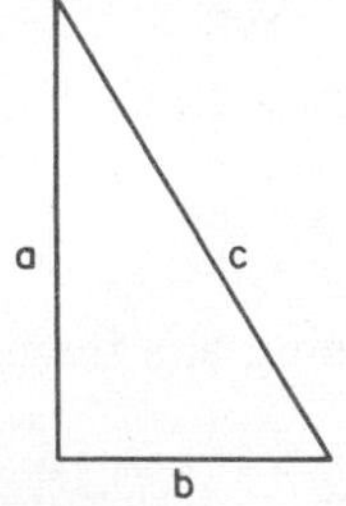

The formula for finding the perimeter of a triangle is:

$$p = a + b + c.$$

Using the formula for the figure on page 170:

$a = 2 \qquad p = a + b + c$

$b = 1\frac{1}{2} \qquad p = 2 + 1\frac{1}{2} + 2\frac{1}{2}$

$c = 2\frac{1}{2} \qquad p = 6$

The perimeter is 6 inches.

Using the formula, find the perimeter of the triangles in Exercises 2, 3, and 4. Illustrate each problem by drawing a triangle and placing the length of each side on it.

2.

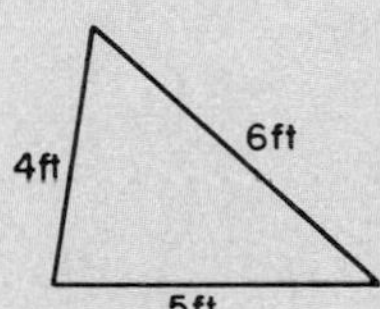

3.

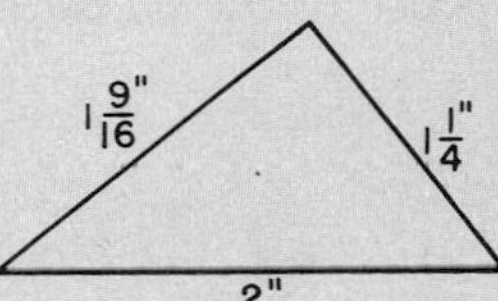

4.

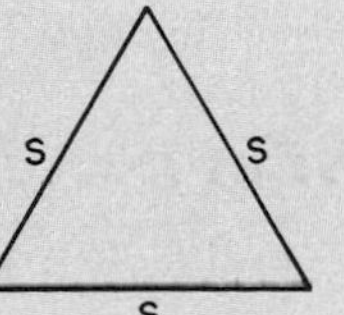

5. Find the perimeter of this equilateral triangle:

6. What formula can you use for finding the perimeter of an equilateral triangle?

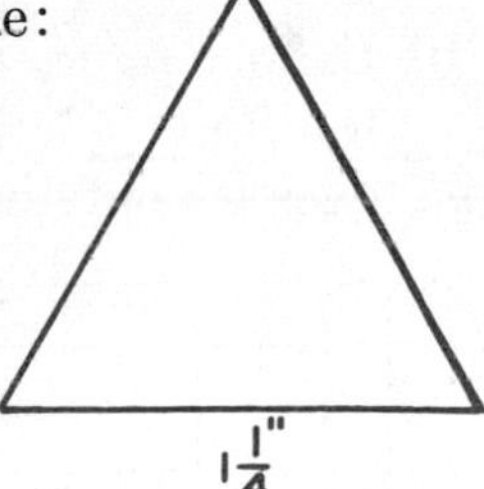

7. Find the perimeter of this isosceles triangle:

8. What formula can you use for finding the perimeter of an isosceles triangle?

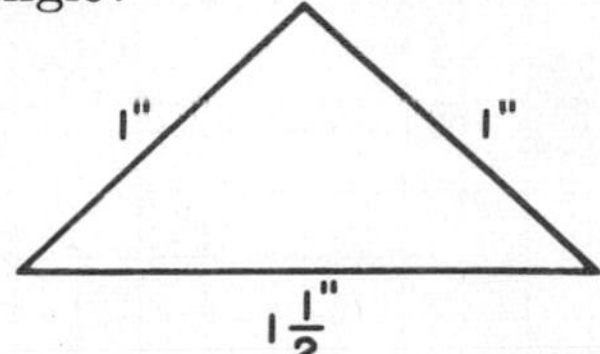

9. Find the perimeters of the following quadrilaterals:

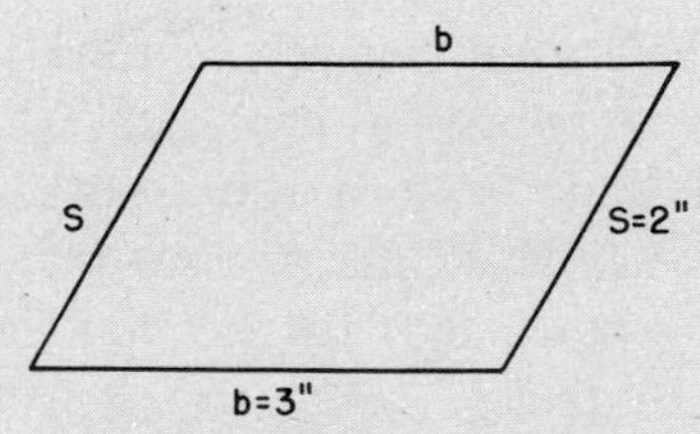

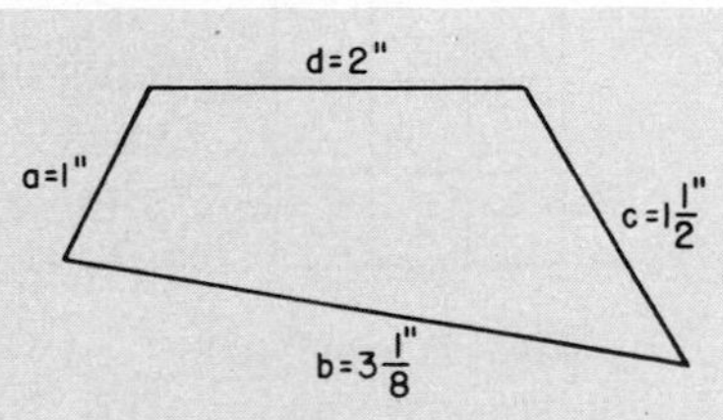

Areas of Rectangles and Squares

ONE
SQUARE
INCH

Areas of polygons are measured in square units. We may measure small areas, like the page of this book, in square inches. The figure is the actual size of a square inch. This square is one inch in length and one inch wide.

Larger surfaces are measured in square feet, square yards, square rods, square miles, and in acres. A square foot is one foot or 12 inches wide and it is one foot or 12 inches long. Similar statements may be made about these other measures of area.

EXERCISES

1. (a) Draw a figure representing a square foot on the board. Mark it into square inches. How many square inches does it contain?

   (b) Draw a figure representing a square yard on the board or on the floor. Mark it into square feet. How many square feet does it contain?

2. 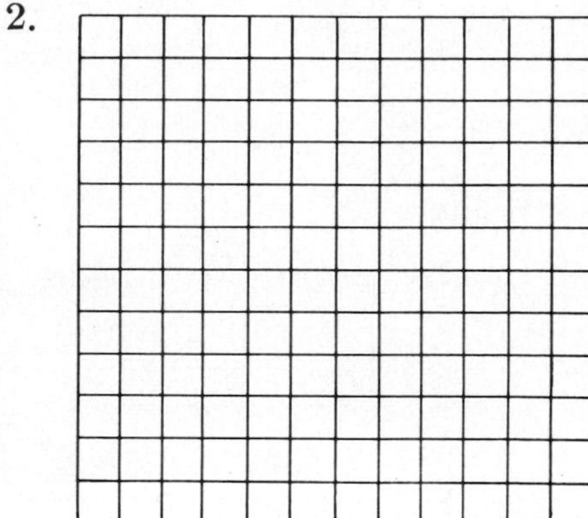

   This figure is not the actual size of a square foot, but it is a scale representation of a square foot. Each little square represents a square inch. (a) How many rows of square inches are there? (b) How many square inches are there in each row? One square foot equals 12×12 or 144 square inches.

3. 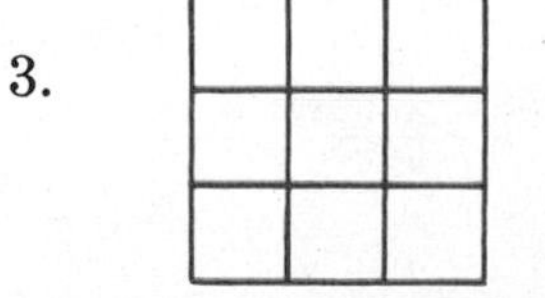

   This figure is not the actual size of a square yard, but is a scale representation of a square yard. Each little square represents here a square foot. (a) How many rows of square feet are there? (b) How many square feet to the row? One square yard equals 3×3 or 9 square feet.

The *Square Measure Table* will be found in the Appendix, page 312.

ONE SQUARE UNIT

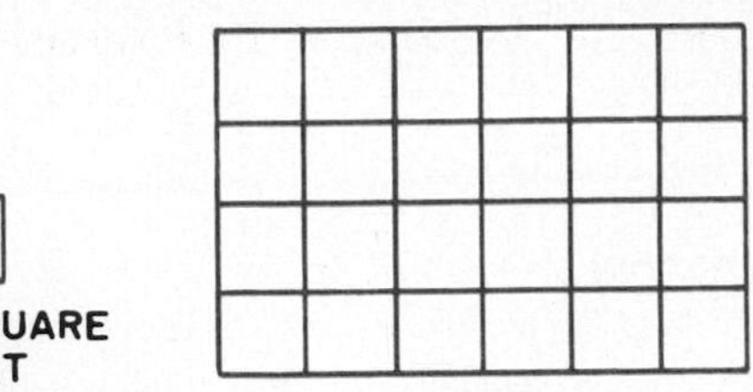

FIG. 1

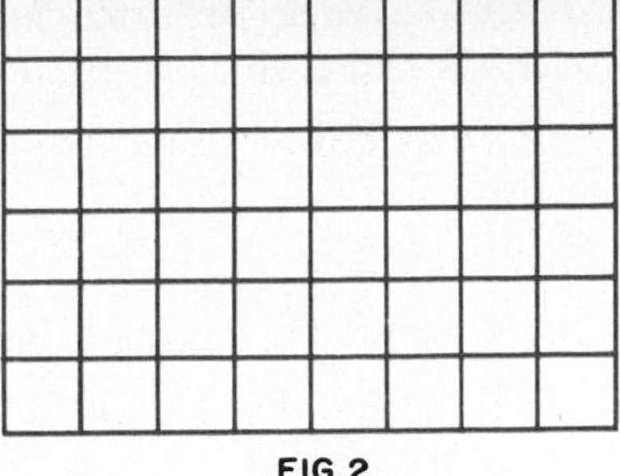

FIG. 2

4. (a) How many square units are there in each row of Figure 1?
   (b) How many rows of square units are there in Figure 1?
   (c) How many square units in Figure 1?
5. (a) How many square units are there in each row of Figure 2?
   (b) How many rows of square units are there in Figure 2?
   (c) How many square units in Figure 2?
6. If A represents the number of square units in the area, and l represents the number of square units in each row, and w represents the number of rows, is this the formula for finding the area of a rectangle?

$$A = l \times w$$

or

$$A = lw$$

Example 1. Using the formula to find the area of Figures 1 and 2, we let each unit in Figure 1 represent a foot and each unit in Figure 2, an inch.

$l = 6$ $\quad A = lw$

$w = 4$ $\quad A = 6 \times 4$

$A = 24$

The area is 24 sq. ft.

$l = 8$ $\quad A = lw$

$w = 6$ $\quad A = 8 \times 6$

$A = 48$

The area is 48 sq. in.

Example 2. Using formula $A = lw$, find the areas of the rectangles having these dimensions:

$2'$ by $6\frac{1}{2}''$

$6\frac{1}{2}''$

$2'$

$l = 24$ $\quad A = lw$

$w = 6\frac{1}{2}$ $\quad A = 24 \times 6\frac{1}{2}$

$A = 156$

The area is 156 sq. in.

$$\begin{array}{r} 24 \\ 6\frac{1}{2} \\ \hline 12 \quad (\frac{1}{2} \times 24) \\ 144 \\ \hline 156 \end{array}$$

We refer to the longer dimension of a rectangle as the length. Before finding the area, both length and width must be expressed in the same unit of measure.

EXERCISES—Find the areas of the rectangles in Exercises 1 through 9:

1. 6′ by 12′
2. 3′ by $11\frac{1}{2}''$ (area in square inches)
3. 6.2 yd. by 3.4 yd.
4. $1\frac{1}{2}'$ by $3\frac{1}{2}'$
5. 3′ by $2\frac{1}{2}$ yd. (area in sq. yd.)
6. 10.2 rd. by 4 rd.
7. $2\frac{1}{2}$ mi. by $1\frac{1}{4}$ mi.
8. $10\frac{1}{2}'$ by 9″ (area in sq. ft.)
9. $6\frac{2}{3}'' \times 1\frac{1}{2}''$

*10. How many square yards of carpet will be required for a room 24′ by 18′?

*11. What is the cost of linoleum to cover a kitchen 9′ by 12′ if linoleum costs $1.75 a square yard?

*12. John is going to seed the lawn with grass seed using 1 pound for each 200 square feet of lawn. How many pounds will he need if the lawn measures 100′ by 30′?

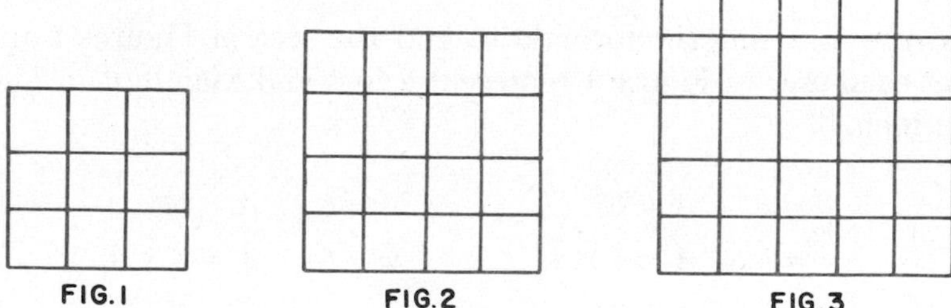

FIG. 1 FIG. 2 FIG. 3

There are 9 square units in Figure 1.
There are 16 square units in Figure 2.
There are 25 square units in Figure 3.

If A represents the number of square units in the area, and s represents the number of units of measure on each side, the formula for finding the area of a square is $A = s \times s$.

This is written $A = s^2$ and is read "A is equal to s square."

The small two is called an exponent. It shows how many times s is used as a factor. s^2 means $s \times s$. See page 10.

3^2 means 3×3 | 4^2 means 4×4 | 5^2 means 5×5

$3^2 = 9$ | $4^2 = 16$ | $5^2 = 25$

EXERCISES

1. What is the meaning of (a) 6^2, (b) 9^2, (c) 10^2?
2. What is the value of (a) 7^2, (b) $(1\frac{1}{2})^2$, (c) $(4.2)^2$?

Find the value of the expressions in Exercises 3 through 17.

3. 11^2	4. 12^2	5. 13^2	6. 14^2	7. 15^2
8. 16^2	9. 17^2	10. 18^2	11. 19^2	12. 20^2
13. 21^2	14. 22^2	15. 23^2	16. 24^2	17. 25^2

It will be helpful to keep the results found in Exercises 3 through 17 and refer to them when they are needed in problems.

Using the formula $A = s^2$, find the areas of the squares in Exercises 18 through 26.

$s = 6\frac{1}{2}$ $\quad A = s^2$

$A = (6\frac{1}{2})^2$

$A = 6\frac{1}{2} \times 6\frac{1}{2}$

$A = \frac{13}{2} \times \frac{13}{2}$

$A = \frac{169}{4}$

$A = 42\frac{1}{4}$

The area is $42\frac{1}{4}$ sq. in.

18. $s = 11'$
19. $s = 24''$
20. $s = 15$ yd.
21. $s = 18'$
22. $s = 1\frac{1}{2}'$
23. $s = 8\frac{1}{2}''$
24. $s = 2.3'$
25. $s = 9.6$ yd.
26. $s = 20.2$ rd.
27. Find the area of a square flower bed $9\frac{1}{2}$ feet on a side.

*28. How many acres are there in a square field if it is 40 rods on a side? (160 sq. rd. = 1 A)

*29. How many acres are there in a ranch that is in the shape of a square 4 miles on a side? (640 A = 1 sq. mile)

Quick Quiz No. 16

1. If a plane is flying 450 miles per hour, how far will it fly in 10 minutes?
2. If you can purchase 2 packages of frozen peas for $0.45, what must you pay if you buy only one package?
3. What part of a gallon is a pint?
4. Correct any errors:
   (a) $\frac{1}{4} = 0.20$ (b) $\frac{1}{8} = 0.375$ (c) $\frac{4}{5} = 0.60$ (d) $\frac{3}{4} = 0.75$
5. $\frac{1}{4}$ is how many times as large as $\frac{1}{8}$?

6. What part of a foot are each of the following?
   (a) 1″ (b) 6″ (c) 10″ (d) 7″ (e) 9″
7. If Mary spent $\frac{1}{4}$ of what she earned baby sitting and saved the rest, what part of her earnings did she save?
8. How many hours and minutes are there from 8:50 a.m. to 3:30 p.m.?
9. If a bushel of potatoes weighs 60 pounds, how many 100-pound bags can a farmer fill if he has 12 bushels of potatoes?
10. If you cut a 16-foot board into 3 equal pieces, what will be the length in feet and inches of each piece?

Areas of Parallelograms

A parallelogram is a quadrilateral in which the opposite sides are parallel.

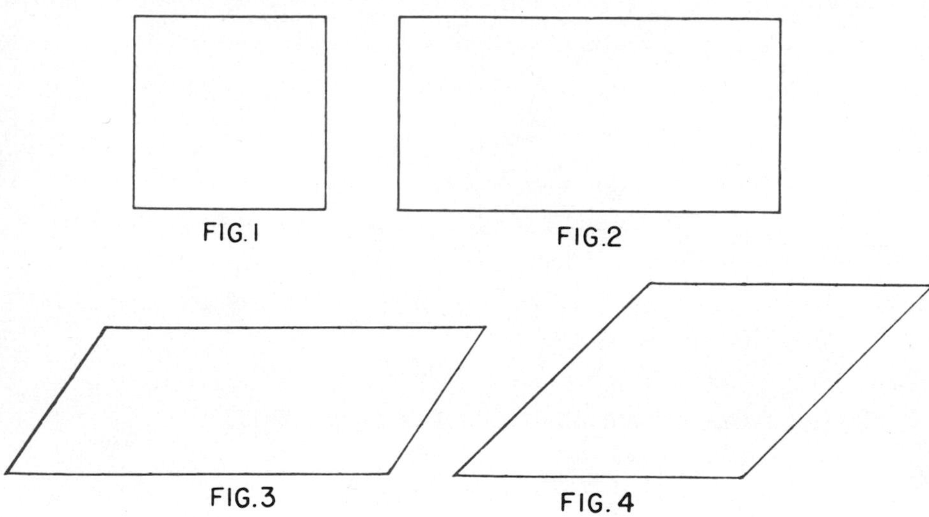

Rectangles and squares are parallelograms with all angles right angles.

Figures 3 and 4 are parallelograms with acute and obtuse angles.

We do not use the words length and width when we talk about parallelograms, but we use base and height (or altitude).

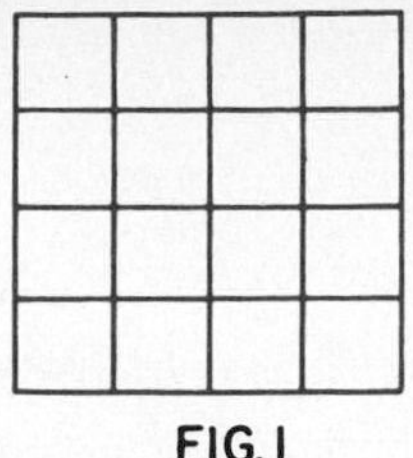

FIG. 1

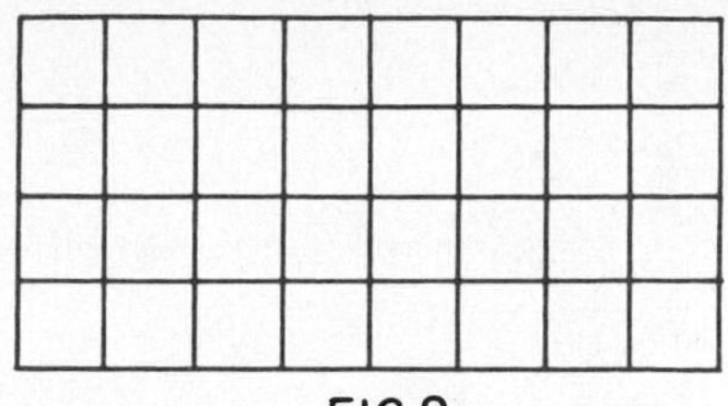

FIG. 2

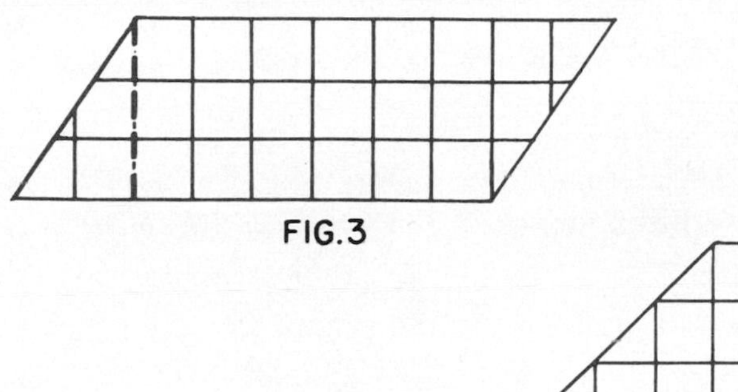

FIG. 3

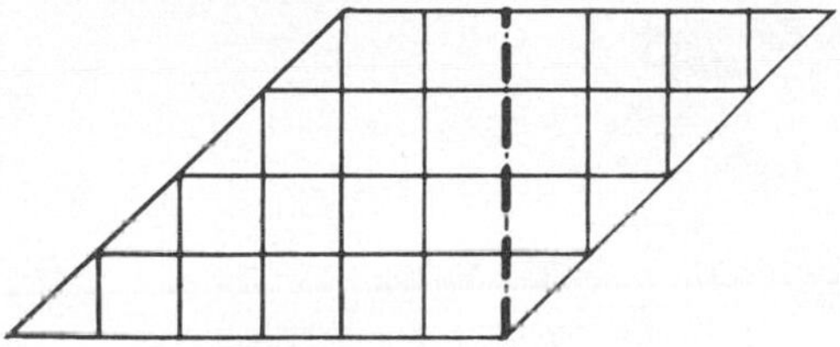

FIG. 4

EXERCISES—Let each of the units of Figures 1, 2, 3, and 4 represent a foot in answering these questions:

1. (a) What is the length of the base of Figure 1?
   (b) What is the height or altitude of Figure 1?
   (c) What is the area of Figure 1?
2. (a) What is the length of the base of Figure 2?
   (b) What is the height of Figure 2?
   (c) What is the area of Figure 2?
3. (a) What is the length of the base of Figure 3?
   (b) What is the altitude of Figure 3? Notice that the altitude of Figure 3 is not equal to its short side, but is the perpendicular distance between the two bases.
   (c) What is the area of Figure 3? (Count the squares)
4. (a) What is the length of the base of Figure 4?
   (b) What is the height (altitude) of Figure 4?
   (c) What is the area of Figure 4? (Count the squares)

Since the words "square" and "rectangle" are used for certain kinds of parallelograms, the use of the word parallelogram generally refers to figures like those in Figures 3 and 4. These parallelograms have special names also. Figure 3 is a *rhomboid* (sides not equal). Figure 4 is a *rhombus* (sides are equal).

Using the formula $A = bh$, we can find the area of the parallelogram in Figure 3.

$b = 8 \quad A = bh$

$h = 3 \quad A = 8 \times 3$

$A = 24$

The area is 24 sq. ft.

Use the formula $A = bh$ to find the areas of the parallelograms in Exercises 5 through 10. Remember, before finding the area, the base and height should be expressed in the same unit of measure.

5. $b = 13''$ $h = 8''$
6. $b = 10\frac{1}{2}'$ $h = 4\frac{1}{2}'$
7. $b = 6.2$ yd. $h = 3.1$ yd.
8. $b = 2'$ $h = 10''$ (area in square inches)
9. $b = 4$ yd. $h = 6'$ (area in square yards)
10. $b = 10'$ $h = 9''$ (area in square feet)

*11. If the area of a parallelogram is 182 sq. ft. and the length of the base is 14 ft., what is the height of the parallelogram?

*12. How many acres are there in a field that is in the shape of a parallelogram, if the base is 60 rods and the perpendicular distance across the field from the base is 40 rods?

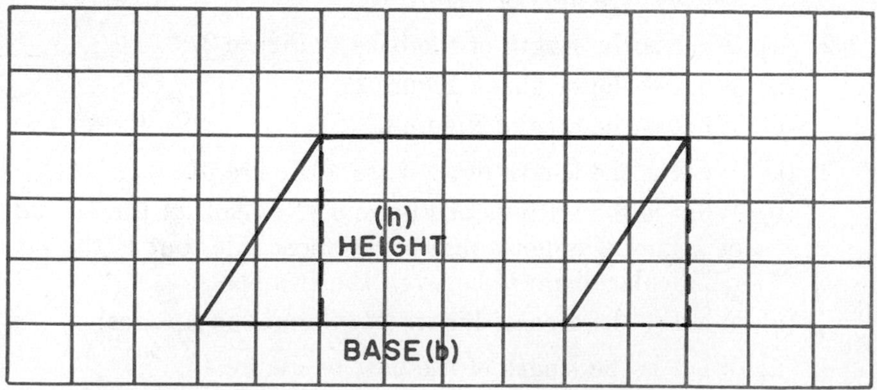

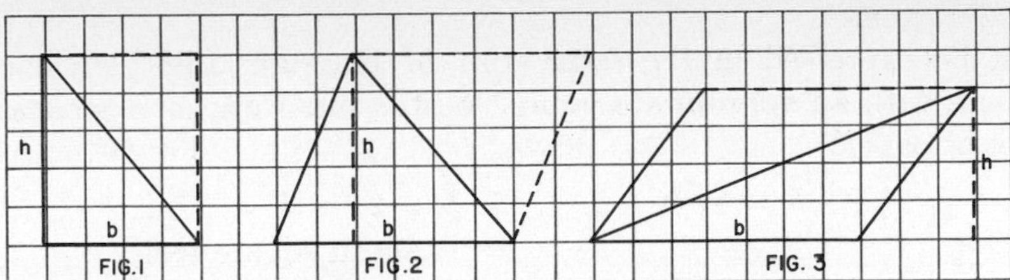

EXERCISES

1. How does the triangle in Figure 1 compare in size with the parallelogram (rectangle) formed by the triangle and the second triangle made by dotted lines?
2. How does the triangle in Figure 2 compare in size with the parallelogram formed there?
3. How does the triangle in Figure 3 compare in size with the parallelogram formed there?
4. What is the formula for the area of a parallelogram?
5. If the area of a triangle is one half the area of a parallelogram having the same base and height, what is the formula for finding the area of a triangle?

The formula for area of a triangle is $A = \frac{1}{2}\,bh$.

A represents the area, b represents the base, h represents the altitude.

Using the formula, we can find the area of the triangles in Figures 1, 2, and 3. (Let each unit on the graph represent one foot.)

Fig. 1	*Fig. 2*	*Fig. 3*
$b = 4 \quad A = \frac{1}{2}bh$	$b = 6 \quad A = \frac{1}{2}bh$	$b = 7 \quad A = \frac{1}{2}bh$
$h = 5 \quad A = \frac{1}{\cancel{2}_1} \times \cancel{4}^{2} \times 5$	$h = 5 \quad A = \frac{1}{\cancel{2}_1} \times \cancel{6}^{3} \times 5$	$h = 4 \quad A = \frac{1}{\cancel{2}_1} \times 7 \times \cancel{4}^{2}$
$A = 10$	$A = 15$	$A = 14$
The area is 10 sq. ft.	The area is 15 sq. ft.	The area is 14 sq. ft.

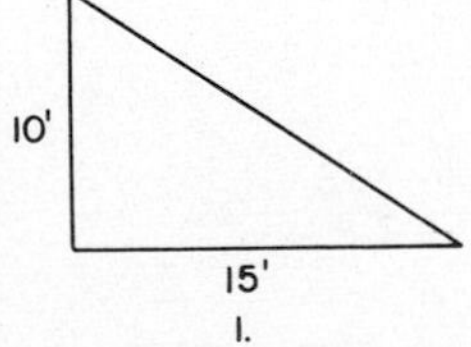

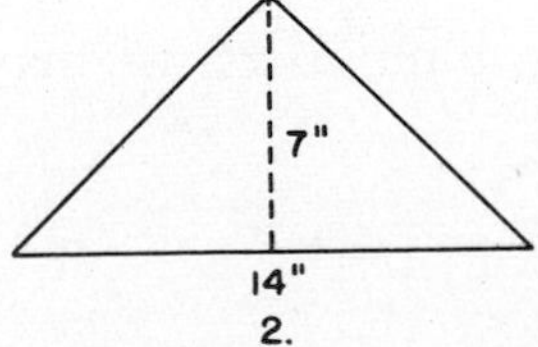

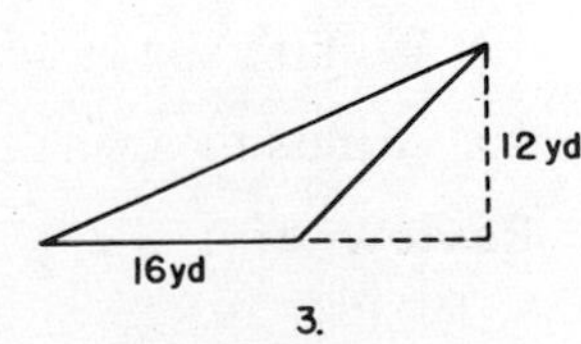

EXERCISES—Using the formula $A = \frac{1}{2}bh$, find the area of these triangles. Remember, before finding the area, the base and height must be expressed in the same unit of measure. Illustrate each exercise with an appropriate figure. Write your work on a separate sheet of paper.

4. $b = 2\frac{1}{2}$ ft., $h = 1\frac{1}{2}$ ft.
5. $b = 2$ ft., $h = 9$ in. (area in square feet)
6. $b = 1.2$ yd., $h = 2.4$ yd.
7. $b = 19$ ft., $h = 7\frac{1}{2}$ ft.
8. $b = 3$ ft., $h = 2$ yd. (area in square yards)
9. $b = 11$ rd., $h = 3\frac{1}{2}$ rd.

*10. What is the area of a dog pen across the corner of a fenced backyard, if the length of the wire fencing used to fence off the corner is 9 feet and the perpendicular distance from the corner to the new wire fencing is 7 feet?

Quick Quiz No. 17

Copy and complete the following sentences by placing *add, subtract, multiply,* or *divide* in each blank to make the sentence true. List your answers by number on a separate sheet of paper.

1. When we want to find the total cost of several differently priced articles purchased in the store, we ______.
2. We ______ to find the price of one article when we know the total cost of a given number of the same kind.
3. To find the product means to ______ the numbers.
4. We ______ to find the difference in the cost of two articles.
5. We add and then ______ to find the average of several numbers.
6. To find the quotient of two numbers means to ______ the numbers.
7. To change fractions to higher terms, we ______ both the numerator and the denominator by the same number.
8. To find the sum of several numbers means to ______ the numbers.
9. To find the ratio of two numbers, we may ______.
10. Minus means ______.

Review of . . .
PERIMETERS AND AREAS

1. The sum of the lengths of the sides of a polygon is called the ______ of the polygon.

2. Write the formula for:
   (a) the perimeter of a rectangle
   (b) the perimeter of a square
   (c) the area of a rectangle
   (d) the area of a square
   (e) the area of a parallelogram
   (f) the area of a triangle
3. Would you find the perimeter or the area of a figure if you wanted to know:
   (a) the amount of fence needed to enclose a rectangular garden?
   (b) the number of square yards of carpeting needed for a bedroom?
   (c) the amount of lace needed to trim the edges of a handkerchief?
   (d) the amount of tape needed to bind the edges of a rectangular place mat?
   (e) the number of acres in a cattle pasture?
   (f) the amount of linoleum for the kitchen floor?
4. Find the perimeters and areas of each of the following figures:

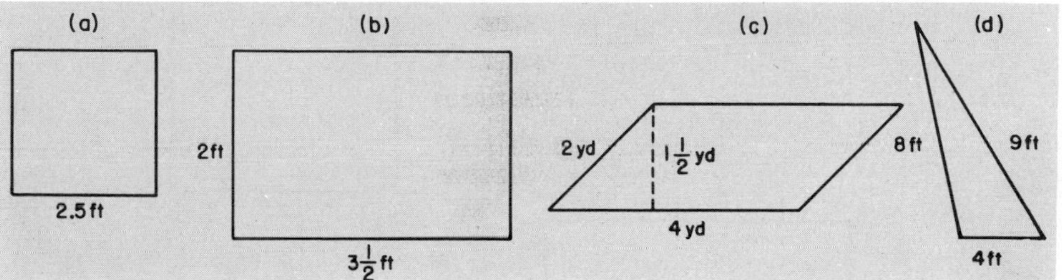

FIG. 3

8.2 yd

9.5 yd

16 yd

5. Find the perimeter of Figure 3.
6. Find the area of Figure 3.

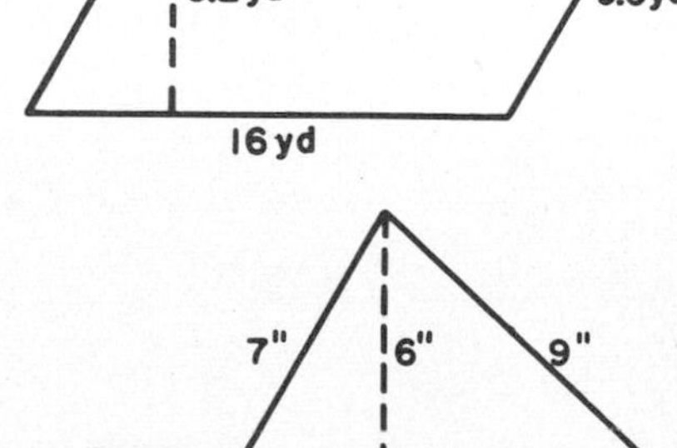

FIG. 4

7. Find the perimeter of Figure 4.
8. Find the area of Figure 4.

9. A rug 9′ by 12′ is on a bedroom floor 10′ by 14′. How many square feet of floor space are not covered?

10. The bases in a baseball diamond are 90 feet apart. How far will a man run who hits a home run if he runs along the base lines?

11. Mr. Mathey had a square garden 16 feet on a side. He enlarged it to 32 feet on a side. How did the area of the new garden compare in size with the area of the old garden?

12. Mr. Orth had a corn field 40 rods by 30 rods. In order to double the area of the field, he increased the field to 80 rods in length but kept it 30 rods wide. Is his field two times as large as the original?

Words you should understand:

1. perimeter 2. dimensions 3. area 4. base 5. height 6. altitude

Chapter Test

1. Find the perimeter of Figure 1.
2. Find the area of Figure 1.
3. Find the perimeter of Figure 2.
4. Find the area of Figure 2.

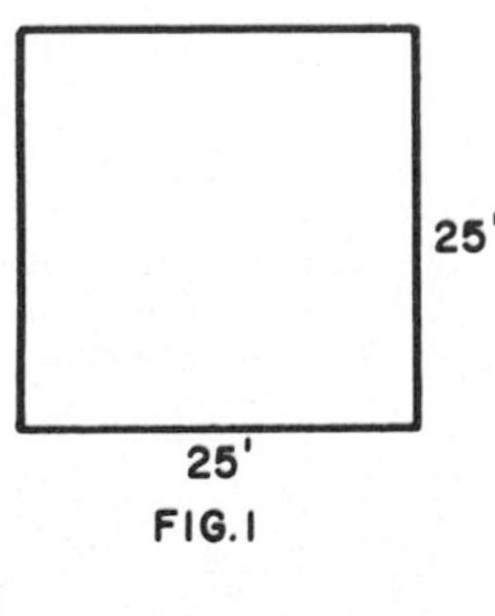

FIG. 1

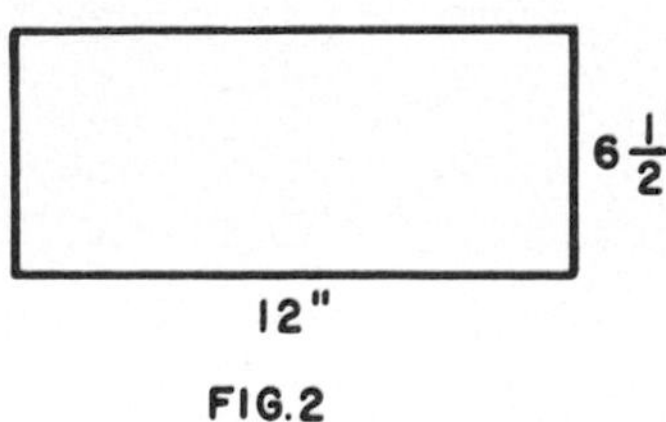

FIG. 2

CHAPTER **ELEVEN**  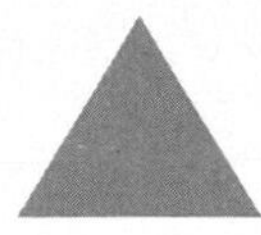  

Exploring Per Cents

In a spelling test of 100 words, Doris spelled 90 words correctly. The grade on Doris' paper was 90%. The symbol "%" means per cent. Charles spelled 85 words correctly. The grade on Charles' paper was 85%.

The word "per cent" is derived from Latin words "per centum" which means "out of a hundred." The word "century," which means a hundred years, came from the same Latin word "centum." Do you know other words which came from the same Latin word "centum"?

Since per cent means out of a hundred, Doris' grade of 90% means 90 out of 100 or $\frac{90}{100}$. This may be written 0.90. Charles' grade of 85% means 85 out of 100 or $\frac{85}{100}$. This may be written 0.85.

Per cents are used to a great extent in industry, in business, and in the world of sports. A shoe store may advertise by the following sign:

Shoe Sale
10% off on all
shoes

Since 10 per cent means $\frac{10}{100}$, the cost of a pair of shoes will be reduced 10 cents out of every dollar. A pair of shoes marked $10.00 may, therefore, be bought at this sale for $9.00. Can you tell why?

A certain bank pays 3% interest on savings. This means that a person will be paid 3 cents ($0.03) a year interest for every 100 cents ($1.00), in his savings account.

EXERCISES

1. See if you can find in newspapers or magazines other uses of per cent.
2. Study the figure to answer these questions:

(a) How many small squares are there in this large square?

(b) If 1% means 1 out of 100, how many squares must be shaded to illustrate 1%?

(c) If one square is shaded, how many squares are not shaded?

(d) If 1% is shaded, what per cent is not shaded?

(e) What % represents the total square?

These statements are true:

$1\% = \frac{1}{100} = 0.01$

$99\% = \frac{99}{100} = 0.99$

$100\% = \frac{100}{100} = 1.00$

3. Is this table correct? Use the figure at the top of the page.

	As a %	As a fraction	As a decimal
Part shaded	10%	$\frac{10}{100}$ or $\frac{1}{10}$	0.10
Part not shaded	90%	$\frac{90}{100}$ or $\frac{9}{10}$	0.90
Total	100%	$\frac{100}{100}$ or $\frac{10}{10}$	1.00

4. (a) 100% of the large square is how much of the square?

(b) $\frac{100}{100}$ or $\frac{10}{10}$ of the large square is how much of the square?

(c) 1.00 of the large square is how much of the square?

Illustrate on squared paper 10 squares long and 10 squares wide the per cents in Exercises 5 through 14. Complete a table for each exercise. See Exercise 3.

5. 25% 6. 20% 7. 50% 8. 40% 9. 80%
10. 30% 11. 17% 12. 22% *13. $33\frac{1}{3}$% *14. $66\frac{2}{3}$%

EXERCISES

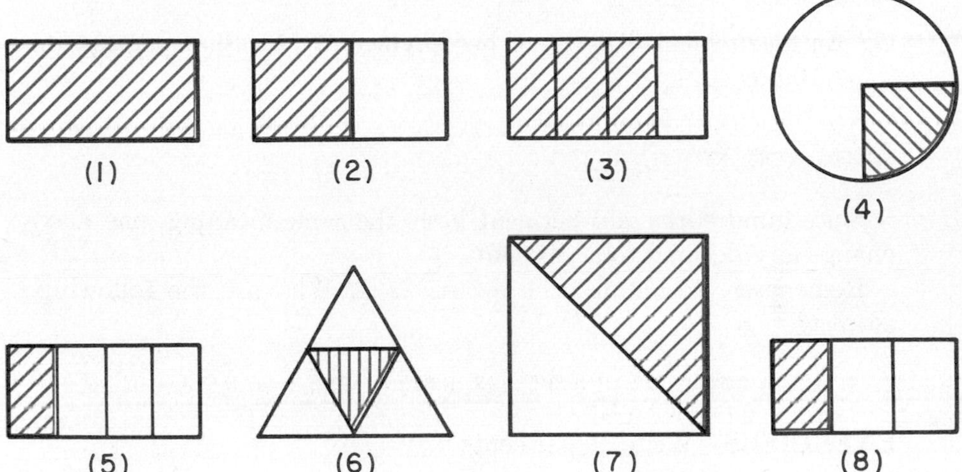

1. In each figure what part is shaded?
2. In each figure what % is shaded?
3. In each figure what part is not shaded?
4. In each figure what % is not shaded?

Illustrate by squares, rectangles, triangles, or circles the per cents in Exercises 5 through 10:

5. 20% 6. 40% 7. $33\frac{1}{3}$% 8. $66\frac{2}{3}$% 9. 80% 10. 100%

11. Susan correctly spelled 80 words out of 100 words. Her score as a fraction was $\frac{80}{100}$. Write this number, using the % symbol.

In Exercises 12 through 17 list the missing numbers, by exercise number, on a separate sheet of paper.

12. Robert correctly spelled 95 words out of 100. His score as a fraction was ?/100 or ______%.
13. Doris correctly spelled 20 out of 25. Her score as a fraction was $\frac{20}{25}$ or $\frac{80}{100}$. Write this fraction as a per cent. Since % means hundredths, by what number were the numerator (20) and the

denominator (25) multiplied to make $\frac{80}{100}$? Is $\frac{80}{100}$ the same as $\frac{20}{25}$?

14. Sam correctly spelled 17 words out of 20. His score was $\frac{17}{20}$ or ?/100 or ______%.
15. Doreen correctly worked 9 problems out of 10. Her score was $\frac{9}{10}$ or ?/100 or ______%.
16. Jim correctly worked 7 problems out of 10. His score was $\frac{7}{10}$ or ?/100 or ______%.
17. Kathleen spent $10 out of her savings of $50. She spent $\frac{10}{50}$ or ?/100 or ______%.

Changing Fractions to Per Cents

Since hundredths and per cent have the same meaning, one may change any decimal to a per cent.

Remember, 25 hundredths means 25%. Why are the following correct?

1. 0.25 = 25% 2. 0.01 = 1% 3. $0.37\frac{1}{2} = 37\frac{1}{2}\%$ 4. 0.375 = 37.5%

EXERCISES—Write as per cents:

1. 0.02	2. 0.08	3. 0.12	4. 0.26	5. $0.12\frac{1}{2}$
6. 0.50	7. 0.83	8. $0.87\frac{1}{2}$	9. 0.42	10. $0.07\frac{1}{2}$
11. 0.01	12. 0.47	13. 0.63	14. $0.37\frac{1}{2}$	15. $0.33\frac{1}{3}$
16. $0.66\frac{2}{3}$	17. $0.16\frac{2}{3}$	18. 1.00	*19. 0.625	*20. 0.875

*21. If Rollin worked 0.75 of the problems assigned, he worked what per cent of them?

*22. If Margaret's weight increased 0.02, her weight increased by what per cent?

*23. If Clyde spent $0.33\frac{1}{3}$ of his money on his vacation, he spent what per cent of his money on his vacation?

*24. If a family spent 0.625 of their income on food and utility bills, they spent what per cent of their income for those things?

The rule for changing a decimal to a per cent is:

A decimal fraction may be changed to a per cent by moving the decimal point two places to the right. Remember to place the per cent sign (%) after the number.

Examples

(a) $\frac{1}{4}$ = ______%

$\frac{1}{4}$ or $\frac{25}{100}$ or 25%

(b) $\frac{9}{12}$ = ______%

$\frac{9}{12}$ or $\frac{3}{4}$ or $\frac{75}{100}$ or 75%

In (a) we multiply the numerator, 1, and the denominator, 4, by 25 to obtain $\frac{25}{100}$. In (b) why did we reduce $\frac{9}{12}$ to $\frac{3}{4}$ before we changed the fraction to hundredths?

EXERCISES—Change the following fractions to per cents:

1. $\frac{1}{2}$	2. $\frac{1}{5}$	3. $\frac{3}{4}$	4. $\frac{3}{10}$	5. $\frac{4}{5}$
6. $\frac{9}{10}$	7. $\frac{3}{20}$	8. $\frac{8}{25}$	*9. $\frac{15}{30}$	*10. $\frac{8}{40}$

*11. If Peter saved $\frac{3}{5}$ of his money, he saved what per cent of his money?

*12. If Esther used $\frac{9}{10}$ of her money for clothes, she used what per cent for clothes?

*13. If Jack could not complete $\frac{1}{4}$ of his problems, he failed to complete what per cent of them?

*14. If $\frac{7}{10}$ of the class are good swimmers, what per cent of the class are good swimmers?

15. If $\frac{10}{10}$ of the class are present, what per cent of the class are present?

$\frac{1}{8}$ = ______%

$\frac{1}{8} = 8\overline{)1.00}$ → $0.12\frac{1}{2} = 12\frac{1}{2}\%$

Since we cannot easily change $\frac{1}{8}$ to a fraction with a denominator of 100, we change the fraction to hundredths by dividing. In this case 1 is divided by 8.

EXERCISES—Change the following fractions to per cents:

1. $\frac{3}{8}$	2. $\frac{5}{8}$	3. $\frac{7}{8}$	4. $\frac{1}{3}$	5. $\frac{2}{3}$
6. $\frac{1}{6}$	7. $\frac{5}{6}$	8. $\frac{1}{16}$	9. $\frac{1}{12}$	10. $\frac{3}{40}$

*11. If $\frac{5}{12}$ of the class had perfect papers on a test, what per cent had perfect papers?

*12. If $\frac{1}{9}$ of the boys at camp received awards for excelling in some sports, what per cent received awards?

What two things did you do in changing these fractions to per cents? How many places did you move the decimal point when you changed the decimal to a per cent?

EXERCISES—Change the following fractions to per cents:

1. $\frac{3}{5}$ 2. $\frac{7}{10}$ 3. $\frac{9}{15}$ 4. $\frac{15}{25}$ 5. $\frac{12}{30}$

6. $\frac{1}{9}$ 7. $\frac{1}{7}$ 8. $\frac{1}{11}$ 9. $\frac{5}{12}$ 10. $\frac{7}{9}$

*11. If $\frac{24}{25}$ of a class made 100% on a test, what % of the class was this?

*12. If $\frac{8}{9}$ of a class are over 4′ 10″ in height, what % of the class is this?

Changing Per Cents to Decimals and Fractions

Since per cent means hundredths, a per cent may be changed to a decimal. Remember 6% means 6 hundredths. The following examples illustrate the relationship.

1. 6% = 0.06 2. 20% = 0.20 3. $62\frac{1}{2}\% = 0.62\frac{1}{2}$ or 0.625

EXERCISES—Write the following per cents as decimals:

1. 4% 2. 21% 3. 52% 4. 88% 5. 96%

6. $33\frac{1}{3}\%$ 7. 4% 8. 100% 9. $1\frac{1}{2}\%$ 10. $3\frac{1}{3}\%$

*11. 40% of Mike's money is the same as what decimal part of his money?

*12. 100% of Alden's money is the same as what decimal part of his money?

Where is the decimal point in a whole number?

The rule for changing a per cent to a decimal is:

A per cent may be changed to a decimal, by moving the decimal point two places to the left. Remember, then the per cent sign is dropped.

$50\% = 0.50$ or $\frac{50}{100}$ or $\frac{1}{2}$

$2\% = 0.02$ or $\frac{2}{100}$ or $\frac{1}{50}$

$12\frac{1}{2}\% = 0.12\frac{1}{2}$ or .125 or $\frac{125}{1000}$ or $\frac{1}{8}$

$33\frac{1}{3}\% = 0.33\frac{1}{3}$ or $\frac{33\frac{1}{3}}{100}$ or ($33\frac{1}{3} \div 100$ or $\frac{100}{3} \times \frac{1}{100}$) or $\frac{1}{3}$

Since any decimal can be changed to a fraction, any per cent can be changed to a fraction.

Remember to reduce all fractions to lowest terms.

EXERCISES—Change the following per cents to fractions reduced to lowest terms:

1. 20%	2. 25%	3. 4%	4. 10%	5. 75%
6. 40%	7. 70%	8. $37\frac{1}{2}$%	*9. $62\frac{1}{2}$%	*10. $66\frac{2}{3}$%

*11. Mr. Grady's salary was increased 12%. The increase was what fraction of his salary?

*12. Hal saved 8% of his earnings. What fraction of his earnings did he save?

Table of Equivalents

EXERCISES—Work out the table of equivalents for the following per cents using the form below:

%	Decimal	Fraction
1. 50%	0.50	$\frac{50}{100}$ or $\frac{1}{2}$
2. 25%	0.25	$\frac{25}{100}$ or $\frac{1}{4}$

1. 50%	2. 25%	3. 75%	4. 20%	5. 40%
6. 60%	7. 80%	8. 10%	9. 30%	10. 70%
11. 90%	12. $33\frac{1}{3}$%	13. $66\frac{2}{3}$%	14. $12\frac{1}{2}$%	15. $37\frac{1}{2}$%
16. $62\frac{1}{2}$%	17. $87\frac{1}{2}$%	*18. $16\frac{2}{3}$%	*19. $83\frac{1}{3}$%	*20. $8\frac{1}{3}$%

Since these per cents and their equivalents are used so frequently it would be useful to memorize them.

Using Per Cents in Solving Problems

There are three kinds of problems involving per cents. We will study all of them at first, so you will understand their relationships. Then we will consider each kind separately to see the various uses of it.

To consider the three types of problems, let's go back to the shoe sale.

10% off on all shoes

1. A pair of shoes is marked $10.00. How much does the customer pay for the shoes? The buyer's problem is: What is 10% of 10? The solution involves finding the per cent of a quantity.

What is 10% of $10?

$N = \frac{1}{10} \times 10$	$\frac{1}{\not{1}\not{0}} \times \not{1}\not{0} = 1$ (cancelled to $\frac{1}{1} \times 1$)
$N = 1$	

If you were buying the shoes you would subtract $1 from the $10 price and pay $9 for the shoes.

First, translate the sentence into a mathematical statement. "What" is an unknown number which we may indicate as any symbol such as N, "is" becomes $=$, 10% may be written as 0.10 or $\frac{1}{10}$, and "of" suggests multiplication. Using these symbols we have $N = \frac{1}{10} \times 10$ or $N = 0.10 \times 10$. This first type involves the same relationship as $N = 6 \times 7$

$N = 42$

Finding the per cent of any quantity, then, is the result of multiplication.

2. The merchant in planning the sale, wishes to take $1 from every $10 of the marked price.

The merchant's problem is, $1 is what % of $10? This involves finding the per cent. First, translate the sentence into a mathematical statement.

$1 is what % of $10?

$1 = N \times 10$

$\frac{1}{10} = N$ What number multiplied by 10 is 1?

$10\% = N$

In this type problem, the product, $1, and one of the factors of the product, in this case $10, are given. The unknown factor may be found by dividing the product by the given factor.

3. The merchant reduces the price of a pair of shoes by $1. This is a reduction of 10% of the original price. Find the original cost.

The question is: $1 is 10% of how many dollars?

This involves finding the original amount.

1 is 10% of how many dollars?

$1 = \frac{1}{10} \times N$	$\frac{1}{\frac{1}{10}} = 1 \div \frac{1}{10}$ or $1 \times \frac{10}{1}$ or 10
$\frac{1}{\frac{1}{10}} = N$	
$10 = N$	

$1 is 10% of $10.

This type problem, like problem 2, gives you the product and one of the factors in the product. In order to find the unknown factor, you may divide the product by the given factor, $\frac{1}{10}$.

Notice that both problems 2 and 3 involve finding an unknown factor when the product and a known factor of the product are given. Since the unknown factors in each are different, these are considered as two separate kinds of problems in per cents.

EXERCISES

1. Do Examples 1, 2, and 3 using 10% = 0.10 instead of $\frac{1}{10}$.
2. Do Examples 1, 2, and 3 by using $12.00 as the marked price of the shoes.

Quick Quiz No. 18

In Exercises 1 through 6, find the products.

1. 4678×29
2. 5678×600
3. 8.26×3.08
4. 0.029×0.086
5. $4\frac{2}{3} \times 4\frac{4}{5}$
6. $225 \times \frac{3}{5}$
7. If an article is sold for 90¢ a yard, $\frac{3}{4}$ of a yard will cost how much?
8. How many pounds of butter fat are there in 210 pounds of milk if it tests 8% butter fat?
9. If $16\frac{2}{3}$% of a circle is shaded, what per cent is not shaded?
10. How much will four boxes weigh if each weighs 18 lb. 9 oz.?

Finding the Per Cent of a Quantity

Examples

1. There were 50 questions on a history test. To make an excellent rating, 90% or more of them must be answered correctly. What is the least number of correct answers that will give a rating of excellent?

What is 90% of 50 questions?

Estimate: 40

$N = 0.90 \times 50$

$N = 45$

$$\begin{array}{r} 50 \\ \underline{0.90} \\ 45.00 \end{array}$$

45 is the least number of correct answers.

These steps will help you in solving problems with per cents:

1. Read the problem carefully.

2. Estimate your answer.

3. Translate into a mathematical statement.

Check:

45 is what % of 50?

$45 = N \times 50$

$\frac{45}{50} = N$

$90\% = N$

$\frac{45}{50} = \frac{9}{10}$ or 90%

4. Do your work neatly as suggested by the example.

5. Check your multiplication, in this case, and see if your answer is close to your estimate.

2. To make a passing grade on the test of 50 questions, you must answer at least 70% correctly. What is the least number of correct answers that will give you a passing score?

What is 70% of 50 questions?

$N = \frac{7}{10} \times 50$

$N = 35$

$\frac{7}{\not{10}_1} \times \not{50}^5 = 35$

35 is the least number of correct answers.

Check:

35 is what % of 50?

$35 = p$ of 50

$\frac{35}{50} = p$

$\frac{7}{10} = p$

$70\% = p$

EXERCISES—Solve the following:

1. 10% of \$450	2. 60% of 120 lb.	3. 1% of \$900
4. 75% of 120 mi.	5. 2% of \$20	6. 15% of 370 A.
7. 30% of 600 pupils	8. 25% of \$160	9. $33\frac{1}{3}\%$ of \$750
10. $12\frac{1}{2}\%$ of \$80	11. $66\frac{2}{3}\%$ of \$420	12. 80% of \$2.40
13. 20% of \$2.50	14. 72% of \$625	15. $37\frac{1}{2}\%$ of 640 lb.

Problems Dealing with 100%

1. If water flowing from a well is 98% pure, what is the per cent of impurities in the water?
2. If a salesman can keep 20% of the money he receives for selling magazines, what per cent will the publishers receive?
3. If ore taken from a mine is 52% metal, what per cent is not metal?
4. If a gold pin is 78% pure gold, what per cent of the pin is alloy, or other metal?
5. If 68% of the people of a country live in towns or cities, what per cent lives on farms?
6. If $33\frac{1}{3}\%$ of corn raised by Mr. Smith is fed to the cattle on his farm and the rest sold, what per cent is sold?
7. If a family spends 20% of their income for rent; 40% for food

and utility bills; 20% for clothes; 15% for savings; and the rest for recreation, what per cent is used for recreation?

8. If 100% of the pupils in a school joined the Junior Red Cross and if there are 829 pupils in the school, how many joined the Junior Red Cross?

9. A family spent 87% of their income and saved the rest. How much did they save if their income was $5,000?

   Hint: 100% − 87% = 13% saved. What is 13% of $5000?

10. A brush salesman keeps 35% of the amount of his sales and sends the rest to the firm manufacturing the brushes. How much should he send to the firm if he sold $450 worth of brushes?

Review Test

1. Change to decimals:

(a) 25%	(b) 1%	(c) $12\frac{1}{2}$%	(d) 75%
(e) $33\frac{1}{3}$%	(f) 8%	(g) 100%	(h) $7\frac{1}{2}$%

2. Change to fractions:

(a) 20%	(b) 10%	(c) $66\frac{2}{3}$%	(d) 40%
(e) $12\frac{1}{2}$%	(f) $16\frac{2}{3}$%	(g) 60%	(h) 32%

3. Change to per cents:

(a) 0.01	(b) 0.06	(c) 0.12	(d) $0.37\frac{1}{2}$
(e) 0.95	(f) $0.08\frac{1}{3}$	(g) $0.33\frac{1}{3}$	(h) 0.625

4. Change to per cents:

(a) $\frac{1}{2}$	(b) $\frac{1}{4}$	(c) $\frac{7}{8}$	(d) $\frac{3}{10}$
(e) $\frac{5}{8}$	(f) $\frac{1}{5}$	(g) $\frac{1}{3}$	(h) $\frac{2}{3}$

5. What is 7% of $450?
6. What is 80% of 750 miles?
7. What is $33\frac{1}{3}$% of $96?
8. What is $12\frac{1}{2}$% of $144?

Oral Work

Do the following exercises orally:

What is $33\frac{1}{3}$% of 600?

$N = \frac{1}{3} \times 600$

$N = 200$

1. What is 10% of:

(a) 20	(b) 400	(c) 95	(d) 340	(e) 62.5

2. What is 20% of:

(a) 45	(b) 75	(c) 550	(d) 1020	(e) 8.25

3. What is $33\frac{1}{3}\%$ of:

(a) 36	(b) 69	(c) 80	(d) 906	(e) 9.75

4. What is $12\frac{1}{2}\%$ of:

(a) 64	(b) 720	(c) 70	(d) 1680	(e) 24.8

5. What is 50% of:

(a) 550	(b) 486	(c) 370	(d) 12.56	(e) 18.5

6. What is 25% of:

(a) 64	(b) 844	(c) 13	(d) 40.20	(e) 8.2

7. What is $66\frac{2}{3}\%$ of:

(a) 12.	(b) 24	(c) 300	(d) 690	(e) 3.96

8. What is 75% of:

(a) 24	(b) 200	(c) 480	(d) 8.4	(e) 20.8

Using More Difficult Per Cents

A man's commission for selling used cars was $6\frac{2}{3}\%$. If he sold Bob Craft's car for $900, what was the amount of his commission?

What is $6\frac{2}{3}\%$ of $900?

$N = 0.06\frac{2}{3} \times \$900$

$$\begin{array}{r} \$900 \\ 0.06\frac{2}{3} \\ \hline 600 \\ 5400 \\ \hline \$60.00 \end{array} \qquad \left(\frac{2}{\cancel{3}_{1}} \times \cancel{900}^{300}\right)$$

The amount of his commission is $60.

Sometimes it is easier to change the per cent to a decimal such as $2\frac{1}{2}\% = 0.02\frac{1}{2}$ or 0.025.

EXERCISES—Find your answers correct to the nearest cent in Exercises 2 through 12.

1. What are the decimal equivalents of the following?
   (a) $4\frac{1}{2}\%$
   (b) $6\frac{3}{4}\%$
   (c) $9\frac{1}{4}\%$

In Exercises 2 through 9, what is:

2. $2\frac{1}{2}\%$ of \$400
3. $2\frac{1}{3}\%$ of \$720
4. $3\frac{1}{2}\%$ of \$75
5. $2\frac{2}{3}\%$ of \$400
6. $2\frac{1}{4}\%$ of \$957
7. $7\frac{3}{4}\%$ of \$150
8. $4\frac{1}{5}\%$ of \$804
9. $3\frac{4}{5}\%$ of \$24
10. If a loan company charged $1\frac{1}{2}\%$ for making a loan of \$30,000, what were the charges?
11. A stock broker received $2\frac{1}{4}\%$ from the sale of stock worth \$45,500. How much did he receive?
12. To receive a prize offered by the publishing company, Kenneth Johnson must increase his February magazine sales of \$750 during the month of March by $7\frac{1}{2}\%$. How much must he increase his sales to win a prize?

Per Cents Greater than 100%

Most of the exercises studied in this chapter talked about per cents that were less than 100%. We will now discuss exercises in which the per cents are greater than 100%.

Example 1. A man's salary has increased to 150% of what it was 10 years ago. 150% of a quantity means 100% of the quantity plus 50% of the quantity. Therefore, 150% of a quantity = 1.50 times the quantity or $1\frac{1}{2}$ times the quantity.

Example 2. A baby's weight has increased 250% since birth. 250% of a quantity means 100% of the quantity plus 100% of the quantity plus 50% of the quantity. 250% of a quantity = 2.50 times the quantity or $2\frac{1}{2}$ times the quantity.

Per cents greater than 100% can be changed to mixed decimals or mixed numbers.

EXERCISES—Change the following to mixed decimals:

130% = 1.30

When we change a per cent to a decimal, we drop the % sign and move the decimal point ______ places to the ______.

1. 150%	2. 125%	3. 140%	4. 105%
5. 200%	6. 250%	7. 183%	8. 101%
9. 300%	10. 350%	11. 104%	12. 1000%

EXERCISES—Change the following to mixed numbers:

$150\% = \frac{150}{100}$ or $1\frac{50}{100}$ or $1\frac{1}{2}$

1. 125%	2. 130%	3. 250%	4. 140%
5. 175%	6. 190%	7. 325%	8. 110%
9. 105%	10. 160%	11. 450%	12. 224%

Example

A company increases the wages of its employees by 10%. A worker's wages will then be 110% of his last wages. If he made $6,500 last year, what will he make during the next year at the new rate?

What is 110% of $6500?

$N = 1.10 \times 6500$

$N = 7,150.$

```
  $6500
   1.10
  -----
  65000
 6500
 ------
$7150.00
```

Answer: $7,150.

If all of Mr. Jenkins' wages this year are 100%, an increase of 10% will make his next year's wages 110% of what they are now.

$110\% = 1.10$ or $1\frac{1}{10}$.

EXERCISES—In Exercises 1 through 6 find the given per cents:

1. 125% of 60 bushels
2. 106% of $450
3. 150% of 300 lb.
4. 225% of 1200 A.
5. 175% of 800 mi.
6. 109% of $80
7. The price of food has increased so that it now is 105% of what it was last year. A family spent $720 for food last year. How much must they allow for food this year if they wish to keep last year's standards?
8. Dave's earnings this year were 125% of what they were last year. He hopes to increase his earnings the same amount next year. What will he need to make next year if he made $460 this year?
9. By using a good grade of fertilizer, a farmer hopes to increase his yield to 140% of what it is now. If he harvested 960 bushels of corn this year, what will he hope to harvest next year by using this fertilizer?

*10. After improving the house which he bought for $15,000, Mr. Jones wished to sell it to make 15%, that is to sell the house for 115% of the original cost. If he sold the house for $18,000, did he make the profit he wished to make?

*11. Douglas will win a prize of a camera if he can increase the number of customers on his paper route to 110% of the number he now has. He had 86 customers and he increased the number to 95. Did he win the camera?

Per Cents Less than 1%

Example 1. A man charged $\frac{1}{2}$% for collecting a bill of $400. How much is this?

$\frac{1}{2}$% means $\frac{1}{2}$ of 1%.

What is $\frac{1}{2}$ of 1% of $400?

$N = \frac{1}{2} \times 0.01 \times 400$

$N = \frac{1}{2} \times 4.00$

$400
0.01
4.00

$\frac{1}{\cancel{2}_1} \times \cancel{4.00}^{2.00} = \$2.00$

$N = 2.00$

$2.00 is $\frac{1}{2}$% of $400.

Example 2. What is 0.9% of $400?

0.9% means 0.9 of 1%.

What is 0.9 of 1% of $400?

$N = 0.9 \times .01 \times 400$

$N = 0.9 \times 4.00$

$N = 3.60$

$400	$4.00
0.01	0.9
$4.00	$3.600

0.9% of $400 is $3.60.

Oral Exercises

What do these per cents mean:

1. $\frac{1}{3}$% 2. $\frac{1}{4}$% 3. $\frac{4}{5}$% 4. $\frac{1}{6}$% 5. $\frac{2}{3}$%

6. 0.1% 7. 0.3% 8. 0.4% 9. 0.8% 10. 0.9%

EXERCISES—Find the given per cents in Exercises 1–12.

1. $\frac{1}{2}$% of $300 2. $\frac{1}{10}$% of 400 bu. 3. $\frac{1}{8}$% of $64

4. $\frac{3}{4}$% of $96 5. $\frac{2}{3}$% of $66 6. $\frac{7}{8}$% of $720

7. 0.1% of $1000 8. 0.6% of 700 lb. 9. 0.7% of 120 bu.

10. 0.9% of $2000 11. 0.3% of 420 mi. 12. 0.8% of $750

13. A tool company found that its sales in June were $\frac{1}{4}$% less than its sales in May. If its sales were $8,000 in May, what was the decrease in sales for June?

14. The total taxes on property to be paid in Kent County was $12,450,000. The treasurer reported that all but 0.7% of the taxes had been paid by February 1. How much was still unpaid?

Review Exercises—Select the answer to make the statement true.

1. Per cent means tenths, hundredths, or thousandths.
2. 5% of a quantity is $\frac{1}{5}$, $\frac{1}{2}$, or $\frac{1}{20}$ of the quantity.
3. 5% of a quantity is 0.05, 0.50, or 0.005 of the quantity.
4. $\frac{1}{4}$ of a quantity = 4%, $\frac{1}{4}$%, or 25% of the quantity.
5. All of a quantity = 50%, 1%, or 100% of the quantity.
6. 200% of a quantity is 20 times the quantity, 200 times the quantity, or 2 times the quantity.

In Exercises 7 through 12, write the word "more" if the per cent represents more than the whole, and the word "less" if the per cent represents less than the whole:

7. 9%	8. $12\frac{1}{2}$%	9. 125%
10. 300%	11. 1%	12. 105%

Select the fraction that is nearest in value to the per cent, in Exercises 13 through 18.

13. 46% is nearest $\frac{1}{3}$, $\frac{1}{2}$, or $\frac{3}{4}$.
14. 9% is nearest $\frac{1}{10}$, $\frac{1}{3}$, or $\frac{1}{8}$.
15. 71% is nearest $\frac{3}{5}$, $\frac{3}{4}$, or $\frac{3}{8}$.
16. 17% is nearest $\frac{1}{17}$, $\frac{1}{6}$, or $\frac{1}{5}$.
17. 29% is nearest $\frac{1}{4}$, $\frac{1}{5}$, or $\frac{3}{10}$.
18. 34% is nearest $\frac{1}{6}$, $\frac{1}{3}$, or $\frac{1}{2}$.

Select the per cent that is nearest in value to the fraction in Exercises 19 through 24.

19. $\frac{15}{16}$ is nearest 100%, 15%, or 16%.
20. $\frac{1}{9}$ is nearest 20%, 9%, or 10%.
21. $\frac{3}{7}$ is nearest 25%, 50%, or 17%.
22. $\frac{4}{17}$ is nearest $16\frac{2}{3}$%, 20%, or 10%.
23. $\frac{11}{12}$ is nearest 12%, 11%, or 100%.
24. $\frac{24}{75}$ is nearest 100%, 90%, or $33\frac{1}{3}$%.

Copy and correct the wrong statements:

25. $\frac{1}{8} = 12\frac{1}{12}\%$ 26. $\frac{1}{6} = 16\frac{2}{3}\%$

27. $\frac{2}{3} = 33\frac{1}{3}\%$ 28. $\frac{3}{8} = 62\frac{1}{2}\%$

29. $\frac{4}{5} = 60\%$ 30. $\frac{7}{8} = 87\frac{1}{2}\%$

Quick Quiz No. 19

1. If today is January 6, what will be the date two weeks from today? four weeks from today?
2. How many days are there in June, July, and August altogether?
3. Mary cut $3\frac{7}{8}$ yards from a piece of cloth containing 10 yards. How many yards were left?
4. If you can walk 3 miles an hour, how long will it take you to walk $\frac{1}{2}$ mile?
5. Arrange these decimals in order of size beginning with the smallest:

   0.5, 0.05, 5.05, 0.1005, 5.5
6. What is the difference between:

   Two hundred and 6 thousandths
   and
   Two hundred 6 thousandths?
7. Round to the nearest tenth:

   (a) 6.72 (b) 4.492 (c) 1.176 (d) 7.59
8. There are how many seconds in 3.1 minutes?
9. What are the next three numbers in this series?

   480, 240, 120, 60
10. Cory Bates saved \$1200. If this is $\frac{3}{8}$ of his income, what is his income?

Other Applications of Per Cents

Examples

1. John saved \$18 out of \$24 earned. What per cent of his earnings did he save?

\$18 is what % of \$24?

$18 = N \times 24$	$\frac{18}{24} = \frac{3}{4}$ or 75%
$\frac{18}{24} = N$	
$75\% = N$	

\$18 is 75% of \$24

2. Mary spent \$3.60 out of her savings of \$30. What per cent did she spend?

\$3.60 is what % of \$30?

$3.60 = N \times 30$	$\frac{3.60}{30} = 30\overline{)3.60}$ → 0.12 (30, 60)
$\frac{3.60}{30} = N$	
$12\% = N$	$0.12 = 12\%$

\$3.60 is 12% of \$30

EXERCISES—Solve the following:

1. 16 in. is what per cent of 32 in.?
2. \$45 is what per cent of \$135?
3. 9 lb. is what per cent of 90 lb.?
4. \$28 is what per cent of \$28?
5. 24 mi. is what per cent of 32 mi.?
6. \$40 is what per cent of \$50?
7. 50 bu. is what per cent of 40 bu.?
8. 80 lb. is what per cent of 60 lb.?
9. 240 bu. is what per cent of 120 bu.?
10. \$75 is what per cent of \$50?
11. \$110 is what per cent of \$100?
12. 640 A. is what per cent of 64 A.?
13. \$3.20 is what per cent of \$64?
14. 120 lb. is what per cent of 800 lb.?
15. 45 bu. is what per cent of 500 bu.?
16. 49 ft. is what per cent of 700 ft.?

*17. \$13.44 is what per cent of \$84?

*18. \$12.96 is what per cent of \$72?

Additional exercises can be found in the Appendix, pages 306-307.

Dwight saved \$5 out of \$51 earned. To the nearest tenth what per cent did he save?

$5 is what % of $51?

$5 = N \times 51$	$0.0980 = 0.098$ or 9.8%
$\frac{5}{51} = N$	$51\overline{)5.0000}$ 459 410 408 20
$9.8\% = N$	

Therefore $5 is 9.8% of $51

1. Why was the division carried to ten thousandths?
2. A decimal to the nearest thousandth gives a per cent to which nearest decimal place?
3. If you were to express this to the nearest per cent, what would it be?

EXERCISES—Solve these exercises expressing the per cent to the nearest tenth:

1. $1 is what per cent of $7?
2. 4 bu. is what per cent of 9 bu.?
3. 15 problems is what per cent of 16 problems?
4. 7 games is what per cent of 12 games?
5. $13 is what per cent of $72?
6. $1000 is what per cent of $1300?
7. 94 ft. is what per cent of 112 ft.?
8. 256 lb. is what per cent of 480 lb.?
9. $82 is what per cent of $51?
10. $64 is what per cent of $44?
11. $82 is what per cent of $31?
12. 450 pupils is what per cent of 1250 pupils?

*13. Do these questions have the same meaning?
(a) 13 doz. is what per cent of 50 doz.?
(b) What per cent of 50 doz. is 13 doz.?
(c) Find what per cent 13 doz. is of 50 doz.

*14. Express this question in as many ways as you can without changing the meaning:
$9 is what per cent of $20?

Example 1. 8 lb. is 10% of what amount?

8 lb. is 10% of what amount?

$$8 = 0.10 \times N$$

$$\frac{8}{0.10} = N \qquad 0.10_{\wedge}\overline{)\,8.00_{\wedge}} = 80.$$

$$80 = N$$

8 lb. is 10% of 80 lb.

Example 2. A boy collected \$8.20 on his paper route which is $66\frac{2}{3}\%$ of the total amount he should collect. How much should he collect?

\$8.20 is $66\frac{2}{3}\%$ of what amount?

$$8.20 = \tfrac{2}{3} \times N$$

$$\frac{8.20}{\frac{2}{3}} = N \qquad \frac{8.20}{\frac{2}{3}} = 8.20 \div \frac{2}{3} = \$\overset{4.10}{\cancel{8.20}} \times \frac{3}{\underset{1}{\cancel{2}}} = \$12.30$$

$$12.30 = N$$

He should collect \$12.30.

EXERCISES—Solve the following exercises:

1. \$320 is 20% of what amount?
2. 6 inches is 60% of how many inches?
3. \$120 is 80% of what amount?
4. 75 bu. is $66\frac{2}{3}\%$ of how many bushels?
5. \$40 is 2% of what amount?
6. \$60 is $1\frac{1}{2}\%$ of what amount?

*7. There are 420 pupils in the seventh grade in Brooks Junior High School. If this is 40% of the total enrollment, how many pupils are there in this school?

*8. Bill has \$360 in the bank. If this is 120% of what he had in the bank last year, how much had he in the bank last year?

Practice with Per Cents

Note that there are three types of percentage problems. It is suggested that you:

(a) Read each problem carefully to determine what you are to find:

1. the per cent of a quantity, or
2. the per cent one quantity is of another, or

3. the original or total amount when a per cent is known.

(b) Estimate your answer.

(c) Make a clear mathematical statement of each problem.

(d) Use the method you prefer to solve the problem.

(e) Check. See whether your answer is reasonably close to your estimate.

1. Andy White earns $62.50 a week. If he puts 10% a week into his savings account, how much does he save each week?
2. A furniture company gives 5% discount for all cash sales. If Mildred Smith bought $750 worth of furniture and paid cash, how much was the discount?
3. A boy bought a $30 radio at a $6 discount. What per cent was the discount?
4. Roberta is 14 years old and her father is 42 years old. Roberta's age is what per cent of her father's age?
5. The Stanton Junior High School gave a play, the proceeds of which were to be used to buy library books. They bought 60 books, which was 4% of what they had before these were purchased. How many books were in the library before the 60 books were added?
6. Bob and Bill each have a savings account. Bob has $28, and Bill $49. Bob's savings is what per cent of Bill's savings?
7. A grocer collected $1,680 one month. If this is 84% of the month's sales, what was the total monthly sales account?
8. There are 60 pounds in a bushel of potatoes. If potatoes are 60% water, how many pounds of water are there in 80 bushels of potatoes?
9. The Jones Fruit Company pays $\frac{3}{4}$% of the value of fruit for shipping-in the fruit. If they shipped $5,000 worth of fruit, what did they pay for shipping charges?
10. Food prices are 102% of what they were last year. How much should a family allow for food this year if they spent $840 last year and wish to maintain the same standard of living?

Quick Quiz No. 20

1. What is 6% of $120?
2. What is 115% of $340?

3. What is $\frac{3}{4}\%$ of \$240?
4. \$6 is what per cent of \$36?
5. What per cent of \$54 is \$36?
6. 48 is what per cent of 12?
7. Find the difference between 112% and 87%.
8. Change to the nearest tenth of a per cent:

   (a) 0.9872 (b) 0.4513 (c) 0.8778 (d) 0.8986
9. How much more time has Ruth to practice on the piano if she has practiced 1 hour 50 minutes and she is supposed to practice 2 hours 30 minutes a day?
10. 20 is what per cent of 45 to the nearest whole per cent?

Per Cent of Increase or Decrease

Example 1. The increase in student pay rose from 45¢ an hour to 50¢ an hour. What was the per cent of increase to the nearest tenth?

The increase is 50¢ − 45¢, or 5¢

5¢ is what per cent of 45¢?

$5 = N \times 45$ $\qquad$ $9\overline{)1.0000}$ = 0.1111 or 11.1%

$\frac{5}{45} = N$

$11.1\% = N$

The per cent of increase in student-help pay is 11.1%

2. The price of grapes dropped from 8¢ a pound to 5¢ a pound. What was the per cent of decrease?

The decrease is 8¢ − 5¢, or 3¢

3 is what per cent of 8?

$3 = N \times 8$

$\frac{3}{8} = N$

$37\frac{1}{2}\% = N$

The per cent of decrease in the price of grapes is $37\frac{1}{2}\%$.

EXERCISES—In the following exercises find the per cent of increase or decrease:

1. The price of wheat dropped from \$2.40 to \$2.00 a bushel.
2. The price of eggs increased from 60¢ a dozen to 65¢ a dozen.

3. The number of pupils in Room 8 increased in one month from 32 pupils to 36 pupils.
4. When the weather gets cool, a girl can decrease the time it takes her to walk to school from 20 minutes to 15 minutes.
5. The pupils' bus fare increased from 10¢ to 15¢.
6. By using the expressway through a city, you can increase your driving speed from 35 mph to 60 mph.
7. A family decreased their gasoline consumption from 55 gallons in July to 45 gallons in August.
8. Mr. Cobb built a house which cost him $9,000 and sold it for $14,500.
9. The population of Wayside increased in five years from 1,500 to 3,000.
10. The fatal accidents decreased in Seymore from 75 to 45 in one year.

Quick Quiz No. 21

1. A girl spent $8.50 for a sweater, $6.75 for shoes, and $3.98 for a purse. How much did she spend in all?
2. A family paid $62.50 a month rent. How much rent did they pay a year?
3. Jim Sneed paid $6.75 for three books. What was the average cost per book?
4. If Jack Metzer can row $2\frac{3}{4}$ miles per hour, how far can he go in $2\frac{1}{2}$ hours?
5. How many pieces of ribbon $3\frac{1}{4}$ inches long can be cut from 78 inches of ribbon?
6. Mrs. Towers bought a piece of cheese that weighed $2\frac{1}{8}$ pounds. If she used $\frac{1}{4}$ of it for lunch, how much was left?
7. A man bought 12 gallons of gasoline at 31.5¢ a gallon. How much change did he get back from a $5 bill?
8. A café paid $210 for 30 cases of peaches. Each case held 24 cans. How much did the peaches cost per can?
9. An airplane traveled 1200 miles in 3 hours 20 minutes. What is its speed in miles per hour?
10. A man bought a lot for $4,000 and built a house costing $16,000 on it. What per cent of the total cost was the cost of the lot?

Using Per Cents in Sports

Example—John had 7 hits out of 12 times at bat and Bill had 8 hits out of 13 times at bat. Compare their batting averages.

What per cent is 7 of 12?	$12\overline{)7.0000}$ quotient $0.5833 = 0.583$
The ratio of 7 to 12 $= \frac{7}{12}$ or 0.583	
John's batting average is 0.583	$13\overline{)8.0000}$ quotient $0.6153 = 0.615$
What per cent is 8 of 13?	7 8
The ratio of 8 to 13 $= \frac{8}{13}$ or 0.615	20 13
Bill's batting average is 0.615	70 65
	50 39

Bill has a higher batting average than John.

Batting averages are usually expressed as decimals to the nearest thousandth.

1. Find the batting averages of the Trojan baseball team after their first week and list the players in order of batting average from highest to lowest.

Player	*At Bat*	*Hits*	*Player*	*At Bat*	*Hits*
1. Sam Jones	24	7	7. Frank Marlow	14	3
2. Bill Smith	20	5	8. Jim Jessup	18	5
3. Phil Rusk	21	6	9. Tom Clark	22	7
4. Jack Deal	22	8	10. Jerry Stout	17	4
5. Fred Brown	19	4	11. Terry Lewis	13	2
6. Jack Snell	22	6	12. Joe Bruner	15	4

2. Compare the pitching averages of these two pitchers: (Express averages as decimals to the nearest thousandth.)
   Englehart pitched 26 games and won 19.
   Carlson pitched 22 games and won 16.
3. Sharon Dobbs got 8 baskets out of 11 trials in eight-court ball, and Kelley Jones got 7 out of 10 trials. Which girl had the better average, expressed as decimals to nearest thousandth?
4. Compare the records of these teams and list them in order of records from highest to lowest.

a. First, find total games played.

b. Second, compare games won with total played. (Express these ratios as decimals to the nearest thousandth.)

Teams	*Games Won*	*Games Lost*
Washington Junior High	6	5
Roosevelt Junior High	8	2
Pershing Junior High	5	6
Hoover Junior High	9	2
Taft Junior High	5	7

Quick Quiz No. 22

1. If zero is added to a number, what is the sum?
2. If zero is subtracted from any number, what is the remainder?
3. If zero is multiplied by any number, what is the product?
4. Can you divide by zero?
5. $724 + 0 = ?$
6. $724 - 0 = ?$
7. $724 \times 0 = ?$
8. Multiply by 10:
   (a) 6 (b) 24 (c) 3.6 (d) 0.36
9. Divide by 10:
   (a) 6 (b) 24 (c) 3.6 (d) 0.36
10. How many zeros will you need to write ten billion?

Review of . . .
PER CENTS

1. What does per cent mean?
2. What per cent of each figure is shaded?

(a)

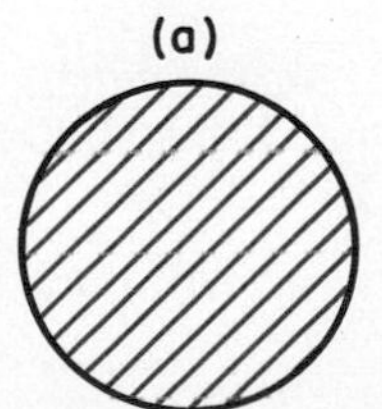

(b)

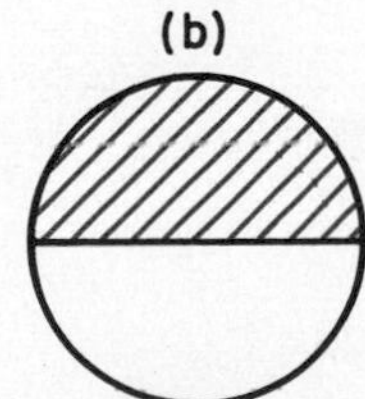

(c)

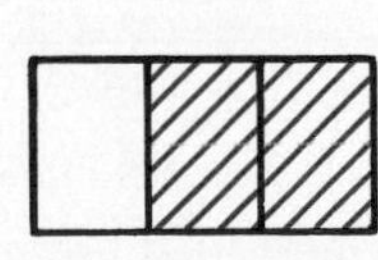

(d)

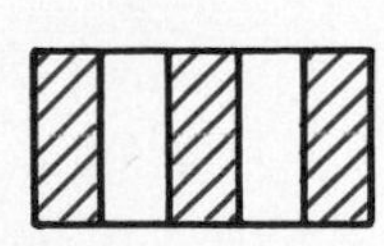

3. Change to per cents:

   (a) 0.02 (b) 1.2 (c) $\frac{1}{8}$ (d) $\frac{11}{12}$

4. Change to decimals:

   (a) 40% (b) 160% (c) $6\frac{1}{2}$% (d) 1.2%

5. Solve the following:

   (a) 6% of \$1250 (b) 150% of 3248 people

   (c) $2\frac{1}{2}$% of \$9.50 (d) $\frac{1}{2}$% of 400 pupils

6. Solve the following:

   (a) What per cent of \$125 is \$75?

   (b) 60 pupils is what per cent of 90 pupils?

   (c) 7 inches is what per cent of 1 foot?

   (d) \$4.20 is 75% of what amount?

7. Solve the following:

   (a) \$12 is 6% of what amount?

   (b) 80 pupils is 40% of how many pupils?

   (c) \$3.50 is 20% of what amount?

   (d) \$4.50 is 25% of what amount?

8. Marian solved correctly 12 problems out of 16 problems. What per cent did she solve correctly?

9. Susan planned to save 40% of all she earned baby sitting. One month she earned \$12.75. If she followed her plan, how much did she save?

10. The enrollment in Franklin Junior High School increased from 790 pupils to 1185 pupils in four years. What was the per cent of increase?

Chapter Test

1. Change to per cents:

   (a) $\frac{3}{4}$ (b) $\frac{1}{8}$ (c) $\frac{1}{5}$ (d) $\frac{8}{9}$

   (e) 0.16 (f) 1.3 (g) 0.005 (h) 0.8

2. Change to decimals:

   (a) 18% (b) $7\frac{1}{2}$% (c) 130% (d) 0.72%

3. (a) What is $5\frac{1}{2}$% of \$230? (b) What is $\frac{1}{4}$% of \$30?

4. (a) 16 is what per cent of 48?

   (b) What per cent of \$200 is \$125?

5. (a) $9 is 10% of what amount?
   (b) $4.50 is 30% of what amount?
6. If Denny saved 30% of his weekly allowance of $4.00, how much did he save?
7. The Washington Junior High School won 7 out of the 9 baseball games they played. What per cent did they win?
8. A boy increased his weight from 85 lb. to 102 lb. during one year. What was the per cent of increase?
9. Helen spelled correctly 42 words out of 50 words on a spelling test. What per cent did she spell correctly?
10. How much sales tax must Mr. Brown pay on a refrigerator if he paid $375 for the refrigerator and the sales tax is 2% of the selling price?

CHAPTER **TWELVE**  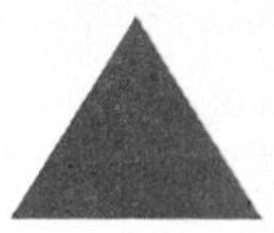  

Business Uses of Per Cent

Commission

People in business use per cents in several ways. One use is with *commission*.

Example—Ralph had outgrown his bicycle. He told Mildred, his sister, that she could keep a 30% commission if she sold the bicycle. She sold the bicycle for $22.50. How much money could she keep as her commission?

What is 30% of $22.50?

$N = 0.30 \times 22.50$	$22.50 0.30 $6.7500
$N = 6.75$	

Mary's commission is $6.75.

Often a person receives a commission for work he has done. For example, real estate agents are paid a certain per cent of the sales prices of the houses they sell. Insurance salesmen are paid a certain

SALE

DESIGNCRAFT

DESKS & TABLES

50% OFF!

Slight imperfections do not mar the beauty of these contemporary style desks. A wide range of sizes, formica tops and colors to choose from. Get them while they last—at 50% savings!

Per cents are essential in business of all kinds.

per cent of the premiums of the insurance they sell. Some people who work on a commission are salesmen, architects, and lawyers. Do you know people who earn their living by working on commission? See if you can find what per cent commission they are paid.

In the above example, Ralph was the employer and Mildred was the agent. The amount of the sale, $22.50, is called the gross proceeds. The amount of money Mildred receives is the commission. The amount Ralph receives is called the net proceeds.

Gross proceeds	= $22.50	$22.50
Commission 30% of $22.50	= $ 6.75	0.30
Net proceeds	= $15.75	$6.7500

EXERCISES—Find the commission:

	Sales	Rate		Sales	Rate
1.	$45	25%	2.	$96	8%
3.	$22	30%	4.	$1.50	40%
5.	$125	10%	6.	$7.50	6%
7.	$4290	15%	8.	$9750	22%

Find the net proceeds:

	Sales	Rate		Sales	Rate
9.	$60	10%	10.	$80	5%
11.	$145	20%	12.	$240	3%
13.	$5250	15%	14.	$6758	25%
15.	$11250	5%	16.	$29650	6%

17. Complete the table.

Commission of Car Salesmen

Salesman	*A*	*B*	*C*	*D*	*E*
Amount of Sales	$5750	$5200	$4500	$3750	$2250
Commission at 8%					
Net Proceeds					

In commission problems we may be interested in:

1. Finding the amount of commission.
2. Finding the net proceeds.
3. Finding the rate of commission.
4. Finding the total sales which will produce a certain amount of commission when the rate of commission is known.

Study these four examples and tell under which of the four headings each belongs.

1. Richard received a commission of $8.00 for selling a $60 bicycle. The commission is what per cent of the sale price?

$8 is what per cent of $60?

$$8 = N \times 60$$

$$\tfrac{8}{60} = N$$

$$13\tfrac{1}{3}\% = N$$

$$\tfrac{8}{60} = 60\overline{)8.00} = 0.13\tfrac{1}{3} \text{ or } 13\tfrac{1}{3}\%$$

$$\begin{array}{r} 60 \\ \hline 200 \\ 180 \\ \hline \frac{20}{60} \text{ or } \frac{1}{3} \end{array}$$

$8 is $13\tfrac{1}{3}\%$ of $60.

2. What will a real estate salesman make if he sells a $9000 house and receives 5% commission?

What is 5% of $9000?

$N = 0.05 \times 9000$

$N = 450$

$$\begin{array}{r} \$9000 \\ 0.05 \\ \hline \$450.00 \end{array}$$

The real estate man makes $450.

3. How much money must Helen send the firm if she sells $55 worth of their cards and receives a 20% commission?

Gross proceeds from the cards	=	$55
Commission 20% of $55	=	11
Net proceeds	=	$44

$\frac{1}{\cancel{5}_1} \times \cancel{55}^{11} = \$11$

Helen will send the firm $44.

4. How many dollars worth of cars must a salesman sell in order to guarantee an income of $500 a month, if he receives a 10% commission?

$500 is 10% of what amount?

$500 = 0.10 \times N$

$\frac{500}{0.10} = N$

$5000 = N$

$$0.10\overline{)\$500.00} = \$5000.$$

The salesman must sell $5000 worth of cars a month to guarantee a $500 commission.

EXERCISES—Find the commission on the following sales:

1. 5% commission on the sale of a $9750 house.
2. 25% commission on the sale of $20 worth of cards.
3. $2\frac{1}{2}$% commission on the sale of $10,000 worth of machinery.
4. 35% commission on an insurance premium of $96.20.

Find the net proceeds on the following:

5. Sale of $940 worth of bonds. Rate of commission 1%.
6. Sale of $9.50 worth of seeds. Rate of commission 10%.
7. Sale of $750 worth of furniture. Rate of commission $3\frac{1}{2}$%.
8. Sale of $8 worth of plants. Rate of commission 12%.

Find the total sales made on the following:

9. Commission on sale of a house $550. Rate of commission 5%.
10. Commission on sale of a pair of shoes $0.90. Rate of commission 10%.
11. Commission on sale of flowers $1.50. Rate of commission 3%.
12. Commission on sale of car $750. Rate of commission 25%.

Find the rate of commission:

13. $10 commission on the sale of $25 worth of books.
14. $6 commission on the sale of $24 worth of needles.
15. $150 commission on the sale of $6000 worth of oil well equipment.
16. $550 commission on the sale of an $11,000 house.

*17. Mrs. Jones sells ladies' coats in a local store. She is paid a salary and 5% commission on all sales. How much commission did she earn if she sold $629 worth of coats one week?

Words you should understand:

1. commission 2. rate of commission 3. net proceeds

Quick Quiz No. 23

1. What is the ratio of $10 to $25?
2. What is the ratio of $30 to $10?
3. If $\frac{3}{4}$ of the cost of a house is $6000, what is the cost of the house?
4. If John works 2 hours and Bill 4 hours and they are paid $6 for the job, what is each boy's share?
5. What is the ratio of the length of a foot ruler to the length of a yardstick?
6. What is the ratio of 4 cents to a dollar?
7. Which ratios are equal to $\frac{1}{2}$ or 1:2?

   (a) $\frac{16}{24}$ (b) $\frac{12}{24}$ (c) $\frac{7}{28}$ (d) $1\frac{1}{2}$:3 (e) 0.5:1
8. If 1″ on a map represents 25 miles, how far apart are two cities if they measure on the map $3\frac{1}{2}$ inches?
9. If a picture is 6 inches wide and 9 inches long, what is the ratio of the width to the length?
10. When a picture is enlarged, the ratio of the width to length is

not changed. How wide will the picture in Exercise 9 be when enlarged, if the enlarged length is $13\frac{1}{2}''$?

Discount

Another important use of per cents in business is in *discount*.

Example—The Conway Boys Shop had a sale on boys' clothes. John's father bought John a new jacket marked \$12.50. The store was giving a 20% discount on all purchases during the sale. What did John's father pay for the jacket?

Marked price of jacket	= \$12.50	$\frac{1}{\not 5} \times \overset{2.50}{\not 12.\not 50} = 2.50$ (with 1 below the cancelled 5)
Discount 20% of \$12.50	= 2.50	
Sale price of jacket	= \$10.00	

Often an article is sold for less than the price at which it is marked to be sold in a store, or at which it is listed in a catalogue. The amount taken off the marked price or list price is called a discount. The rate of discount may be expressed as a per cent or as a fraction, as in "Sale 20% off" or "Sale $\frac{1}{5}$ off" The sale price or net price equals the marked price or list price less the discount.

EXERCISES—Find the discount and the net price or sale price:

1. Marked price on a dress is \$25. Rate of discount is 10%.
2. List price on a bicycle is \$65. Rate of discount is 20%.
3. Marked price on a pair of shoes is \$10.50. Rate of discount is 10%.
4. Marked price on a table is \$76. Rate of discount is 25%.
5. List price on a television set is \$350. Rate of discount is 20%.
6. Marked price on a chair is \$150. Rate of discount is 15%.
7. List price on a tennis racket is \$25. Rate of discount is 30%.
8. Marked price on a baseball is \$5. Rate of discount is 25%.

Complete the following tables:

9. Prices of Shoes

Marked Price	\$22.50	\$15.00	\$9.50	\$8.50	\$7.00
Discount @ 10%					
Sale Price					

10. Prices of Suits

Marked Price	$156	$96	$72	$54	$36.75
Discount @ $33\frac{1}{3}\%$					
Sale Price					

11. Prices of Chairs

List Price	$128	$104	$88	$42.40	$36.80
Discount @ $12\frac{1}{2}\%$					
Net Price					

12. Prices of Toys

List Price	$12.96	$10.08	$9.36	$6.30	$4.50
Discount @ $16\frac{2}{3}\%$					
Net Price					

In problems involving discounts we may be interested in:

1. Finding the discount.
2. Finding the sale price or the net price.
3. Finding the rate of discount.
4. Finding the marked price or list price when the sale price or net price and the rate of discount are known.

Study these four examples and tell under which of the above headings each belongs.

1. At a January sale a girl bought a sweater marked $5 for $4. What per cent was the sweater reduced?

$5 − $4 = $1 (the amount of reduction)

$1 is what per cent of $5?

$1 = N \times 5$

$\frac{1}{5} = N$

$20\% = N$

The sweater had been reduced 20%.

2. A store advertises 8% discount for paying cash for a piano. How much will the Smith family save, if they pay cash for a piano marked $960?

What is 8% of $960?

$N = 0.08 \times 960$

$N = 76.80$

$960
0.08
$76.80

The Smith family will save $76.80 by paying cash.

3. The employees in the Cox Department Store are given an 8% discount on any article bought in the store. What will an employee pay for a lamp marked $12.50?

Marked price of lamp	= $12.50	$12.50
Discount 8% of $12.50	= 1.00	0.08
Net price of lamp	= $11.50	$1.0000

The employee will pay $11.50 for a lamp marked $12.50

4. Carl paid $45 for a coat. The rate of discount was 25%. What was the original marked price on the coat?

$100\% - 25\% = 75\%$

$45 is 75% of what amount?

$45 = \frac{3}{4} \times N$

$\frac{45}{\frac{3}{4}} = N$

$\frac{45}{\frac{3}{4}} = 45 \div \frac{3}{4} \text{ or } \overset{15}{\cancel{45}} \times \frac{4}{\underset{1}{\cancel{3}}} \text{ or } 60$

$60 = N$ The original price of the coat was $60.

EXERCISES—Find the amount of discount.

In computing discounts, many firms disregard all fractions of a cent. In the following problems drop all fractions of a cent in finding discounts.

1. Marked price of lamp is $14. Rate of discount is 25%.
2. List price of coat is $25. Rate of discount is 30%.
3. Marked price of table is $29. Rate of discount $2\frac{1}{2}$%.
4. List price of divan is $212.50. Rate of discount 12%.

Find the net price:

5. Marked price of gloves $6.50. Rate of discount 8%.
6. List price of radio $125. Rate of discount 5%.
7. Marked price of stove $223.50. Rate of discount 20%.

8. List price of car $2250. Rate of discount 10%.

Find the rate of discount:

9. Original price of hat $10. Sale price $9.
10. Original price of suit $28. Sale price $21.
11. Original price of picture $12.50. Sale price $10.00.
12. Original price of gloves $2.25. Sale price $1.75.

Find the original marked price:

13. Sale price of stove $240. Rate of discount 20%.
14. Sale price of stove $260. Rate of discount 25%.
15. Sale price of sweater $16.00. Rate of discount 20%.
16. Sale price of book $2.88. Rate of discount 4%.

*17. Hal Briggs bought a $100 flute for $80. What was the rate of discount?

*18. All employees of the Brent Department Store are allowed a 5% discount on all purchases. Find how much a clerk will pay for the following:

1 dress	$39.75
1 blouse	6.98
1 pair gloves	4.50

Quick Quiz No. 24

1. All of anything is ______ per cent.
2. What part of the whole is:

   (a) 25% (b) $33\frac{1}{3}$% (c) 75% (d) 10% (e) $12\frac{1}{2}$%
3. Change to decimals:

   (a) 6% (b) 12% (c) 5% (d) $33\frac{1}{3}$% (e) $37\frac{1}{2}$%
4. Change to per cents:

   (a) $\frac{1}{2}$ (b) $\frac{1}{5}$ (c) $\frac{3}{10}$ (d) $\frac{3}{4}$ (e) $\frac{1}{4}$
5. Change to per cents:

   (a) 0.06 (b) 0.10 (c) 1.25 (d) 0.875 (e) 2
6. 75% of a foot is how many inches?
7. $66\frac{2}{3}$% of a yard is how many feet?
8. How many ounces are there in $12\frac{1}{2}$% of a pound?
9. How many quarts are there in 25% of a gallon?
10. 10% of a mile is how many feet?

Interest

Dan borrowed \$80 from his father. Dan agreed to repay the loan in one year, and, in addition, he agreed to pay his father 5% of \$80. This is 5% *interest* for the use of the money.

1. The money borrowed is called the *principal*. (The letter "p" is used to represent the principal.) What is the principal (p) in the above problem?
2. The per cent of interest paid for the use of the money is called the *rate of interest*. (The letter "r" is used to represent the rate of interest.) 5% interest means at the rate of 5% a year. What is the rate of interest (r) in the above problem?
3. The length of time for which the money is borrowed is called the time. (The letter "t" is used to represent the time.) What is the time (t) in the above problem?
4. The money that is paid for the use of money is called the interest. (The letter "i" is used for interest.) How would you find the interest in the above problem?
5. The money borrowed, which is the principal (p), plus the money paid for the use of the money borrowed, which is the interest, (i), is the amount.

Solving Dan's Problem

The interest for one year is 5% of \$80.

$p = 80$	$i = 0.05 \times 80$	\$80
$r = 5\%$ or 0.05	$i = 4$	0.05
$t = 1$		\$4.00

The interest for one year is \$4.00.

1. What does 5% interest mean?
2. When you find 5% of \$80, you find the interest for how long?
3. Since the principal plus the interest equals the amount, what amount would Dan pay his father at the end of the year?

EXERCISES—Find the interest for 1 year on:

1. \$50 at 2%	2. \$75 at 4%	3. \$100 at 5%
4. \$800 at 6%	5. \$225 at 8%	6. \$1975 at 5%
7. \$2150 at 8%	8. \$226 at 6%	9. \$3750 at 8%
10. \$4750 at 1%	*11. \$450 at $2\frac{1}{2}$%	*12. \$780 at $4\frac{1}{2}$%

Finding the Amount

Marie borrowed $50 from her father to pay for art lessons. She agreed to pay 6% interest and to repay the loan at the end of the year. How much money will she owe her father at the end of the year?

The interest for 1 year is 6% of $50.

$p = 50$	$i = 0.06 \times 50$	$50
$r = 6\%$ or 0.06	$i = 3$	0.06
$t = 1$		$3.00

The amount = principal + interest

$$A = \$50 + \$3$$

$$A = \$53$$

The letter, A, is used to represent the amount.

When you borrow money, you not only need to pay the interest but also the principal. What is the sum of the principal and interest called?

EXERCISES—Find the amount at the end of the year on:

1. $50 at 5%	2. $80 at 4%	3. $120 at 6%
4. $360 at 3%	5. $1,250 at 8%	6. $970 at 9%
7. $1,280 at 6%	8. $3,250 at 5%	9. $7,520 at 4%
10. $296 at $2\frac{1}{2}$%	*11. $1,246 at $3\frac{1}{2}$%	*12. $872 at $4\frac{3}{4}$%

There are many reasons why people borrow money. A man might borrow money to buy a home. A business firm might borrow money to enlarge the business. A student might borrow money to pay his way through college. In order to borrow money, a person must show the lender that he will be able to repay the loan and the interest when it becomes due.

1. Give some situations in which you think it might be wise to borrow money.
2. Give some situations in which you think it might be unwise to borrow money.

Banks and loan companies make a business of lending money. The interest may be based on a yearly rate. 6% interest means 6% a year. The length of time money is borrowed varies from a few days to years.

Example—Find the interest on \$100 at 6%:

The interest for one year is 6% of \$100.

$i = 0.06 \times 100$ | \$100 × 0.06 = \$6.00

$i = 6$

The interest for one year is \$6.00.

For 1 month ($\frac{1}{12}$ year) the interest will be $\frac{1}{12}$ of \$6.00 or 50 cents.

For 2 months ($\frac{1}{6}$ year) the interest will be $\frac{1}{6}$ of \$6.00 or \$1.00.

For 3 months ($\frac{1}{4}$ year) the interest will be $\frac{1}{4}$ of \$6.00 or \$1.50.

EXERCISES—Find the interest on \$100 at 6% for:

(a) 4 months ($\frac{1}{3}$ year)
(b) 5 months ($\frac{5}{12}$ year)
(c) 6 months ($\frac{1}{2}$ year)
(d) 7 months ($\frac{7}{12}$ year)
(e) 8 months ($\frac{2}{3}$ year)
(f) 9 months ($\frac{3}{4}$ year)
(g) 10 months
(h) 11 months
(i) 2 years
(j) 2 years 6 months ($2\frac{1}{2}$ years)

Writing a Formula for Finding Interest

Sue borrowed \$30 at 8% for 6 months. What interest will she owe?

The interest for 1 year is 8% of \$30.

$p = 30$ $i = 0.08 \times \$30$

$r = 8\%$ or 0.08 $i = \$2.40$ (1 yr.)

time 6 *mo.* $= \frac{1}{2}$ yr.

$t = \frac{1}{2}$

The interest for $\frac{1}{2}$ year $= \frac{1}{2} \times \$2.40 = \$1.20$.

How was the interest for $\frac{1}{2}$ year found?

The product of what three quantities gave us the interest?

The interest equals the product of the principal, the rate, and the time.

$$\mathbf{i = p \times r \times t} \quad \text{or} \quad \mathbf{i = prt}$$

In products like $p \times r \times t$, the "$\times$" signs may be omitted.

Using a formula to solve above problem

$p = 30$ $\qquad i = prt$

$r = 8\%$ or 0.08 $\qquad i = 30 \times 0.08 \times \frac{1}{2}$ (15 / 1 cancellation)

time 6 *mo.* $= \frac{1}{2}$ yr.

$t = \frac{1}{2}$ $\qquad i = 1.2$

Sue owes $1.20 in interest.

What is the advantage in using the formula?

Using a formula, find the interest on $340 at 5% for 2 years 1 month.

$p = 340$ $\qquad i = prt$

$r = 5\%$ or 0.05 $\qquad i = 340 \times 0.05 \times 2\frac{1}{12}$

$t = 2\frac{1}{12}$ $\qquad i = 35.42$

The interest is $35.42.

```
   340
  0.05
 17.00
  2 1/12
  ----
   142
  3400
 35.42
```

EXERCISES—Using the formula, find the interest on:

1. $200 at 6% for 3 months.
2. $450 at 4% for 2 months.
3. $800 at 3% for 1 month.
4. $1250 at 5% for 6 months.
5. $1000 at 8% for 2 years.
6. $780 at 4% for 2 years 6 months.
7. $870 at $4\frac{1}{2}\%$ for 1 year.
8. $350 at $3\frac{1}{2}\%$ for 3 years.
9. $560 at 6% for 9 months.
10. $78 at 8% for 8 months.
11. $900 at 8% for 4 months.
12. $100 at $2\frac{1}{2}\%$ for 1 year 6 months.

*13. $80 at $6\frac{1}{2}\%$ for 1 year 3 months.

*14. $70 at $4\frac{1}{2}\%$ for 2 years 9 months.

*15. What amount will the Jones Company need to pay the bank if they borrow $2,000 at 8% for 3 months?

16. What amount will an oil company need to pay the bank if they borrow $10,000 at 6% for 2 months?

More practice on business uses of per cents is found in the Appendix, pages 307-308.

Finding Interest When Time Is Given in Days

When computing the interest, we usually consider 360 days in a year and 30 days in a month.

Example—Find the interest on $360 at 4% for 20 days.

$p = 360$	$i = prt$	$\overset{20}{\$\not{3}\not{6}\not{0}} \times 0.04 \times \dfrac{1}{\underset{1}{\not{1}\not{8}}} = \$0.80$
$r = 4\%$ or 0.04	$i = 360 \times 0.04 \times \frac{1}{18}$	
$t = \frac{20}{360}$	$i = 0.8$	
The interest is $.80.		

EXERCISES—Find the interest on each of the following:

1. $40 at 6% for 90 days.
2. $720 at 6% for 30 days.
3. $540 at 8% for 20 days.
4. $1000 at 5% for 60 days.
5. $700 at 4% for 120 days.
6. $1900 at 5% for 72 days.
7. $200 at 4% for 45 days.
8. $1350 at 4% for 30 days.
9. $250 at 6% for 4C days.
10. $1000 at 8% for 10 days.

Words you should understand:

1. principal 2. rate of interest 3. time
4. interest 5. amount

Test on Uses of Per Cents

Select the correct answer:

1. The agent's share of a sale is called (commission, net price, profit).
2. The amount a price is reduced is called (profit, commission, discount).
3. The money borrowed is called (interest, principal, amount).
4. The principal plus the interest is called (principal, rate, amount).
5. The amount left after the commission is subtracted is called (net proceeds, profit, discount).
6. Which is greater, (60% of the number, 0.62 of a number, or $\frac{5}{8}$ of the number)?

7. 200% of \$2.50 is (\$5.00, \$50, 50¢).
8. Three times a number is (3%, 100%, 300%) of it.
9. One-sixth of a number is about (10%, 15%, 60%) of it.
10. The interest on \$1000 at 8% for 1 year is (\$20, \$8, \$80).
11. 12 problems correct out of 15 gives a score of (90%, 70%, 80%).
12. The ratio of 6 to 12 is ($\frac{1}{2}$, $\frac{2}{1}$, $\frac{3}{4}$).
13. The ratio of 12 to 6 is ($\frac{1}{2}$, $\frac{2}{1}$, $\frac{3}{4}$).
14. 40 is what per cent of 100? (4%, $\frac{2}{5}$%, 40%).
15. $5\frac{1}{2}$% of \$200 is (\$10, \$20, \$11).
16. 0.8 is what per cent of 8? (100%, 1%, 10%).
17. The ratio of 1 ounce to 1 pound is ($\frac{1}{1}$, $\frac{1}{4}$, $\frac{1}{16}$).
18. A newsboy doubles his money. His profit is (100%, 200%, 5%).
19. If $\frac{3}{4}$ of a number is 12, the number is (9, 16, 15).
20. If 20% of a number is 100, the number is (20, 2, 500).

Review of . . .
USING PER CENT

1. When a commission is paid for selling,
   (a) who receives the commission?
   (b) who receives the net proceeds?
2. Find the commission:
   (a) Sales \$25 Rate of commission 15%
   (b) Sales \$15,000 Rate of commission 5%
3. Find the net proceeds:
   (a) Sales \$425 Rate of commission 20%
   (b) Sales \$30,000 Rate of commission 8%
4. Skip Williams received \$5.00 for selling \$25.00 worth of greeting cards. What was the rate of commission?
5. How many dollars worth of farm machinery must a salesman sell during a year to make a yearly income of \$6000 if he is paid a 12% commission on all sales?
6. Find the net price on the following articles:
   (a) Marked price of a chair \$56.00 Rate of discount 8%
   (b) List price of a table \$92.00 Rate of discount 20%

7. Find the rate of discount:
   (a) Marked price of a sweater $12.00 — Sale price $10.00
   (b) List price of a bedroom suite $450 — Sale price $405
8. Find the original marked price:
   (a) Sale price of a sweater $8.00 — Rate of discount 20%
   (b) Sale price of a piano $585.00 — Rate of discount 10%
9. James Tucker bought a bicycle marked $60 for $50. What was the rate of discount?
10. If a gas company allows a 5% discount on all bills paid by the 10th of the month, how much will a family save on a bill of $16.75 if it is paid by the 10th of the month?
11. Find the interest on $240 at 3% for 6 months.
12. Find the interest on $850 at 8% for 90 days.

Chapter Test

1. Find the commission:
   (a) Sale of house $10,000 — Rate of commission 5%
   (b) Sale of greeting cards $12.50 — Rate of commission 20%
2. Find the net proceeds:
   (a) Sale of books $300 — Rate of commission 25%
   (b) Sale of shoes $975 — Rate of commission 15%
3. Find the net price:
   (a) Marked price of coat $32 — Discount 15%
   (b) Marked price of radio $45 — Discount 5%
4. Find the interest on:
   (a) $75 at 6% for 3 months (b) $100 at 8% for 60 days
5. Bill Rose borrowed $50 from his father. He agreed to pay his father 6% interest and to pay the loan at the end of 6 months from his earnings. How much will Bill have to pay his father at the end of 6 months?
6. At a sale a $2.50 book was sold for $2.00. What per cent was the book reduced?
7. A magazine company allowed the music department of Bell High School a commission of 30% on all magazine subscriptions obtained during the month of February. If the department sold $650 worth of subscriptions, how much did the department make?
8. The Smith family sold their house for $13,250. They paid a real estate agent 5% for selling the house. How much did the family have left from the sale after paying the agent?

CHAPTER **THIRTEEN**  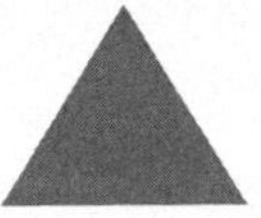  

Exploring The Circle

A circle is an important geometric plane figure. Compasses are usually used to construct circles. Figure 1 illustrates a circle.

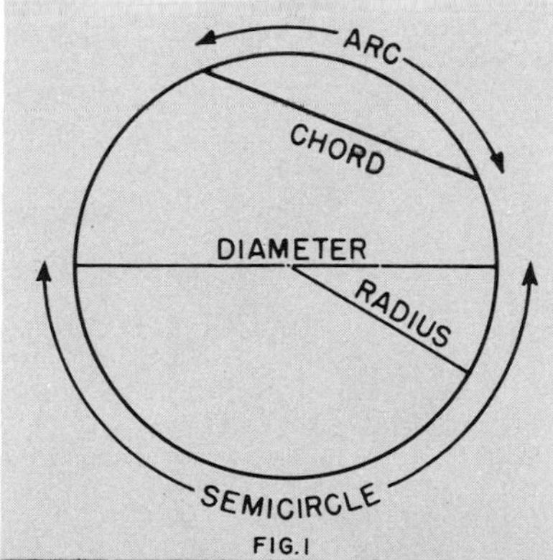

FIG. I

The circle is a closed curve in a plane all points of which are the same distance from a point called the center.

The length of the circle is called the circumference. A part of the circle is called an arc.

Study the illustration on page 227 and list the correct word to complete the sentence on a separate sheet of paper.

1. A half of a circle is a ______.
2. A line segment from the center to any point on the circle is a ______.
3. A line segment that joins two points on a circle and contains the center of circle is a ______.
4. A line segment whose ends lie on the circle is a ______.
5. The diameter of a circle is twice as long as the ______.

Making Designs with Circles

How many circles can you see in this picture?

If we want a circle with a two inch diameter, we open the compasses one inch measured along a ruler. The distance between the two points on the compasses will be the length of the radius of the circle. The plural of radius is radii.

Make a circle whose diameter is 2″ (radius 1″). Using the same radius of 1″, make six arcs around the circle. Then draw the six chords. This figure is a *regular hexagon* (six-sided figure with equal sides and equal interior angles).

See if you can make these designs.

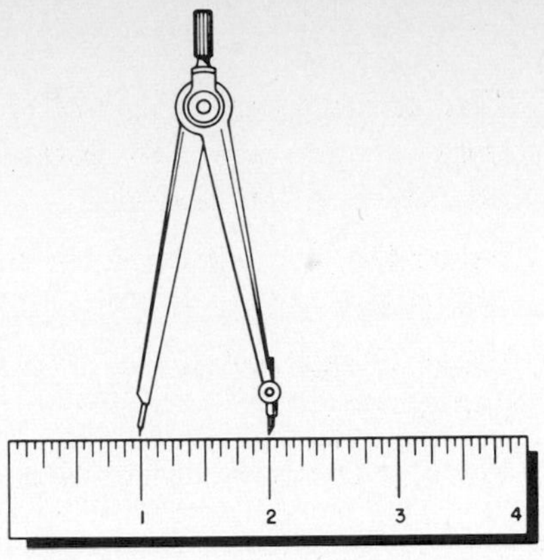

Quick Quiz No. 25

1. What is the sum of 0.2, 0.7, 0.9, 0.8, and 0.4?
2. Add: $6\frac{1}{2}$ lb., $3\frac{3}{4}$ lb., $7\frac{7}{8}$ lb., and $4\frac{1}{16}$ lb.
3. What is total mileage covered in five days, if a man drove the following number of miles: 420 miles, 375 miles, 289 miles, 575 miles, and 408 miles?
4. 75% + 10% + 3% + ?% = 100%.
5. Add: 16 ft. 4 in., 9 ft. 8 in., and 7 ft. 10 in.
6. On a trip a family spent \$18.78 for gasoline, \$156.25 for food and lodging, and \$16.75 for incidentals. How much did the trip cost?

7. Find the average weight of the players on a basketball team, if their weights are 126 pounds, 111 pounds, 107 pounds, 105 pounds, and 102 pounds.
8. Select the best estimate for this sum:
   $780 + 460 + 310 + 296$ (1700, 1800 or 1900).
9. What is the perimeter of a triangle whose sides are $3\frac{1}{2}''$, $4''$, and $3\frac{3}{4}''$?
10. What is the perimeter of a rectangle $18'' \times 16''$?

The Relation of the Circumference to the Diameter of a Circle

45° segment of a discharge elbow on a drainage pump for the Florida Everglades.

Since the circumference is dependent upon the length of the radius we would expect to find a relationship between the circumferences of circles and the lengths of their diameters.

A boy measured the length of the diameter of a plate. The diameter measured 9″. He made a mark on the circumference of the plate and placed this mark on a mark on a line drawn on the floor. He rolled the plate carefully along this line until the mark on the plate again touched the line on the floor. He measured the distance between the marks on the line on the floor which is the same as the circumference. The circumference measured 28.25″. He divided the length of the circumference by the length of the diameter carrying out the division to the nearest hundredth. He carried out the same experiment with three other circles.

The boy tabulated his measurements in this manner:

Object	*Diameter*	*Circumference*	*Circumference ÷ Diameter*
1. Plate	9″	28.25″	$\frac{28.25}{9} = 3.14$
2. Half dollar	1.2″	3.75″	
3. Bicycle wheel	28″	88″	
4. Can	10″	31.25″	

EXERCISE 1

(a) Complete the table obtaining each quotient to the nearest hundredth.

(b) Find the average of the four quotients.

Another method of measuring circular objects is to use a tape line.

EXERCISE 2

(a) Find three circular objects and measure the length of the diameter and the circumference of each.

(b) Make a table as in Exercise 1 and obtain the average of the three quotients.

Mathematicians have computed the ratio of the circumference of a circle to the length of its diameter and have found this ratio to be 3.1416 when rounded to ten-thousandths. Useful approximations of this ratio are $3\frac{1}{7}$ or 3.14. To designate this ratio we use the Greek letter π (pronounced pi).

π is approximately $3\frac{1}{7}$ or 3.14

A formula for finding the circumference is:

$$\mathbf{C = \pi d} \quad \text{or} \quad \mathbf{C = 2\pi r}$$

where d is length of the diameter and r is the length of the radius. Since the diameter is equal to two times the radius, $\mathbf{\pi d = 2\pi r}$.

Example 1:

$d = 9$ $\quad C = \pi d$

$C = 3.14 \times 9$

$C = 28.26$ or 28.3

The circumference is about 28.3 inches.

Example 2:

Find the circumference of a circle whose radius is 7 inches in length.

$r = 7$ $\quad C = 2\pi r$

$C = 2 \times \frac{22}{\underset{1}{7}} \times \overset{1}{7}$

$C = 44$

The circumference is about 44 inches.

EXERCISES

1. If the length of the diameter of a circle is 24 feet, what is the length of the radius?
2. If the length of the radius of a circle is 2.5″, what is the length of the diameter?
3. Using $\pi = 3\frac{1}{7}$, find the circumference of the following:
   (a) $d = 14''$ (b) $r = 21''$ (c) $r = 42$ ft.
   (d) $d = 7$ yd. (e) $r = 108$ ft. (f) $d = 1.4$ ft.
   (g) $r = 10.5$ ft. (h) $d = 8.4$ yd.
4. Using $\pi = 3.14$, find the circumference rounded to the nearest tenth of a unit of the following circles:
   (a) $d = 10$ ft. (b) $r = 5$ in. (c) $d = 1.2$ ft. (d) $r = 5$ yd.
5. From the examples in Exercises 3 and 4 can you tell when it is convenient to use $3\frac{1}{7}$ for the value of π?
6. What is the circumference of a circular flower bed 12 feet in diameter?

*7. How many plants 6 inches apart can you put around the outer edge of a circular pool 7 feet in diameter?

*8. The front wheel of Mildred's bicycle is 20″ in diameter. How many feet does the bicycle travel if the wheel revolves 500 times?

*9. A bicycle wheel is 28″ in diameter. How many times will the wheel revolve in going a mile?

*10. If you know the length of the circumference of a circle, how could you find the length of the diameter of this circle?

Quick Quiz No. 26

1. Fill in the missing number:
   (a) If the length of the radius of a circle is 6″, how many inches are there in the length of the diameter?
   (b) If the length of the diameter of a circle is $\frac{7}{8}$″, how many inches are there in the length of the radius?
2. Which is larger, 2 square inches or a square 2 inches on a side?
3. What is the perimeter of a circular flower bed 4 ft. in diameter? (use $\pi = 3.14$)
4. Approximately how many plants will you need to go around the outside of the flower bed in Exercise 3, if you put them 4 inches apart?
5. What is the interest on $500 at 8% for 3 months?
6. $20 is what per cent of $35 to the nearest whole per cent?
7. How much does an agent earn if he is paid 15% commission and he sells $1800 worth of goods?
8. A merchant wishes to sell a chair for 25% more than it cost him. If the chair cost $90, for what price must the chair be sold?
9. What is the cost of linoleum, at $5.25 a square yard, for a room 12 feet square?
10. A man's hourly wage was increased from $2.40 to $2.60 an hour. What was the per cent increase?

The tops of these oil tanks are circular in shape.

The Formula for Finding the Areas of Circles

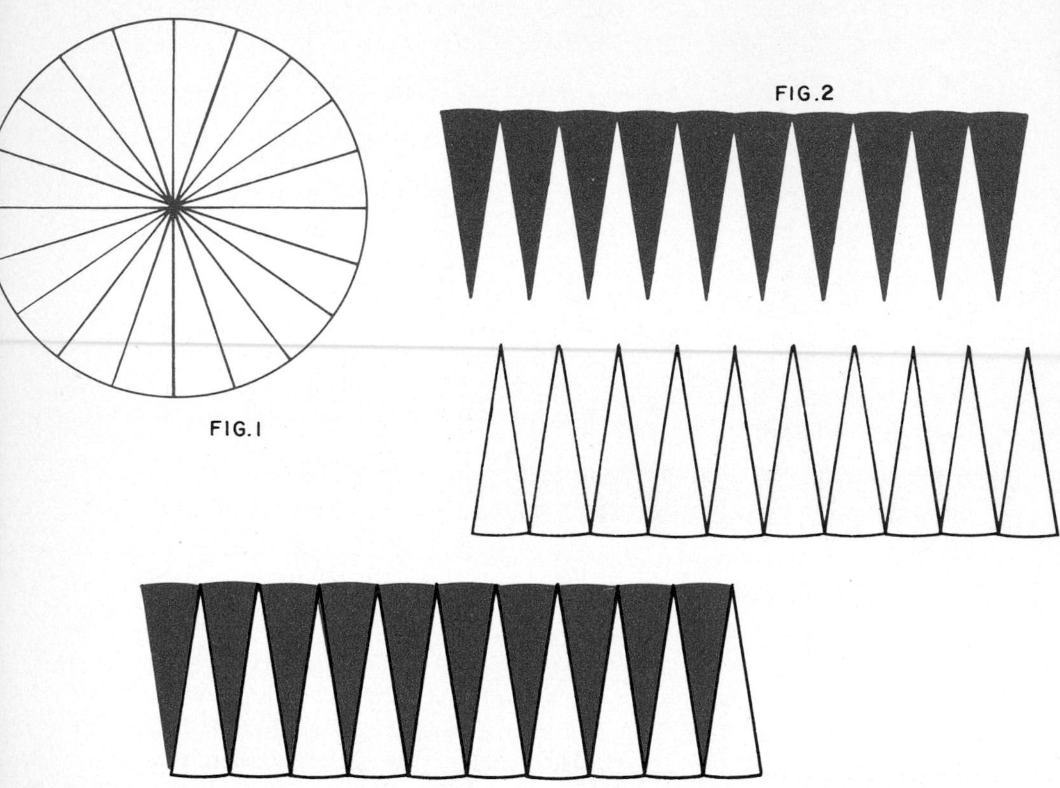

FIG. 1

FIG. 2

FIG. 3

Harold divided a circle into 20 equal sectors as in Figure 1. He then cut the ten equal parts of each semi-circle as shown in Figure 2. He fitted the top semi-circle into the bottom semi-circle as in Figure 3.

1. If we consider the base as a straight line, what does Figure 3 appear to be?
2. What is the formula for finding the area of a parallelogram?
3. What part of the circumference is each base?
4. What corresponds to the height of the parallelogram?
5. If the formula for the circumference is $C = 2\pi r$, what is the formula for one-half of the circumference? If the base of Figure 3 appears to be one-half of the circumference and the height appears to be the radius (r), the area A of a circle would be πr times

r, or:

$$A = \pi r^2$$

Remember $r \times r$ can be written r^2.

Harold has shown that this formula is a reasonable formula for finding the area of a circle.

Example 1.

Find the area of a circle if the length of the radius is 1 inch.

$r = 1 \qquad A = \pi r^2$

$A = 3.14 \times 1 \times 1$

$A = 3.14$

The area is 3.1 to the nearest tenth of a square inch.

Example 2.

Find the area of a circle whose diameter is 6″ in length.

$d = 6 \qquad A = \pi r^2$

$r = 3 \qquad A = 3.14 \times 3 \times 3$

$A = 28.26$

$$\begin{array}{r} 3.14 \\ 9 \\ \hline 28.26 \end{array}$$

The area is 28.3 to the nearest tenth of a square inch.

EXERCISES—Find the areas of each of the circles in Exercises 1 through 8. (Use $\pi = 3.14$) Express all areas to the nearest tenth of a square inch, square foot, or square yard. r and d represent the length of the radii and diameters.

1. $r = 2$ ft.
2. $d = 12$ in.
3. $r = 5$ yd.
4. $r = 2.1$ ft.
5. $d = 4.8$ in.
6. $r = 1\frac{1}{2}$ ft.
7. $r = 3\frac{1}{3}$ in.
8. $d = 2\frac{2}{3}$ in.

*9. The diameter of the top of a circular table is 36 inches. How many square inches are there in the top of this table?

*10. How many square feet are there in the top of the table in Exercise 9?

*11. A circular flower bed is 10 feet in diameter. If Mrs. Steward is to put chrysanthemum plants in it and is going to allow 2 square feet for each plant, how many plants will she need?

*12. A mirror company makes circular mirrors and charges $0.15 a square inch for them. How much will a circular mirror cost the length of whose diameter is 12″?

Quick Quiz No. 27

1. $7382 = 7000 + 300 + 80 + ?$

2. Write a number with zero in tens place, 5 in ones place, and 6 in hundreds place.

3. Find the pay a man would receive who works from 8:30 to 4:30 with an hour off for lunch, at $2.20 an hour.

4. How many hours are there from 6:30 A.M. one day to 6:30 P.M. the following day?

5. How late is a train that was due to arrive at 2:45 P.M. but arrived at 3:17 P.M.?

6. How many days are there from March 10 to and including April 22?

7. How many million is a billion?

8. $124 + 276 + 30 = ?$

9. $7000 - 5624 = ?$

10. What is the cost of $2\frac{1}{2}$ yards of cloth at $1.80 a yard?

Review of . . .

CIRCLES

1. In the circle in the figure, what are the following line segments called: (a) AOB, (b) OC, (c) DE

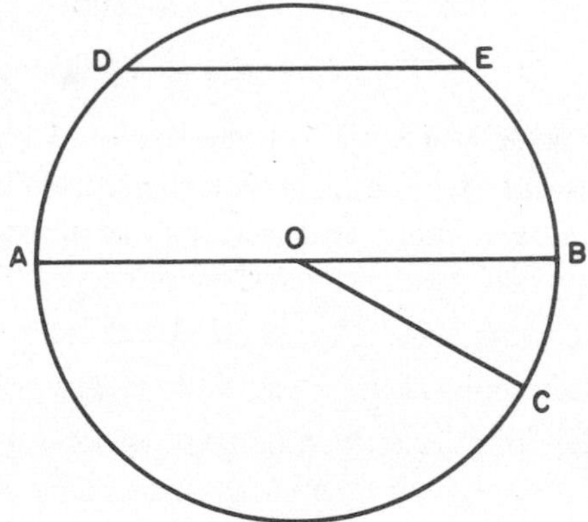

2. How may one find an approximate value of π?

3. Give two approximations of π which can be used in finding the circumference of a circle if the diameter is known.

4. Give two formulas for finding the circumference of a circle.

5. Give a formula for finding the area of a circle.

6. Find the circumference and area of each of the following circles; d and r represent the lengths of the radii and diameters.
   (a) $d = 12'$ (b) $d = 1.5''$ (c) $r = 7''$ (d) $r = 3\frac{1}{2}$ ft.

7. How far is it around a circular flower bed 6 feet in diameter? Give answer to nearest tenth of a foot.
8. How many square inches of surface has a circular mirror whose radius is 21″?
9. How many plants can be placed around the edge of a circular flower bed 10 feet in diameter if the plants are placed 10 inches apart?

Chapter Test

1. Give two approximate values of π that are used in finding the circumference or area of a circle.
2. Write two formulas for finding the circumference of a circle.
3. Write the formula for finding the area of a circle.
4. Find the circumference of the circle in Figure 1. (Use $\pi = 3\frac{1}{7}$)
5. Find the area of the circle in Figure 1. (Use $\pi = 3\frac{1}{7}$)

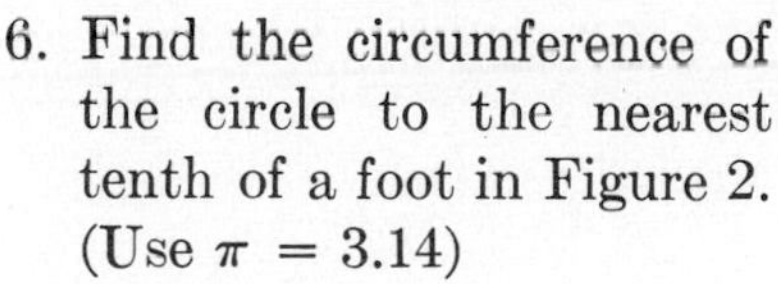

6. Find the circumference of the circle to the nearest tenth of a foot in Figure 2. (Use $\pi = 3.14$)
7. Find the area of the circle to the nearest tenth of a square foot in Figure 2. (Use $\pi = 3.14$)

FIG. I

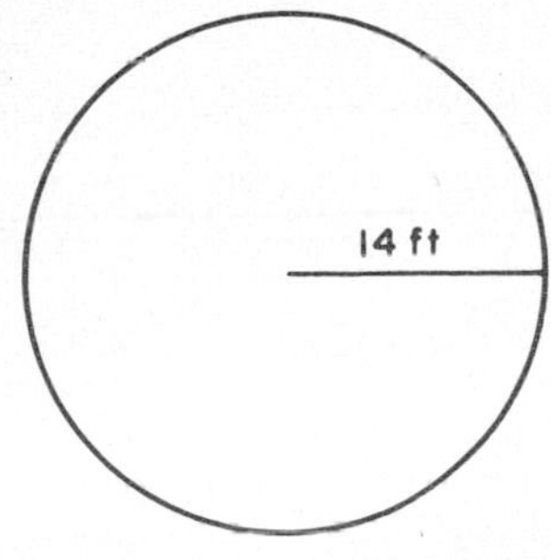

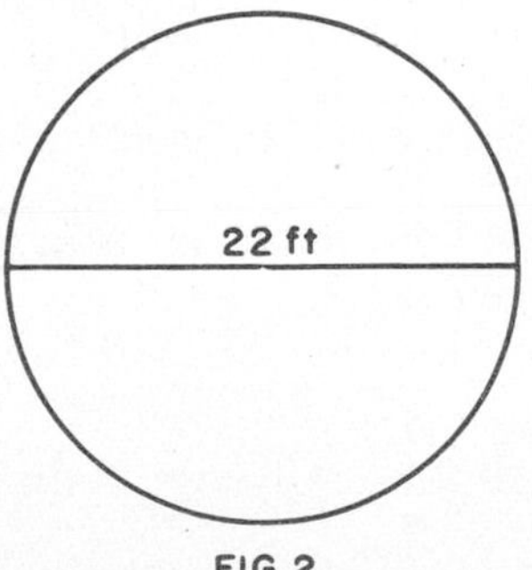

FIG.2

8. A test driver drove a new car around a circular track which had a diameter of 40 feet. To the nearest foot, how many feet did he drive the car in making one trip around the track?

9. A lamp shade has a circle at the top which is 12 inches in diameter and a circle at the bottom which is 18 inches in diameter. How many inches of tape will be needed to go around both circles?

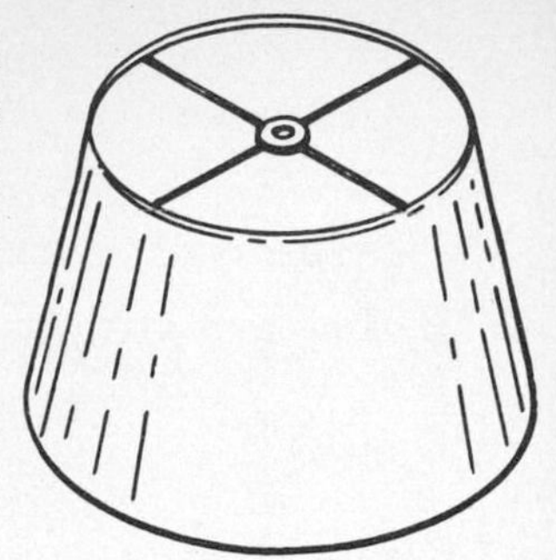

10. A bomb destroyed everything within a radius of 0.5 miles from where it fell. How many square miles of total destruction is this?

CHAPTER **FOURTEEN**  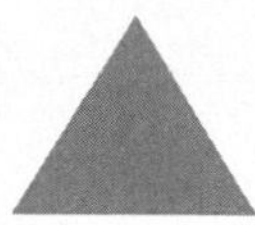  

Polygons and Rectangular Solids

Some Kinds of Polygons

A closed straight line figure lying in a plane is called a *polygon*. You have already studied about two special polygons called triangles and quadrilaterals.

Several common polygons are illustrated by the figures on the following page.

EXERCISES

1. What word will correctly complete the following sentences:
   (a) A ______ is a polygon with three sides.
   (b) A ______ is a polygon with six sides.
   (c) A ______ is a polygon with five sides.
   (d) A ______ is a polygon with four sides.
   (e) An ______ is a polygon with eight sides.

See figures on page 240.

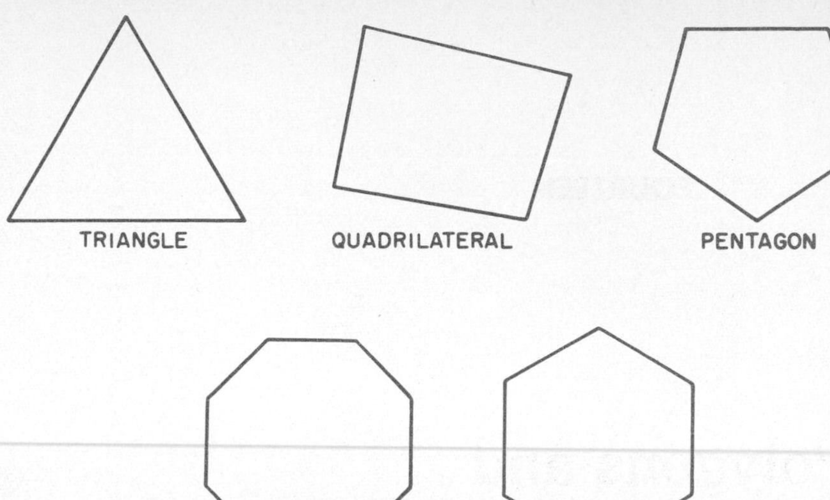

2. (a) Draw a figure to illustrate a polygon with more than eight sides.
   (b) Write a definition for a polygon.
   (c) Why is a circle not a polygon?

3. Regular Polygons. A regular polygon is a polygon with equal sides and equal interior angles.
   (a) Which kind of triangle is a regular polygon?
   (b) Which kind of quadrilateral is a regular polygon?

Using the circle, draw some regular polygons.

4. Pentagon:

Since a pentagon has five sides, if we mark five equal arcs on the circle we can draw five equal sides.

Things to think about:

(a) How many angle degrees are there at the center of the circle?

(b) How many central angles (angles at the center of the circle) will be required for five equal arcs on the circle?

(c) How many degrees are there in each central angle?

5. Draw a regular pentagon.

Step 1. Construct circle O any size and draw radius OB.

Step 2. Draw central angle BOC equal to 72° using a protractor.

Step 3. Draw chord BC and measure BC with the compasses.

Step 4. Starting at point C and using the same radius found in Step 3, make equal arcs cutting circle at points D, E, and F.

Step 5. Draw chords CD, DE, EF, and FB.

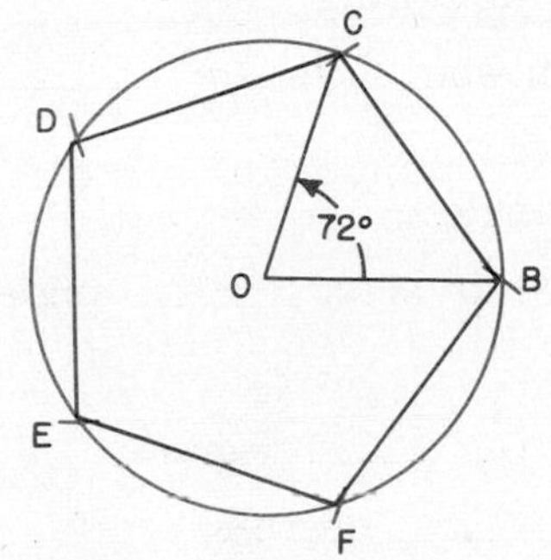

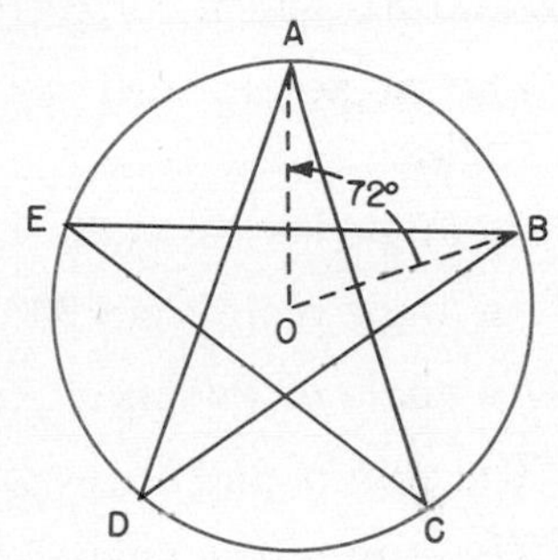

6. Draw a five-pointed star.

7. Construct a regular hexagon.

Step 1. Construct circle O any size and draw radius OA.

Step 2. Using the same radius, OA, and with A as a center, draw an arc cutting the circle at B.

Step 3. With the same radius and B as a center, draw an arc cutting circle at C.

Step 4. Continue in the same way to locate points C, D, E, and F.

Step 5. Connect points A, B, C, D, E, and F.

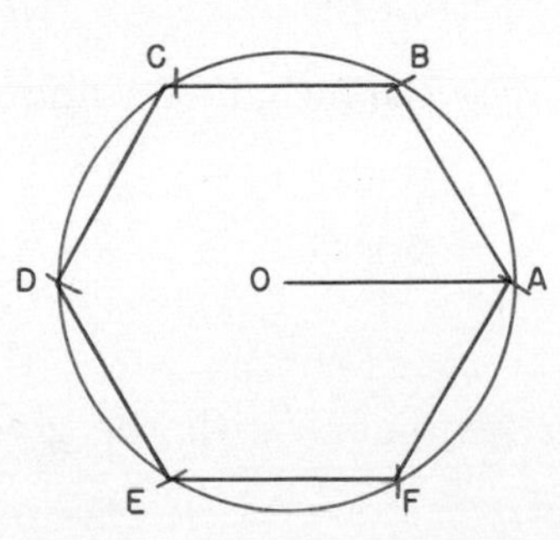

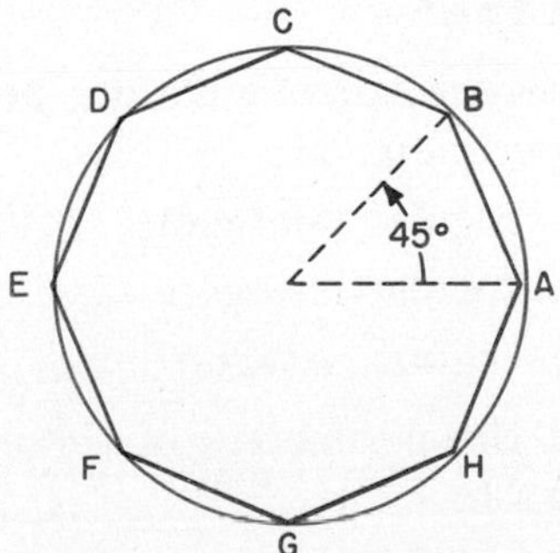

*8. Draw a regular octagon.

*9. Draw an original design based on regular polygons.

*10. Look for designs outside of the classroom which use regular polygons. If possible, bring them to class.

11. Make a design using polygons for a quilt pattern design, a jewelry design, or a floor design.

Words you should understand:
1. polygon 2. pentagon 3. hexagon 4. octagon

Quick Quiz No. 28

List words which correctly complete the following:

1. The angles formed by two perpendicular lines are ______ angles.
2. An angle less than 90° is an ______ angle.
3. An angle more than 90° and less than 180° is an ______ angle.
4. An angle of 180° is a ______ angle.
5. The sum of the angles of any triangle is ______ degrees.
6. The sum of the angles of a square is ______ degrees.
7. The sum of the angles of any rectangle is ______ degrees.
8. A triangle with all sides equal length is called an ______ triangle.
9. A triangle with only two sides equal length is called a ______ triangle.
10. A triangle with no two sides equal length is called a ____ triangle.

Perimeter of a Regular Pentagon

A regular polygon has all sides and all interior angles equal.

EXERCISES

1. If S is one side of a regular polygon, write the formula for finding the perimeter of:
   (a) a regular pentagon
   (b) a regular hexagon
   (c) a regular octagon
2. Find the perimeters of these regular pentagons with the given length of side s.
   (a) $s = 16$ inches
   (b) $s = 1\frac{3}{4}$ feet
   (c) $s = 2.5$ yards

3. Find the perimeter of these regular hexagons with the given length of side s.
   (a) $s = 13$ inches
   (b) $s = 2\frac{1}{4}$ yards
   (c) $s = 15.6$ feet

4. Find the perimeter of these regular octagons with the given length of side s.
   (a) $s = 16$ feet
   (b) $s = 2$ feet 9 inches
   (c) $s = 4.2$ yards

Indians employed many geometric figures in their designs.

Volume of Rectangular Solids

Your school room has three dimensions: length, width, and height. The angles at all the many corners are right angles. If the walls, the ceiling, and the floor are all rectangles, the room is an example of a rectangular solid. We often need to find the volume of rectangular solids.

The volume is measured in cubic measures such as cubic inches, cubic feet, or cubic yards. Name some rectangular solids.

EXERCISES

1. The sketch illustrates a cubic inch.

(a) How long is it? (b) How wide is it? (c) How high is it? Its volume is a cubic inch. Therefore, it is also called an inch cube.

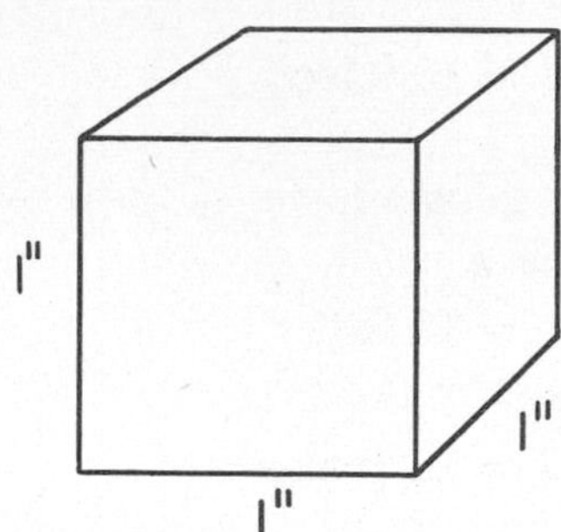

2. This is a scale drawing of a rectangular solid made up of blocks. Each block represents a cubic inch.

(a) How many inches long is this rectangular solid? (b) How many inches wide? (c) How many inches high? (d) How many cubic inches make up this rectangular solid?

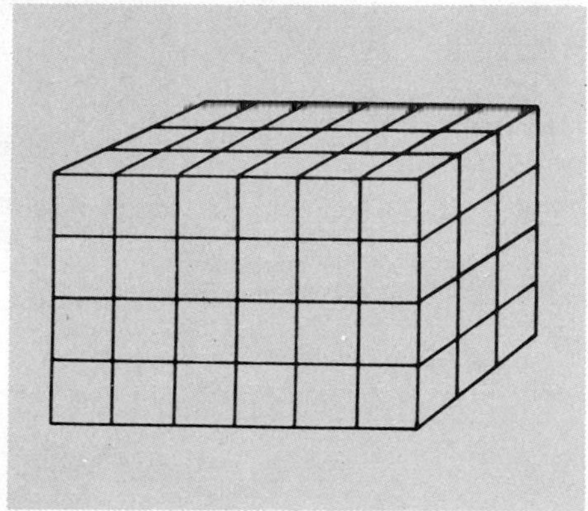

3. (a) How many cubic inches are there in a cubic foot? How many inches long is a cubic foot, how many inches wide, and how many inches high?

4. See Figure 2.

(a) How can we find the volume, without counting the blocks, if we know the length, width, and height? Notice all three dimensions are in inches.

The number of cubic units in the volume of a rectangular solid is the product of the number of units in the length, the width, and the height.

The formula is

$$V = l \times w \times h$$

or

$$V = lwh.$$

If this formula is used the units in the length, width, and height must be in the same unit of measure.

Find the volume of a rectangular solid whose length is 5″, width 3″, and height 4″.	Find the volume in cubic inches of a rectangular solid whose length is 2′, width 6″, and height $1\frac{1}{2}$″.
$l = 5$ $V = lwh$	$l = 24$ $V = lwh$
$w = 3$ $V = 5 \times 3 \times 4$	$w = 6$ $V = 24 \times 6 \times 1\frac{1}{2}$
$h = 4$ $V = 60$	$h = 1\frac{1}{2}$ $V = 216$
The volume is 60 cubic inches.	$24 \times 6 \times 1\frac{1}{2} = 24 \times \overset{3}{\not 6} \times \frac{3}{\underset{1}{\not 2}}$ or 216
	The volume is 216 cubic inches.

A cubic foot is 12 in. long, 12 in. wide and 12 in. high. How many cubic inches are there in a cubic foot?

1728 cu. in. = 1 cu. ft.

5. How many cubic inches are there in
   (a) 6 cu. ft. (b) $3\frac{1}{2}$ cu. ft. (c) 2.5 cu. ft. (d) $\frac{3}{4}$ cu. ft.
6. How many cubic feet are there in
   (a) 5184 cu. in. (b) 7776 cu. in. (c) 17280 cu. in.
   (d) 576 cu. in.

EXERCISES—Find the volume of these rectangular solids:

1. $l = 8'$ $w = 7'$ $h = 4'$
2. $l = 24''$ $w = 16''$ $h = 10''$
3. $l = 2\frac{1}{2}'$ $w = 1\frac{1}{3}'$ $h = 6\frac{1}{2}'$

4. $l = 7.5$ yd. $w = 2.1$ yd. $h = 6.4$ yd.
5. $l = 2'$ $w = 7''$ $h = 4''$
6. $l = 7'$ $w = 4'$ $h = 6''$
7. $l = 6'6''$ $w = 4'3''$ $h = 1'3''$
8. $l = 9'6''$ $w = 2'2''$ $h = 4'$
9. Find the number of cubic feet of air in a room $30' \times 28' \times 9'$.
10. How many cubic feet of water are needed to fill a pool $60' \times 20' \times 5'$?
11. How many gallons will it take to fill the pool in problem 10 if $7\frac{1}{2}$ gallons equals one cubic foot?
12. (a) What is the volume of a wheat bin $18' \times 16' \times 9'$?
    (b) Approximately how many bushels will the bin hold if 0.8 bushel will occupy approximately 1 cubic foot of space?

*13. How many cubic yards of dirt will be taken from an excavation for a new building if the excavation is $60' \times 40' \times 18'$?

*14. How many cubic yards of concrete will be needed to pave a street 300 feet long and 30 feet wide if the concrete paving is to be $4''$ thick?

*15. Make a model of a cubic foot out of cardboard. If your class makes enough cubic feet to occupy a cubic yard of space, how many will be needed?

Quick Quiz No. 29

Draw a figure to illustrate each of the following:

1. Curved line
2. Vertical parallel lines
3. Straight angle
4. Perpendicular lines
5. Obtuse angle
6. Broken line
7. Acute angle
8. Quadrilateral
9. Right angle
10. Horizontal parallel lines

Review of . . . POLYGONS AND RECTANGLES

1. What kind of lines enclose a polygon?

2. What name is given to each of the following:
   (a) a three sided polygon?
   (b) a four sided polygon?
   (c) a five sided polygon?
   (d) a six sided polygon?
   (e) an eight sided polygon?
3. If a circle is used in drawing regular polygons, how large is the central angle of the circle to determine a side of each of the following:
   (a) a square?
   (b) a regular pentagon?
   (c) a regular octagon?
4. What is the formula for finding the volume of a rectangular solid?
5. Change:
   (a) 16 cu. ft. to cu. in.
   (b) 6912 cu. in. to cu. ft.
   (c) 9 cu. ft. to cu. yd.
   (d) 243 cu. ft. to cu. yd.
6. Find the number of cubic feet of space in a room 28′ × 20′ × 8′.

*7. Draw a decagon and then draw all the diagonals from one vertex to the other vertices.
   (a) Into how many triangles is the decagon divided?
   (b) If the sum of the angles of a triangle is 180°, what is the sum of the angles of the decagon?

Chapter Test

1. Using a circle, draw the following:
   (a) a square
   (b) a hexagon
2. Copy and fill in the blanks:
   (a) ______ cu. in. = 1 cu. ft.
   (b) ______ cu. ft. = 1 cu. yd.
3. Change:
   (a) 9 cu. ft. to cu. in.
   (b) 4320 cu. in. to cu. ft.
   (c) 6 cu. yd. to cu. ft.
   (d) 279 cu. ft. to cu. yd.

4. If it takes approximately $7\frac{1}{2}$ gallons of water to fill one cubic foot, how many gallons will it take to fill an aquarium 2 feet long by $1\frac{1}{2}$ feet wide to a depth of 1 foot?
5. Find the number of cubic yards of dirt needed to cover a lawn 100 feet by 36 feet if the dirt is to be 1 inch thick all over the lawn.

CHAPTER **FIFTEEN**  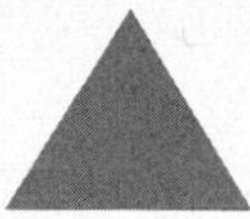  

Graphs

Pictographs

Data, or a collection of information, may be illustrated by a graph. A common type of graph is a pictograph. As the name suggests, pictures are used to show comparisons.

The Southside Bank used the following pictograph to show their sale of government bonds for one week in March.

Bond Sale *Southside Bank* *March 10–14*

One Bond = $37.50 Worth of Sales Face Value $50

Girls

Boys

Women

Men

Answer these questions:

1. Each bond represents how much in purchase value (amount paid for the bond)?
2. Each bond represents how much in face value (value of the bond at end of 10 years)?
3. How much money was invested this week in bonds by girls? By boys? By women? By men?
4. What is the total face value of the bonds purchased this week by girls? By boys? By women? By men?
5. What part of the total number of bonds purchased this week were purchased by girls? By boys? By women? By men?

How to make a pictograph:

Step 1. Select the scale. Let each picture represent a convenient number. For example, if one apple may represent 50 bushels. In this case, a half apple would represent 25 bushels.

Step 2. Arrange pictures in an attractive manner. Colors may be used to help catch the eye.

Step 3. Be sure the scale is written on graph. Place title in, above, or below graph.

Make pictographs of the following data:

1. The number of bushels of apples sold from five large orchards are: Smith orchard—550 bushels; Brown orchard—400 bushels; Henry orchard—825 bushels; Jones orchard—350 bushels. (Suggestion: Let = 50 bushels.)
2. Number of calories needed for different kinds of work: work done chiefly at a desk, about 2,500 calories; work done chiefly standing or walking, about 3,000 calories; muscular work, about 3,500 calories; heavy muscular work, about 5,000 calories. (Suggestion: 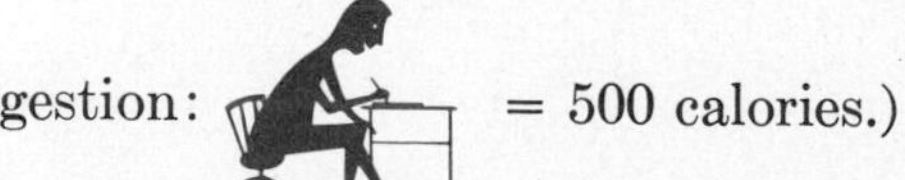 = 500 calories.)
3. Make a pictograph showing the number of boys and number of girls in class.

4. Make a pictograph showing how many pupils of different age groups there are in the class, how many 12 year olds, how many 13 year olds.

*5. Make a pictograph showing how many senior high schools, how many junior high schools, how many elementary schools there are in your school system.

Quick Quiz No. 30

Select the best estimated answer for each of the problems below:

1. 4286 + 3929 + 926 + 2100 = (9,000; 11,000; 12,000)
2. 5200 − 3920 = (500; 1,000; 1,500)
3. 58 × 99 = (600; 5,400; 6,000)
4. 7740 ÷ 40 = (100; 150; 200)
5. 29.6 + 31.3 + 42.8 + 75.1 = (150; 160; 170)
6. 329.2 − 187.4 = (100; 200; 300)
7. 75.9 × 29.2 = (2000; 2400; 3000)
8. 24.6 ÷ 1.9 = (10, 12, 15)
9. $33\frac{1}{3}\%$ of $2965 = ($500; $1000; $1500)
10. $10 is what per cent of $90? (1%; 10%; 20%)

Bar Graphs

Horizontal and vertical bar graphs are also used to show comparisons. See Chapter 9 on "Comparing Quantities," page 161. In making these graphs, we follow certain steps.

Example—Make a bar graph of the following data:

Results of Review Test for First Hour Mathematics Class

Rating	Excellent	Good	Fair	Poor
Number of Pupils	10	18	8	4

Step 1. Decide whether to make a horizontal or vertical graph.

Step 2. Select a suitable scale in order to make the bars a convenient length. It is usually best to begin the number scale at zero in order to present a true picture.

Step 3. Decide on the width of the bars and spaces between the bars. In bar graphs, the bars are usually of uniform width and the spaces between the bars the same width as the bars.

Step 4. Leave enough margin space to the left and at the bottom to write the necessary information.

Step 5. Label the horizontal line, in this case, 5, 10, 15, 20, and the vertical line, in this case, Poor, Fair, Good, and Excellent.

Step 6. Make the bars the proper length using the scale that you selected in Step 2. Shade or color each bar.

Step 7. Place the title of the graph at the top.

Step 8. Round data to nearest convenient decimal place.

Results of Review Test for First Hour Mathematics Class

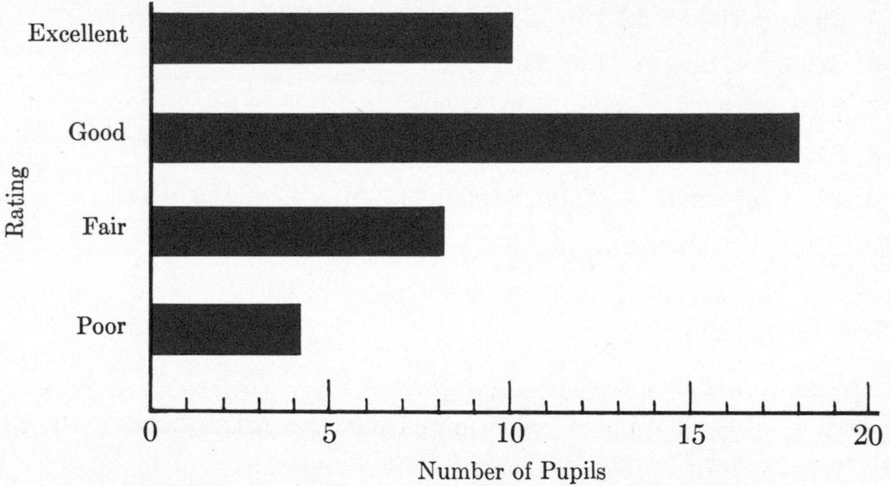

EXERCISES—Make bar graphs for each collection of data:

1. The enrollment in Horace Mann Junior High School by grades: Grade IX—340; Grade VIII—375; Grade VII—410.
2. The week's attendance in a classroom: Monday—40; Tuesday—42; Wednesday—42; Thursday—39; Friday—42.
3. The number of 7th grade pupils making 100% on the week's spelling test: Room 1—24; Room 2—30; Room 3—20; Room 4—16; Room 5—21; Room 6—18; Room 7—25; and Room 8—19.
4. The heights of famous monuments: Washington's Monument, 555 feet; The Statue of Liberty (from sea level to tip of torch), 305 feet; and the Bunker Hill Monument, 221 feet.

*5. Areas of continents: Asia—16,494,217 square miles; Africa—11,529,480 square miles; North America—9,363,868 square miles; South America—7,096,656 square miles; Antarctica—5,362,626 square miles; Europe—3,781,407 square miles, and Australia—2,974,581 square miles. (Round to nearest million square miles.)

*6. Find other interesting data to graph. Some suggestions:
   (a) Your school's enrollment by grades.
   (b) The number of boys and the number of girls in each grade in your school.
   (c) The height or weight of five classmates compared with your height or weight.
   (d) Number of calories in food servings.
   (e) Height of the tallest buildings in your town or city.
   (f) Growth of population of your town or city.
   (g) Growth of population of the United States.
   (h) The number and causes of fatal accidents in your town or city for a definite period of time.
   (i) Any data from your science or social studies classes.

Quick Quiz No. 31

1. Find the sum of $56.50, $8.08, $9.25, and $.38.
2. What is the difference between $13.98 and $14.50?
3. The product of $47.50 and 28 is what?
4. What is the quotient if the dividend is $31.75 and the divisor 25?
5. What is the difference between the smallest and the largest integers you can write with the digits 6, 2, 1, and 3?
6. A candy manufacturer can pack 12 five-pound boxes of candy in a carton. How many cartons will the manufacturer need for packing 180 five-pound boxes?
7. A railroad timetable gives the distance from Washington, D. C., to Pittsburgh, Pennsylvania, as 296 miles. If the distance on the timetable from Washington, D. C., to Ellerslie, Maryland, by the same route is 152 miles, how far is it from Ellerslie to Pittsburgh?
8. Mr. Lunn decided to fertilize his dairy pastures by using 450 pounds of fertilizer to an acre. How many tons of fertilizer will he need to fertilize 40 acres of pasture?

9. Mr. Gordey harvested the corn in three fields. From the first field he harvested 320 bushels, from the second 528 bushels, and from the third 840 bushels. How many bushels to the acre did the corn yield if there were 40 acres in the three fields?

10. Is this sum correct? If it is not correct, find the correct sum.

$$\begin{array}{r} 9672 \\ 1871 \\ 386 \\ \underline{24} \\ 12{,}953 \end{array}$$

Broken-line Graphs

Fixed values or amounts such as the height of buildings, lengths of rivers, etc. are represented on bar graphs. Changing values and amounts such as temperatures, population of cities, etc. are shown on line graphs. Thus the bar graph compares two or more subjects which are related in some way, whereas, the broken-line graph compares two or more values of the same subject.

Broken-line graphs may be used to show price changes, temperature changes, and changes that occur from hour to hour, day to day, and so forth. In making these graphs, it is best to follow these steps.

Example—Make a broken-line graph of the following data:

Changes in Temperature

Hour	6 A.M.	7 A.M.	8 A.M.	9 A.M.	10 A.M.	11 A.M.	12 Noon
Temperature	52°	54°	56°	56°	50°	45°	35°

Step 1. Draw a horizontal line and a vertical line. These are called the horizontal axis and the vertical axis. Label each axis as suggested by the numbers in the table. In this case, the horizontal axis is labeled with numbers from 6 to 12 while the vertical axis starts from 35 and is numbered to 60 in groups of fives. (Time is always shown on the horizontal axis.)

Step 2. Each point is located by a pair of numbers. One number tells how far to count on the horizontal axis and the other number tells how far to count on the vertical axis.

Step 3. Locate the points and join them in succession.

Step 4. Label your scales and place a title on the graph. What changes are illustrated by the graph?

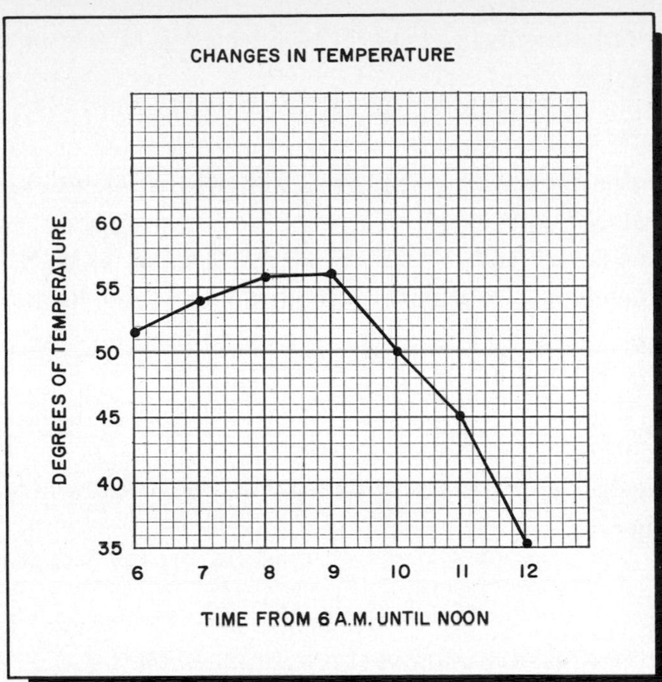

EXERCISES—Make a broken-line graph for each set of data. It may be helpful to first write the data in table form.

1. Changes in temperature from noon until 6 P.M.: 12 noon—81°; 1 P.M.—83°; 2 P.M.—86°; 3 P.M.—88°; 4 P.M.—92°; 5 P.M.—92°; and 6 P.M.—88°.
2. A boy's weight on the first day of each month for a year: January—82 pounds; February—82 pounds; March—83 pounds; April—84 pounds; May—86 pounds; June—88 pounds; July—90 pounds; August—90 pounds; September—91 pounds; October—93 pounds; November—92 pounds; and December—93 pounds.
3. The per cent of pupils making a perfect score on the weekly mathematics tests for 9 weeks: 1st week—5%; 2nd week—8%; 3rd week—9%; 4th week—10%; 5th week—9%; 6th week—10%; 7th week—10%; 8th week—12%; and 9th week—15%.
4. The amount of rainfall per month on the Davis Ranch: January—2.2 inches; February—2.4 inches; March—2.5 inches; April—3 inches; May—3.4 inches; June—2 inches; July—1.8 inches; August—0.8 inches; September—1.6 inches; October—2 inches; November—2.2 inches, and December—1.8 inches.

*5. Mary kept a record of her earnings from baby-sitting for one year: January—\$2.50; February—\$3.00; March—\$3.25; April—\$3.00; May—\$2.00; June—\$5.50; July—\$6.25; August—\$7.50; September—\$2.00; October—\$3.50; November—\$3.00; and December—\$5.50.

*6. Find other interesting data to graph with broken-line graphs. Some suggestions are:
   (a) The enrollment in your school for the last 10 years.
   (b) The change in prices of a food, such as eggs, during a year.
   (c) The change in population of your town or city for 10 years.
   (d) The rainfall in your city for a year.
   (e) The growth in population of the United States during this century.
   (f) The amount spent for fuel by your family each month for a year.

Quick Quiz No. 32

1. Supply the missing numbers in the following:
   (a) $\frac{1}{4} = \frac{?}{8}$ (b) $\frac{?}{4} = \frac{9}{12}$ (c) $\frac{10}{12} = \frac{5}{?}$ (d) $\frac{?}{24} = \frac{2}{3}$
2. Correct any errors in these:
   (a) $8\frac{9}{8} = 9\frac{1}{8}$ (b) $7\frac{5}{4} = 6\frac{1}{4}$ (c) $12\frac{10}{9} = 13\frac{1}{10}$ (d) $4\frac{8}{6} = 5\frac{2}{6}$
3. $3\frac{3}{4}$ $+2\frac{1}{8}$
4. $7\frac{1}{16}$ $-2\frac{5}{8}$
5. $4\frac{2}{3} \times 7\frac{1}{2}$
6. $18 \div 4\frac{1}{2}$
7. If you multiply 80 by any proper fraction, will the answer be larger or smaller than 80?
8. If you multiply 80 by any mixed number, will the answer be larger or smaller than 80?
9. If you divide 80 by any proper fraction, will the answer be larger or smaller than 80?
10. If you divide 80 by any mixed number, will the answer be larger or smaller than 80?

Circle Graphs

Circle graphs show the relations of parts to a whole and the relations between parts.

Words you should understand:
1. central angle 2. arc 3. sector

EXERCISES

1.

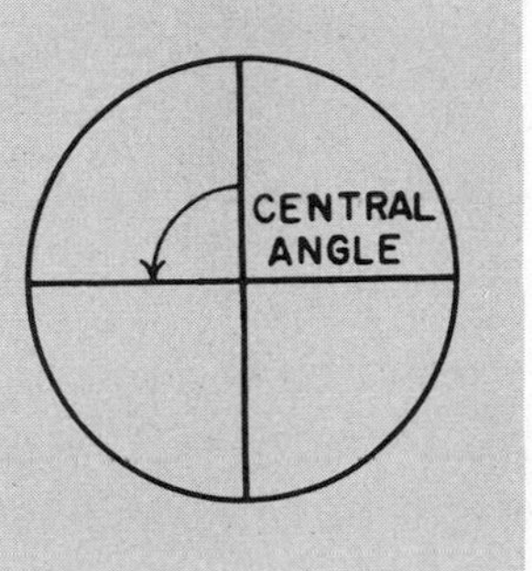

(a) Into how many parts has this circle been divided?

(b) If all the arcs are equal what kind of angles are formed at the center of this circle?

(c) How many degrees are there in each of the central angles of this circle?

(d) What is the sum of the degrees of the four central angles of this circle?

(e) Can a circle have more than four central angles?

(f) What is the sum of the degrees of all the central angles?

(g) An angle that has its vertex at the center of a circle is called a ______.

2.

If the central angles of each of these circles are equal:

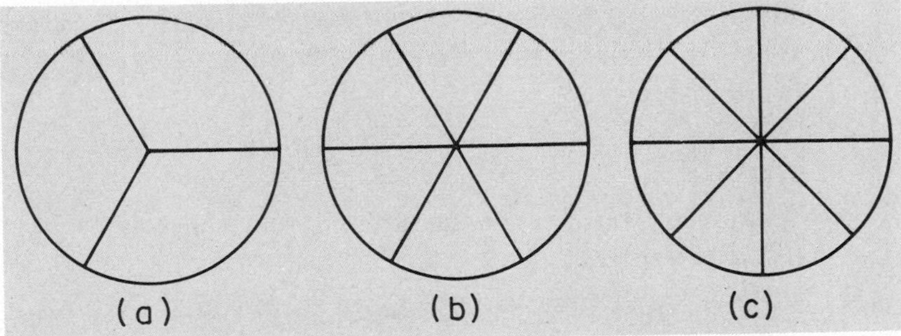

(a) How many degrees are there in each central angle of circle (a)?

(b) How many degrees are there in each central angle of circle (b)?

(c) How many degrees are there in each central angle of circle (c)?

3.

(a) How many degrees in the largest central angle of circle (d)?

(b) How many degrees in the smallest central angle of circle (e)?

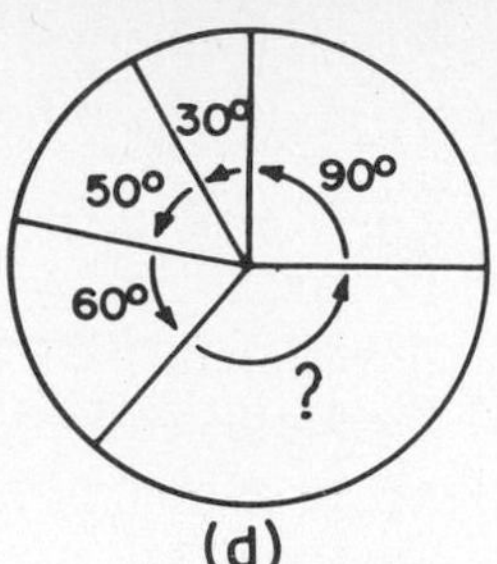

4.

(a) Into how many parts has the circumference of this circle been divided?

(b) What is each part called? The length of an arc can be measured by any unit of linear measure of length, such as inches, feet, or yards.

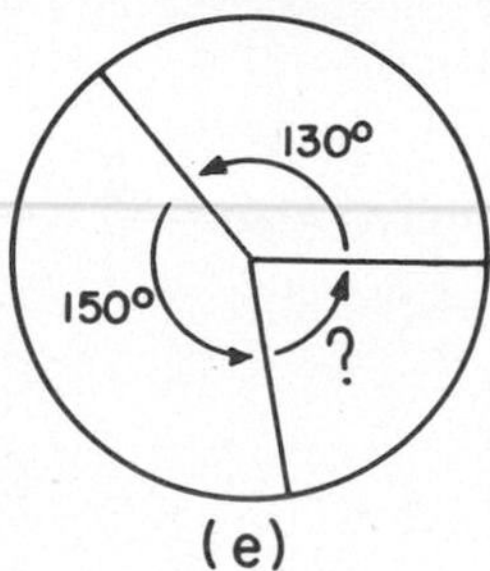

An arc is measured by the same number of degrees as the central angle which determines the arc.

(c) Each arc is measured by how many degrees?

(d) What fractional part of the circumference is each arc in this circle?

(e) What fractional part of the circumference is each arc in circle (a) of Exercise 2?

(f) In Exercise 2, circle (a), each arc is measured by how many degrees?

(g) What fractional part of the circumference is each arc in circle (b) of Exercise 2?

(h) In Exercise 2, circle (b), each arc is measured by how many degrees?

(i) What fractional part of the circumference is each arc in circle (c) of Exercise 2?

*(j) What fractional part of the circumference is each arc in circle (d) of Exercise 3?

*(k) In circle (e), Exercise 4, each arc is measured by how many degrees?

*(l) What fractional part of the circumference is each arc in circle (e) of Exercise 3?

*(m) In circle (d), Exercise 3, each arc is measured by how many degrees?

5.

(a) What fractional part of the circumference of circle *A* is arc *a*? Hint: 60° is what part of 360°?

(b) Arc *a* is measured by how many degrees?

(c) What fractional part of the circumference of circle *B* is arc *b*?

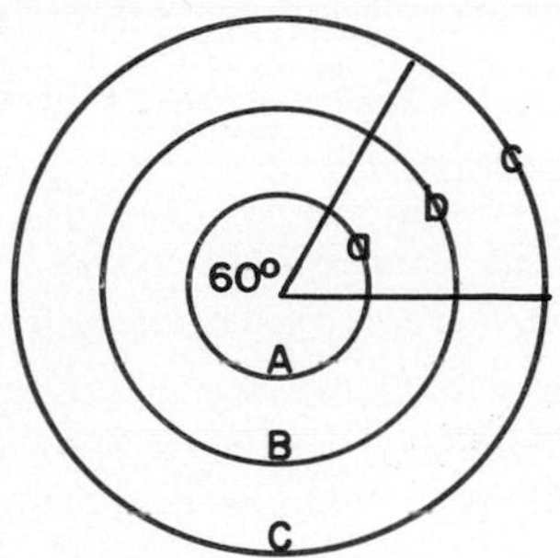

(d) Arc *b* is measured by how many degrees?

(e) What fractional part of the circumference of circle *C* is arc *c*?

(f) Arc *c* is measured by how many degrees?

(g) Does the number of degrees that measure an arc depend on the size of the circle?

(h) Does the length of an arc depend on the size of the circle?

(i) Any part of a circumference of a circle is called an ______.

6. This circle is divided into sectors.

(a) How many sectors does this circle have?

(b) Do these sectors appear to be equal?

(c) If the sectors are equal what fractional part of the area of the circle is each?

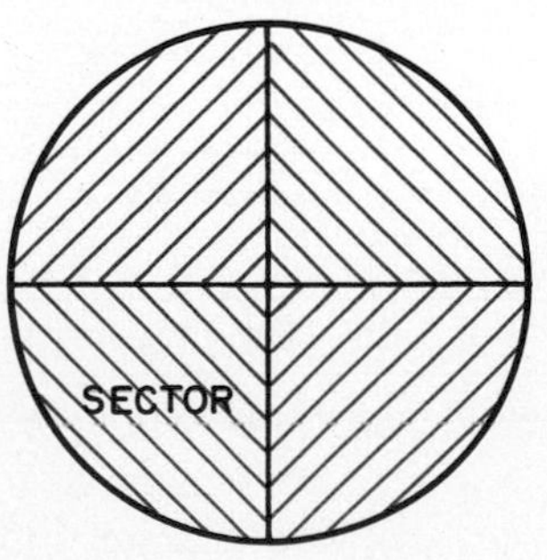

7. (a) How many equal sectors are there in circle (a) of Exercise 2? What fractional part is each sector of the total area?
   (b) How many equal sectors are there in circle (b) of Exercise 2? What fractional part is each sector of the total area?
   (c) How many equal sectors are there in circle (c) of Exercise 2? What fractional part is each sector of the total area?
   (d) How many unequal sectors are there in circle (d) of Exercise 3? *What fractional part is each sector of the total area?
   (e) How many unequal sectors are there in circle (e) of Exercise 3? *What fractional part is each sector of the total area?
   (f) What is the part of a circle formed by two radii and an arc called?

Making Circle Graphs

Example—According to recent statistics, approximately 25% of the drivers of cars involved in fatal accidents in our country are under 24 years of age, 70% are between the ages of 24 to 64, and 5% are over 65 years of age. Make a circle graph to illustrate this data.

Step 1. The sectors of a circle graph depend on the size of the central angles. It is convenient to arrange the data in table form.

This table shows the per cent changed to fractional parts of the whole circle and then to size of central angles.

Age of Drivers in Fatal Car Accidents

Ages of drivers	*Per cent of whole*	*Fractional part of whole*	*Size of central angle*
Under 24 years	25%	$\frac{25}{100} = \frac{1}{4}$	25% or $\frac{1}{4}$ of 360° = 90°
24 to 64 years	70%	$\frac{70}{100} = \frac{7}{10}$	70% or $\frac{7}{10}$ of 360° = 252°
Over 64 years	5%	$\frac{5}{100} = \frac{1}{20}$	5% or $\frac{1}{20}$ of 360° = 18°
Totals	100%	$\frac{20}{20}$	360°

Step 2. Make a large enough circle to show this information.

Step 3. To start the construction of the first central angle, draw a radius like OA in the graph. Place the center of the protractor on the center of the circle (O) and have the zero on the scale on a line with OA. Find the number of degrees on the protractor for the first central angle (90°) and make a mark, in this case *B*. Draw line *OB*. This sector represents 25% of the circle, or the per cent of drivers under 24 years of age.

To make the second central angle, place the center of the protractor at center (*O*) and have zero on the scale on a line with *OB* and measure the angle (18°). This sector represents 5% of the circle or the per cent of drivers over 64 years of age. Since our circle only represents three classes of information, the rest of the circle should be an angle of 252°. This sector represents 70% of the circle, or the per cent of drivers from 24 to 64 years of age.

Step 4. Label each sector.

Step 5. Each sector can be colored or shaded to attract the eye.

Step 6. Place the title above or below the circle.

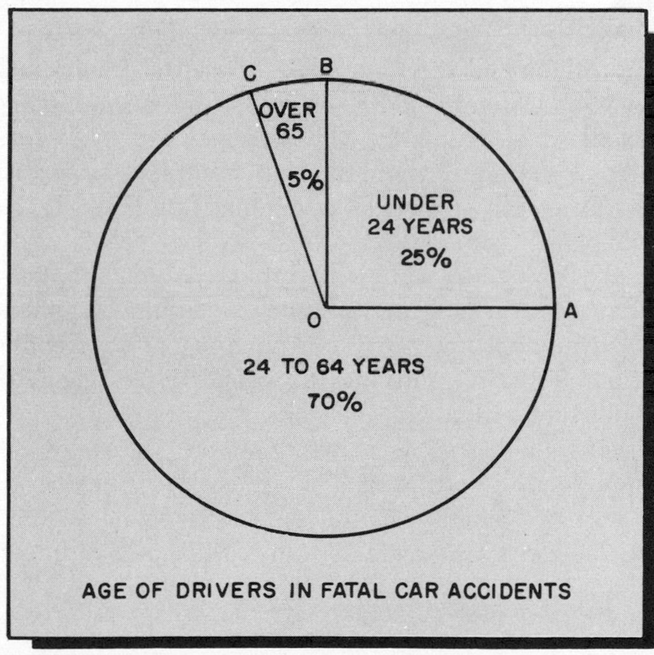

AGE OF DRIVERS IN FATAL CAR ACCIDENTS

EXERCISES—Make a circle graph for each set of data:

1. In Pershing Junior High School, 55% of the pupils are girls and 45% are boys.
2. Water is $33\frac{1}{3}$% oxygen and $66\frac{2}{3}$% hydrogen.

3. A family made the following budget: 20% for food, 40% for home payment, 25% for clothing, 10% for savings, and 5% for recreation.
4. According to recent statistics, approximately 80% of fatal car accidents occur on clear days, 15% on rainy days, 3% on snowy days, and 2% on foggy days. (Round the size of central angles to nearest degree.)
*5. How 40 students in Room A of Park Junior High School spent the major portion of their vacations: 10 went to camp, 8 traveled in the United States, 4 worked on farms of relatives, 9 attended summer school, and 9 worked and played at home. (Find what per cent of 40 is in each group.)
*6. Joe Bryce spent a typical school day in the following way: school, 6 hours; sleep, 10 hours; eating and home duties, 3 hours; study, 2 hours; and recreation, 3 hours.

The Number Line

The Egyptians and the Babylonians used geometry primarily to solve problems which helped them build and survey. In contrast to this application of geometry, the Greeks were more interested in geometry as a system of thought. For example, by use of logic they proved many of the properties of geometric figures. In high school courses in plane geometry, the methods and proofs of the Greeks are studied. The Greeks did some thinking about numbers but they had little interest in relating numbers to geometric figures.

In the seventeenth century a French scientist, René Descartes, invented a method of studying the properties of geometric figures by applying the methods of algebra.

Coordinate geometry, as the method of Descartes is called, is based upon the association of a point with a number or numbers. Starting with a point associated with 0 on a line, points equally spaced to the right are associated with the positive integers. Thus,

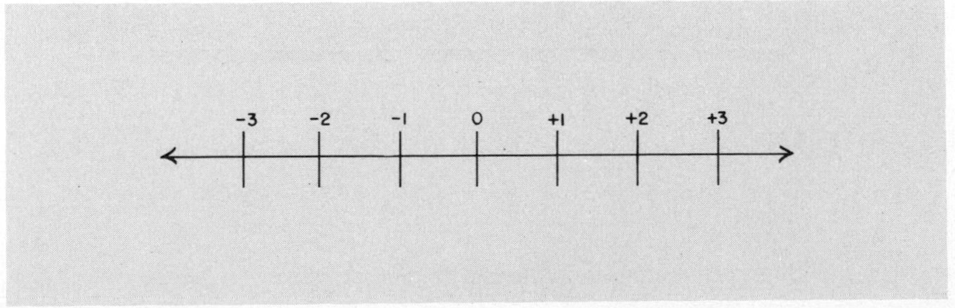

$+1$ is the number assigned to the point one unit to the right of 0; $+2$, two units to the right of 0; $+3$, three units to the right of 0, and so on. $+1$, $+2$, and $+3$ are read "positive one," "positive two," and "positive three."

Corresponding points on the line to the left of zero are designated by negative numbers. Thus, -1 is assigned to the point one unit to the left of 0; -2, two units to the left of 0; -3, three units to the left of 0, and so on. -1, -2, and -3 are read "negative one," "negative two," and "negative three." For the positive integers this, of course, corresponds to the markings on a ruler which are equally spaced. The number assigned to a point is called the *coordinate* of the point.

Fractions, also, are assigned to points on this same line. $+\frac{1}{2}$ would be the coordinate of the point one-half unit to the right of 0; $-\frac{1}{2}$ is the coordinate of the point one-half unit to the left of 0; and so on.

Not all of the points on the line have been assigned numbers. In later study of mathematics other points on the same line are associated with other kinds of numbers. We will use only positive and negative integers, positive and negative fractions, and 0 on our line. This system establishes a one-to-one correspondence between a number and a certain point on the line. This means that for each number there is a point corresponding to it, and for each point on the line to which we have assigned a number there is a number corresponding to it. Also, notice that positive and negative numbers on the line indicate direction from 0. Positive numbers are in the direction to the right of zero and negative numbers are to the left of zero. Due to this relationship, positive and negative numbers are sometimes called "directed numbers."

EXERCISES

1. Make a number line (number scale) using the integers -10 through $+10$.
2. (a) Using the line that you made in Exercise 1, how many units are there from $+2$ to $+8$?
   (b) How many units are there from $+1$ to $+10$? from -1 to $+3$? from -3 to $+6$? from -6 to $+10$?
3. Mark points on the line with the following coordinates: $+\frac{1}{2}$, $-\frac{1}{4}$, $+2\frac{1}{2}$, $-4\frac{1}{2}$, $-6\frac{1}{8}$.
4. How many units are there from $+\frac{1}{2}$ to $+6$? $-\frac{1}{4}$ to $+2\frac{1}{2}$? and $-4\frac{1}{2}$ to $+\frac{1}{2}$?
5. How many points could be represented by a number scale?

6. On the number line (scale) $x = +3$ is a point and $x = -4$ is a point, and so on. Written as coordinates these are generally written $(+3)$ and (-4).

Write the following as coordinates:

(a) $x = +1$ (b) $x = +5$ (c) $x = -7$ (d) $x = -\frac{1}{4}$

(e) $x = +4\frac{1}{2}$ (f) $x = -8\frac{3}{4}$ (g) $x = +23$ (h) $x = a$

*7. If $x = +4$ is a point on the line, $x > +4$ means all the points, but not including $+4$, to the right of $+4$. The following drawing shows this algebraic statement expressed geometrically:

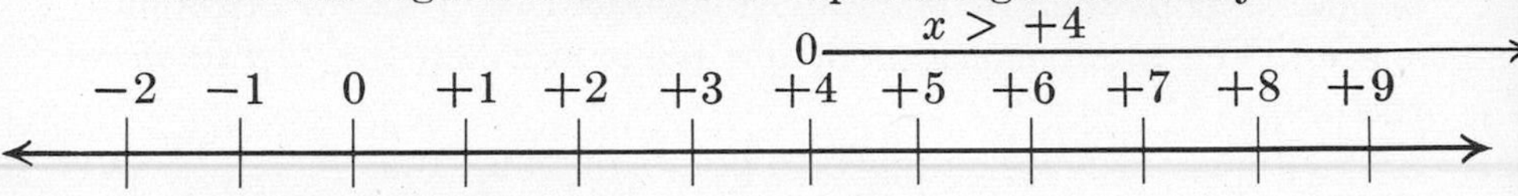

This is called a half-line.

Make a similar drawing for (a) $x > +4$; (b) $x > 0$; (c) $x > -3$; (d) $x < +5$; (e) $x < -2$.

*8. The expression $+4 < x < +6$ is read "x is greater than $+4$ and less than $+6$." A geometric drawing for this algebraic statement would be:

$+4 < x < +6$

0 0

−2 −1 0 +1 +2 +3 +4 +5 +6 +7

Make a similar drawing for:

(a) $+3 < x < +8$ (b) $-1 < x < +5$

(c) $-5 < x < +2$ (d) $0 > x > -4$

(e) $+6 > x > -2$

*9. In Exercises 7 and 8 above, the end points were not included in the half-line or line segment. These points can be included by writing $+4 \leq x \leq +6$. This is read "x is equal to or greater than $+4$ and equal to or less than $+6$."

Write algebraic expressions for and make geometric drawings for:

(a) x is equal to or greater than $+5$ and equal to or less than $+10$.

(b) x is equal to or greater than -1 and equal to or less than $+4$.

(c) x is equal to or greater than -8 and equal to or less than 0.

(d) x is equal to or less than 0.

(e) x is equal to or greater than 0.

(f) x is less than -4 and greater than -10.

(g) x is equal to or greater than -3.

(h) x is 4 units to the left of 0.

(i) x is equal to $+15$.

Quick Quiz No. 33

1. Which is larger?
   (a) 0.5 or 0.005 (b) 0.25 or 0.249
2. Arrange in order of size, beginning with the smallest:
   1.1, 0.2, 0.01, 1, 0.99.
3. Correct any errors:
   (a) $\frac{1}{4} = 0.25$ (b) $\frac{1}{8} = 0.375$ (c) $\frac{3}{4} = 0.75$ (d) $\frac{1}{5} = 0.30$
4. What is the value of the underlined digit?
   $27.076\underline{3}1$
5. $9.0 + 0.3 + 26.6 + 7.0 = ?$
6. $700 - 1.25 = ?$
7. $4.93 \times 1.25 = ?$
8. Divide to nearest hundredth:
   $5.4\overline{)0.442}$
9. A fast train traveled 78.2 miles in 68 minutes; how many miles is this per minute?
10. A plane climbed 25,000 feet in 12.4 minutes. How many feet per minute did this average? (To nearest tenth of a foot.)

Lines in a Plane

In order to associate points in the plane with numbers, two lines perpendicular to each other will be used. The figure below shows the required sketch for the method we will use. The two lines are marked x and y (or xx' and yy'). The vertical line is called the y-axis (yy') and the horizontal line is called the x-axis (xx').

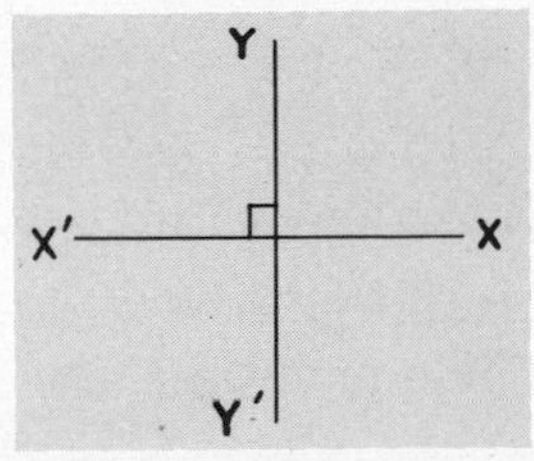

All points in the plane one unit to the right of the line which we call the y-axis are described by the equation $x = +1$. You will recall that in one dimension (that is, on one line) $x = +1$ was a point. However, in two dimensions (that is, on a plane) $x = +1$ is a line. This is reasonable if we think of all the points in the plane which are one unit to the right of the y-axis. There are an unlimited number of points which qualify and the set of them is called a line. Therefore, $x = +2$ would be a line parallel to the y-axis and 2 units to the right of it. Also, $x = -1$ would be a line parallel to the y-axis and one unit to the left of it, and $x = -4$ would be a line parallel to the y-axis and 3 units to the left of it.

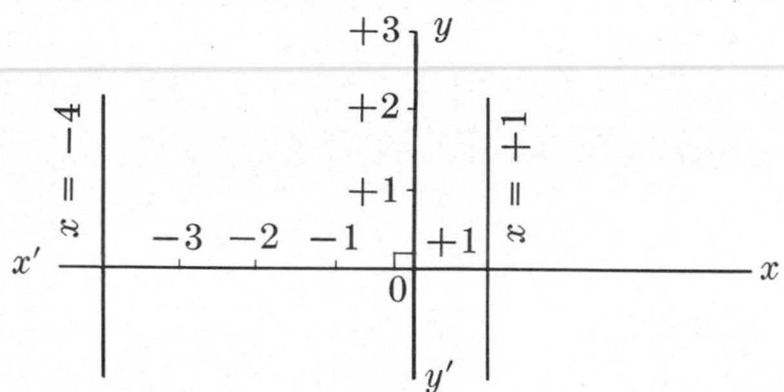

Lines in the plane above and below the x-axis (xx') and parallel to it may be designated by equations. $y = +1$ is a line parallel to x (xx') and one unit above the x-axis. This equation represents all the points in the plane which are one unit above the x-axis and, therefore, is the equation of a line.

EXERCISES

1. Draw two number lines represented by perpendicular axes as in the figure above.
2. Draw and label the following lines in the plane (a) $x = +1$; (b) $x = +2$; (c) $x = +3$; (d) $x = +5$; (e) $x = -1$; (f) $x = -4$; and (g) $x = -5$.
3. Draw and label the lines (a) $y = +1$; (b) $y = +3$; (c) $y = +5$; (d) $y = -1$; (e) $y = -2$; and (f) $y = -6$.
4. What is the line $y = 0$?
5. What is the line $x = 0$?
6. At what point does the line $x = +4$ intersect the x-axis? What relationship does this line have to the y-axis?
7. At what point does the line $y = +3$ intersect the y-axis? What relationship does the line have to the x-axis?

8. How are lines $x = +4$ and $x = -2$ related to each other?

9. How are lines $y = +5$ and $x = +6$ related to each other?

10. How does a road map use lines to establish positions?

*11. Since $x = +4$ is an algebraic way to express a line in a plane (two dimensions), $x > +4$ would represent an unlimited number of parallel lines from $x = +4$ (not including +4) to the right. Geometrically, this would look like the following sketch and would be a half-plane starting from $x = +4$ and extending to the right indefinitely.

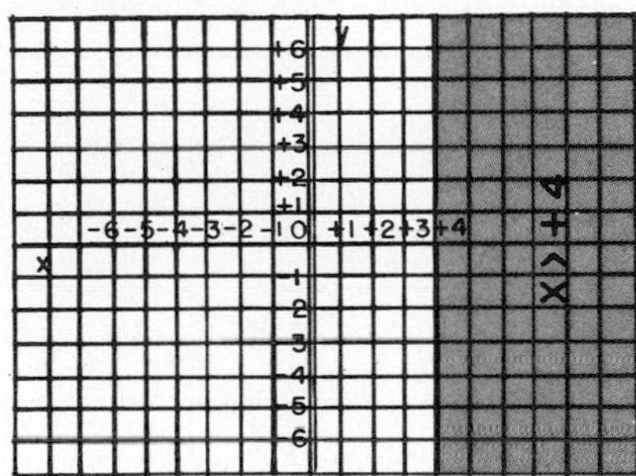

Sketch the following in a plane:

(a) $x > +3$ (b) $x > +7$ (c) $x > -3$

(d) $x < +4$ (e) $x < -3$

*12. The algebraic expression $+4 \leq x \leq +6$ in a plane (two dimensions) geometrically would be:

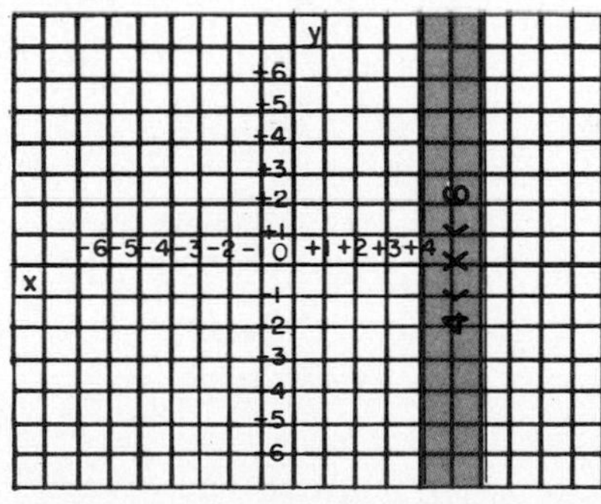

Sketch the following: (a) $+3 \leq x \leq +5$; (b) $-2 \leq x \leq +1$.

*13. Sketch in a plane: (a) $y = +4$; (b) $y > +4$; (c) $y < -3$.

Example: Make a sketch in the plane of the expressions $x > +3$ and $y > +2$.

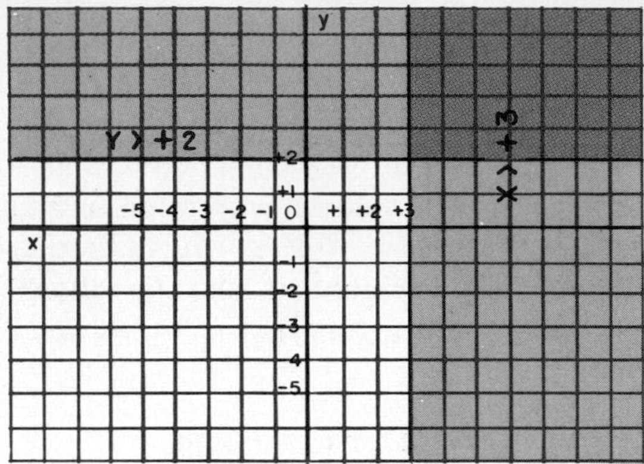

*14. (a) Make a sketch in the plane of $x > +2$, and $y > -1$.

(b) Make a sketch in the plane of $+2 < x < +4$ and $+3 < y < +4$.

*15. Make a sketch in the plane of $-3 < x < 0$ and $-2 < y < +3$.

Assigning Numbers to Points on the Plane

In a plane a point may be established by intersecting lines. The lines $x = -4$ and $y = +3$ intersect at one and only one point. Instead of writing both equations for the point it is labeled $(-4, +3)$. This point is 4 units to the left of the y-axis and 3 units above the x-axis. The lines $x = -6$ and $y = -3$ intersect at a point labeled $(-6, -3)$. The first number, -6, tells that the point is 6 units to the left of the y-axis and the -3 tells that the point is 3 units below the x-axis. The figure shows these two points, $(-4, +3)$ and $(-6, -3)$. $(-4, +3)$ and $(-6, -3)$ are called *ordered number pairs*. The first number of the pair is called the *abscissa*. The abscissa tells where the point is in relation to the y-axis. The second number of the pair is the *ordinate*. The ordinate tells where the point is in relation to the x-axis. The abscissa and ordinate together are also called coordinates of a point in a plane. In this system a pair of numbers is assigned to each point in the plane. This is an example of one-to-one correspondence since every point in the plane is assigned coordinates and every pair of coordinates is assigned to a point in the plane.

Example—Sketch the x- and y-axes and locate the points $(-4, +3)$ and $(-6, -3)$.

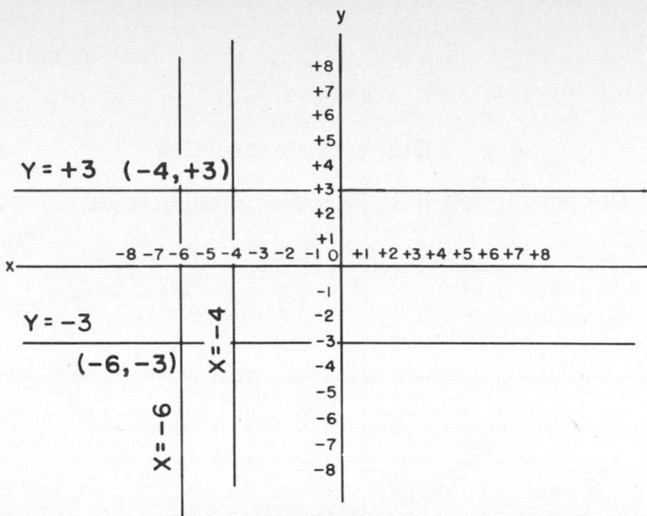

EXERCISES—Sketch the x- and y-axes and plot the following points.

1. (a) $(+3,+4)$; (b) $(+4,+2)$; (c) $(+4,+1)$; (d) $(+2,0)$.
2. (a) $(-3,+2)$; (b) $(+2,-4)$; (c) $(-1,0)$; (d) $(+4,-1)$.
3. (a) $(-2,-3)$; (b) $(0,-3)$; (c) $(-3,-3)$; (d) $(+4,-5)$.

In Exercises 4 through 6 join the points in succession and identify the figure.

4. $(0,0)$, $(+4,0)$, and $(+2,+3)$.
5. $(0,+1)$, $(+4,+1)$, $(+4,-3)$, and $(0,-3)$.
6. $(-3,0)$, $(0,+3)$, $(+3,0)$, and $(0,-3)$.
7. Write the coordinates of each point in the sketch.

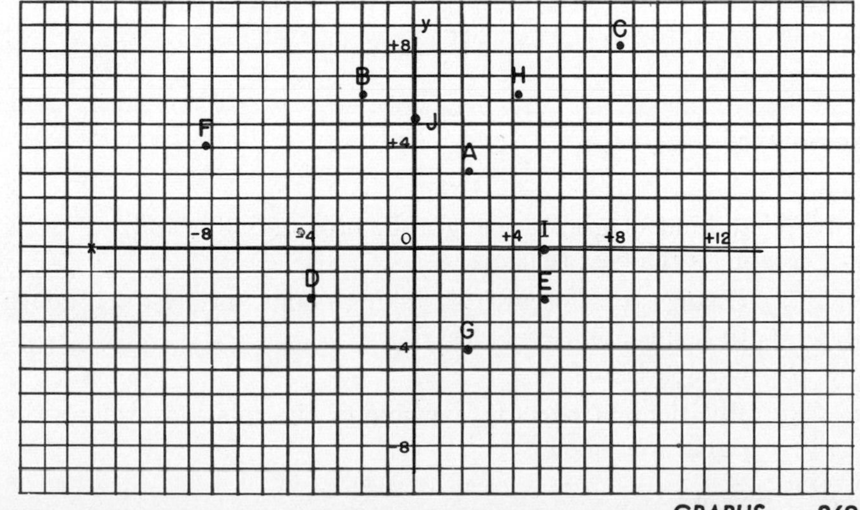

*8. Make a design on a pair of axes using line segments and label each point with coordinates.

Quick Quiz No. 34

Find the perimeters and the areas of each of these figures:

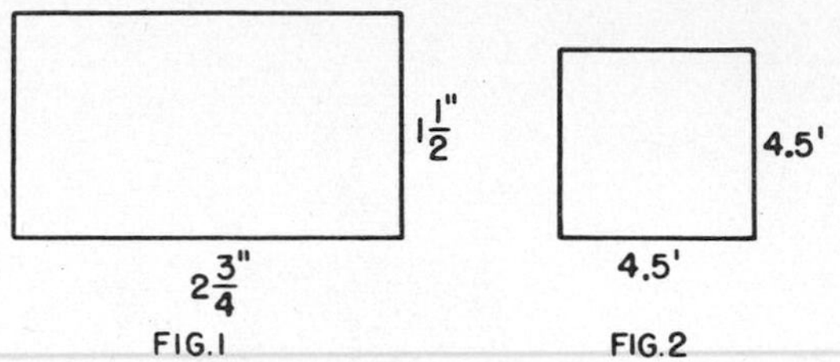

FIG. 1 FIG. 2

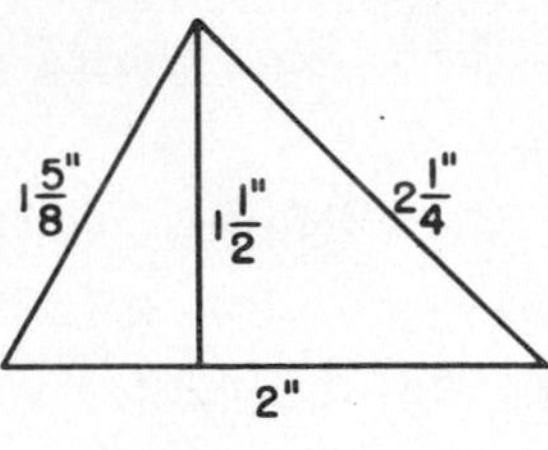

FIG. 3

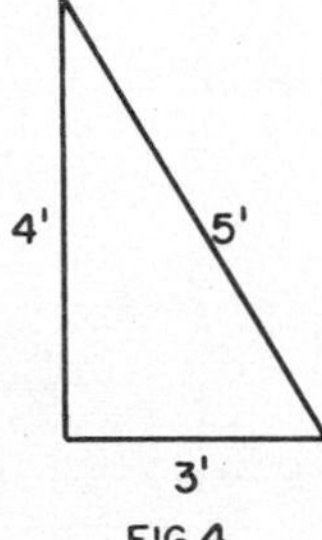

FIG. 4

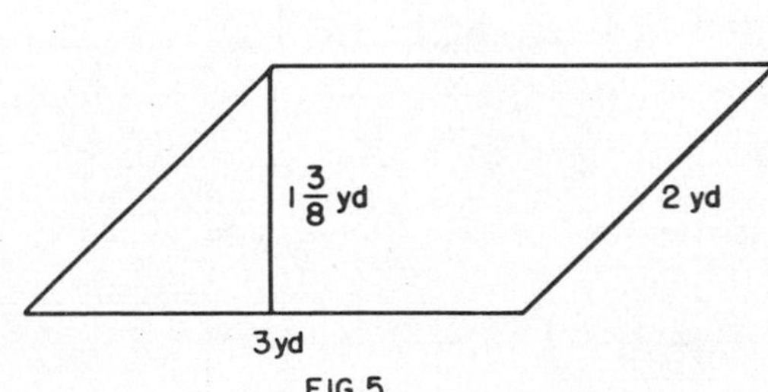

FIG. 5

Review of . . .

GRAPHS

1. What kind of graph, bar graph, broken-line graph, or circle graph, is the best to show:
   (a) Changes that occur from hour to hour, day to day, month to month, or year to year?
   (b) Comparisons?
   (c) Relations of parts to a whole or the relations among the parts of a whole?

2. Answer these questions about the graph below:
   (a) What kind of graph is this graph?
   (b) What story does this graph tell?
   (c) What is the unit on the horizontal scale?
   (d) How many pupils belong to each club?

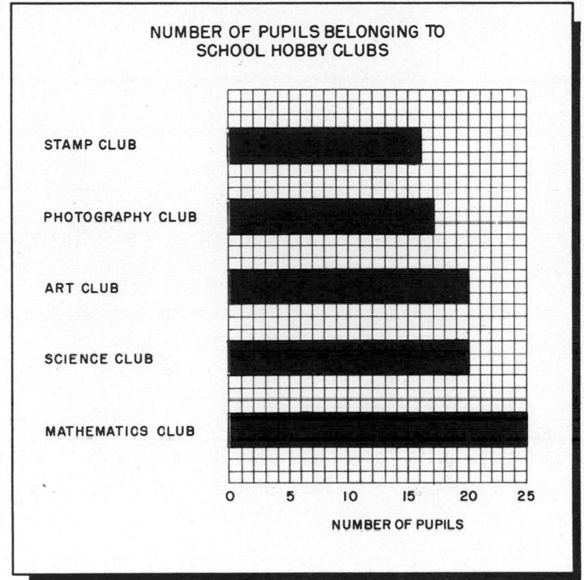

3. Compare the number belonging to the mathematics club with the number belonging to each of the other clubs.

4. Make a broken-line graph to show Barbara Sonen's record on Quick Quizzes 1 to 9.

Number of Exercise	1	2	3	4	5	6	7	8	9
Score	5	6	6	7	7	7	6	8	9

5. Make a circle graph to show how Robert Kirk spent his allowance.

Expenditures	Lunches	School Supplies	Amusements	Church
Per cent spent	70%	5%	15%	10%

6. Name the coordinates of the points in the figure below:

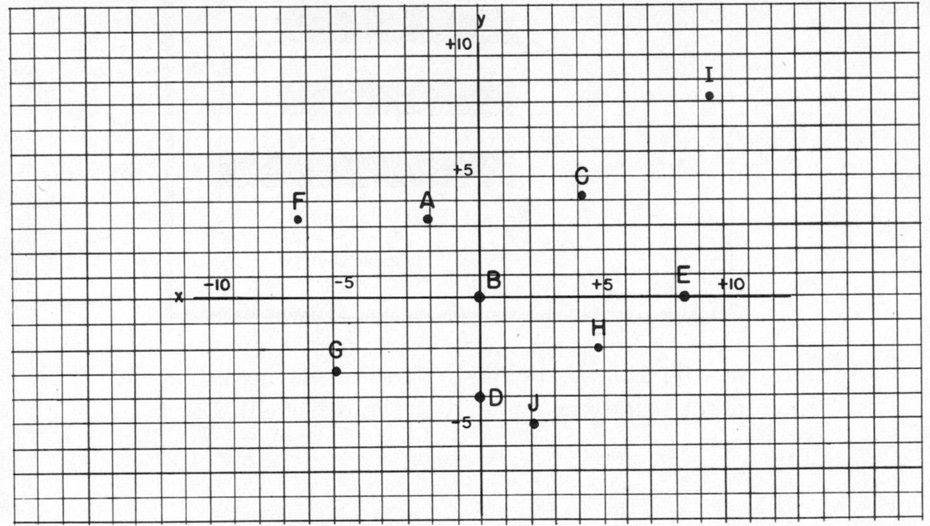

7. Plot the following number pairs with reference to an x- and y-axis and join them in succession: $(-4,+4)$, $(0,+2)$, $(+4,+4)$, $(+2,0)$, $(+4,-4)$, $(0,-2)$, $(-4,-4)$ and $(-2,0)$.

8. Find the distance between the following pairs of points:
   (a) $(+5)$ and $(+14)$ (b) (-4) and $(+6)$
   (c) (-12) and (-6) (d) (-8) and (0)

*9. Sketch the following algebraic expressions in one dimension:
   (a) $x = +3$ (b) $x > -2$
   (c) $x > -4$ (d) $+4 \leq x \leq +8$
   (e) $-2 \leq x \leq +6$ (f) $-1 \geq x \geq -5$

*10. Sketch the following algebraic expressions in two dimensions:

(a) $x = +2$ (b) $y = -3$

(c) $x = -1, x = +3$ (d) $x > +2$

(e) $y > +4$ (f) $x < -4$

(g) $+3 \leq x \leq +7$ (h) $-\frac{1}{2} \leq x \leq 0$

(j) $-1 \leq y \leq +1$

Chapter Test

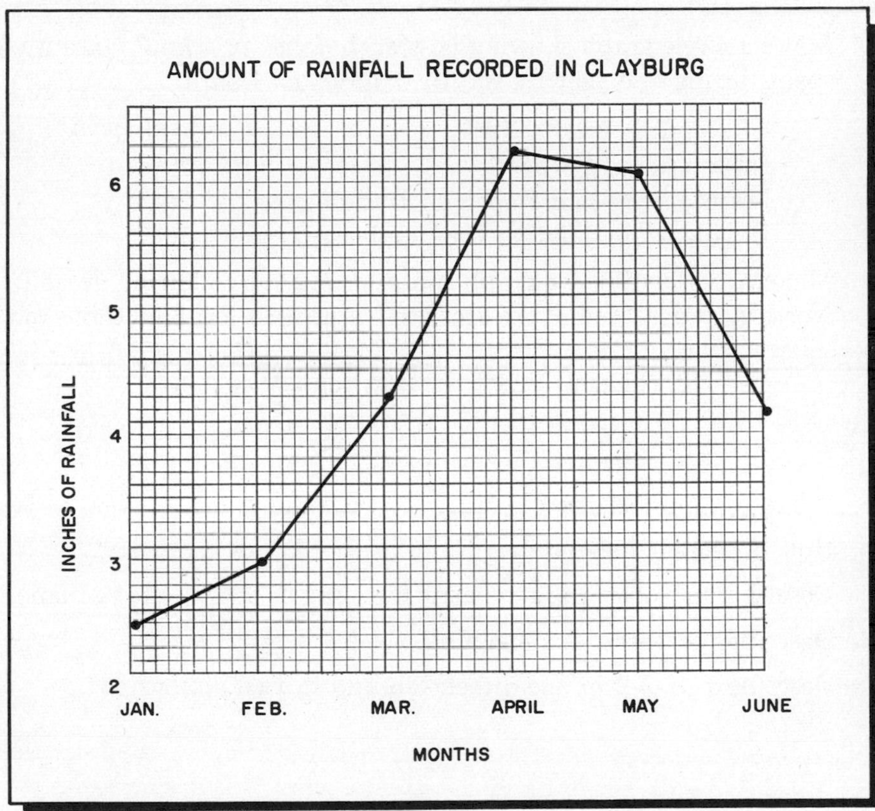

1. Answer these questions about the graph above:
   (a) What kind of graph is this?
   (b) What story does this graph tell?
   (c) What is the unit on the horizontal scale?
   (d) What is the unit on the vertical scale?
   (e) How many inches of rainfall were recorded for each month?
   (f) What month received the greatest amount of rainfall?

(g) What month received the least amount of rainfall?

(h) How did the amount of rainfall in April compare with the amount in June?

2. Make a vertical bar graph to show the amount of waste paper collected by each row in Room 10 for the Junior Red Cross fund.

Row	1	2	3	4	5	6
Weight of Paper	200 lb.	140 lb.	250 lb.	110 lb.	100 lb.	210 lb.

3. Make a circle graph showing how each dollar of school taxes was spent during one year by the Bristol School Board.

Expenditure	*Per Cent spent*
Instructional Purposes	70%
Maintenance and Repair of Buildings	20%
Payment on Building Indebtedness	10%

4. Make a horizontal bar graph representing the following areas in North America. Round the areas to the nearest hundred thousand square miles.

Mexico	760,290 sq. mi.
United States	3,608,787 sq. mi.
Canada	3,849,997 sq. mi.

5. What is a number line?

6. How is a point located in a plane in coordinate geometry?

7. Describe, in words, the geometric meaning of $x = +4$ for a plane.

8. Describe, in words, the meaning of $(+3, +4)$.

9. Describe $x > +2$ in one dimension and in two dimensions.

CHAPTER SIXTEEN    

Estimating and Central Tendency

Estimating Sums and Products

In many exercises in this course, you have been asked to estimate answers. Sometimes an estimate is all that is needed in a problem situation. It will be useful to be able to estimate a sum or product quickly. It is always good to know if an answer is reasonable and an estimate always serves as a check of the reasonableness of a result. In this chapter we will place emphasis on learning to make good estimates for computations.

Suppose a man knows he has a balance of \$214.35 in his checking account. In order to pay his bills he needs to write checks in the following amounts: \$19.25, \$49.00, \$1.98, \$65.63, \$18.25, and \$21.75. If he thought "$20 + 50 + 2 + 70 + 20 + 20 = 182$," he would know that he could pay his bills and not overdraw his account. An estimate of a sum gives him the answer to an important question.

Or suppose you were dividing fractions like $2\frac{1}{2} \div 1\frac{1}{2}$. You can see that the quotient is between 1 and 2. If in actually doing the work your answer was not between 1 and 2, you would know from your estimate that you made an error.

Interior of IBM's System 360 computer. This magnetic "memory" has a billion character storage capacity with arithmetical and logical processing ability.

EXERCISES

In all of the following exercises, estimate the answer. Carry out the computation upon direction of your teacher.

In Exercises 1 through 10 find the sums:

1. $1492 + 2036 + 897 + 463 + 513$
2. $86 + 94 + 15 + 19 + 48 + 73 + 89 + 38$
3. $99 + 199 + 299 + 399 + 499 + 599$
4. Of all multiples of 5 between 44 and 99. Hint: $45 + 50 + 55$, and so on.
5. Of the first 30 even numbers.
6. $4{,}347{,}617 + 1{,}299{,}083 + 3{,}567{,}999$
7. $2\frac{3}{4} + 3\frac{1}{2} + 1\frac{3}{4} + 7\frac{3}{4}$
8. $1.03 + 8.16 + 7.89 + 9.86 + 2.06$
9. $367 + 478 + 589 + 690 + 701 + 812 + 923$
10. $5\frac{1}{4} + 6\frac{1}{2} + 7\frac{1}{4} + 8\frac{1}{2} + 9\frac{1}{4} + 10\frac{1}{2}$

In Exercises 11 through 20 find the products:

11. 413×311
12. $1\frac{3}{4} \times 2\frac{1}{2}$
13. 9.7×8.14
14. 0.813×0.00764
15. $\frac{3}{4} \times \frac{7}{8} \times \frac{6}{7}$
16. $4\frac{2}{3} \times 6\frac{3}{4}$
17. 3096×463
18. $33\frac{1}{3} \times 66\frac{2}{3}$
19. $5\frac{1}{4} \times 6\frac{1}{3} \times \frac{7}{8}$
20. $49 \times 39 \times 29$

In Exercises 21 through 30 perform the indicated operations:

21. $1{,}000{,}000 - 69{,}396$

22. $456 + 345 - 277$

23. $\frac{1}{2} + \frac{1}{3} + \frac{1}{4}$

24. $23\frac{1}{2} - 19\frac{3}{4}$

25. $468 \div 23$

26. $0.693 \div 3.6$

27. $1\frac{3}{4} \times 5\frac{1}{6}$

28. $4\frac{3}{4} \div 1\frac{1}{2}$

29. $11.09 - 7.96 - 2.63$

30. $4\frac{1}{2} + 5.4 + 6\frac{1}{3} + 11.05$

Estimating with Per Cents

In Chapter 11 we studied the fractional equivalents of certain per cents. Some of these were:

$50\% = \frac{1}{2}$ $\quad 25\% = \frac{1}{4}$ $\quad 75\% = \frac{3}{4}$ $\quad 33\frac{1}{3}\% = \frac{1}{3}$ $\quad 12\frac{1}{2}\% = \frac{1}{8}$

These equivalents can be very useful in estimating answers involving per cents, as well as also being useful in actual computation.

Example 1.

Find 75% of 483.
Since $\frac{3}{4}$ of 480 is 360, 75% of 483 is a little more than 360. $483 \times 0.75 = 362.25$.
One might also observe that $\frac{3}{4}$ of $3 = \frac{9}{4} = 2\frac{1}{4}$.
Using the distributive principle, we see that

$$0.75 \times 483 = 0.75\,(480 + 3) = 360 + 2\tfrac{1}{4} = 362.25.$$

Example 2.

What per cent of 92 is 12?
We know that $\frac{12}{96} = \frac{1}{8}$, and since $\frac{1}{8} = 12\frac{1}{2}\%$, we estimate that 12 is a little more than $12\frac{1}{2}\%$ of 92. We say a "little more" because 12 is a larger part of 92 than it is of 96.
Dividing 12 by 92 we find 0.130, correct to thousandths. 13.0% compares favorably with our estimate.

EXERCISES

In Exercises 1 through 15 give the results at sight:

1. $33\frac{1}{3}\%$ of 300

2. $12\frac{1}{2}\%$ of 88

3. 25% of 4040

4. 75% of 360

5. $66\frac{2}{3}\%$ of 30,000

6. 6 is what per cent of 12?

7. 8 is what per cent of 80?

8. 100 is what per cent of 300?

9. 19 is what per cent of 38?

10. 100 is what per cent of 50?

11. 300 is what per cent of 60?

12. 2 is what per cent of 200?

13. $\frac{1}{2}$ is what per cent of 100?

14. $37\frac{1}{2}$ is what per cent of 80?

15. $62\frac{1}{2}$ is what per cent of 75?

16. A boy saves 15% of his earnings. If he earns $164 during the month of July, what did he save that month?

17. Mr. Jones makes a commission of 8% on all sales. In January his sales totaled $1200, for February, $1500, and for March, $1624. What was his commission for the three months?

18. Four per cent interest is paid on a loan of $410. What is the interest on this loan for $1\frac{1}{2}$ years?

19. The enrollment in Benton Junior High School is 75 more than last year. If the enrollment this year is 915, what was the per cent of gain over last year?

20. Arthur is 5 feet 10 inches tall today. Last year his height was 5 feet 7 inches. What was the per cent gain in his height?

21. Increase 500 by 13%, and decrease the result by 15%.

22. A state income tax is 1% of the first $1000 of net income; $1\frac{1}{4}$% of the next $1000; $1\frac{1}{2}$% of the next $1000; and 2% of all income over $3000. What is the income tax on $6735 in that state?

23. In Springfield, property is assessed at 60% of its market value. The Joseph property is assessed at $10,000. What is the market value of the Joseph property?

24. The sales tax in a certain state is $2\frac{1}{2}$%, but there is no sales tax on food. In a store the clerk is given a twenty-dollar bill to pay for the following items: meat, $1.50; soap, 75 cents; canned fruit, $1.48; paper towels, $1.25; cleaning fluid, $2.10. What will the change be?

25. It is estimated that the population of Roseville will increase 10% each year for the next five years. Today the population is 40,000. What is the estimated population for five years from today? What per cent of today's population is this estimate?

Averages

Suppose your grades on five tests were 80, 85, 90, 95, and 100. Your average grade would be $\frac{80 + 85 + 90 + 95 + 100}{5} = \frac{450}{5} = 90.$

The *average* of n numbers is the sum of the numbers divided by n. This average is also called the *mean*. See page 129.

An artist's concept of a nuclear rocket missile. Even in such long range rockets as this, mathematics plays a vital part.

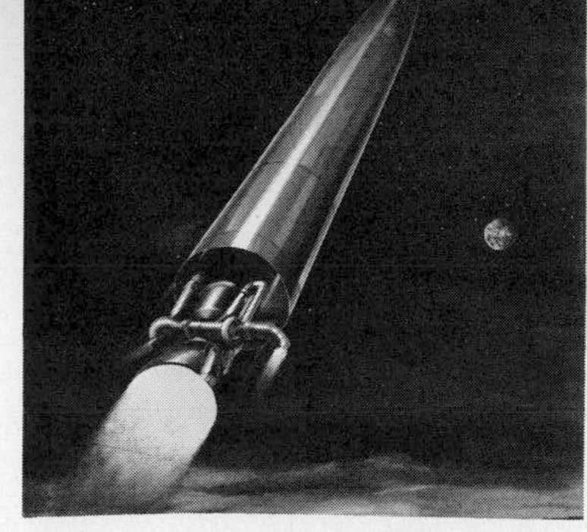

In the above example we could have estimated the average, or mean, by noticing that 90 seems to be about the "middle" grade. We notice that 80 is as much less than 90 as 100 is more than 90, and 85 is as much less than 90 as 95 is more.

Example 1.

Estimate the average of the grades: 70, 78, 80, 80, 82, 83. Then compute the actual average and compare this with your estimate.
Because 70 is quite a bit less than 80, we might estimate the average to be 78 or 79.

The average is $\frac{70 + 78 + 80 + 80 + 82 + 83}{6} = \frac{473}{6} = 78\frac{5}{6}$.

We could have found the average in another way. Suppose we estimated the average to be 80.

$80 - 70 = 10$, and $80 - 78 = 2$ $\qquad 10 + 2 = 12$
$82 - 80 = 2$, and $83 - 80 = 3$ $\qquad 2 + 3 = 5$

We can say the sum of the deviations of the grades less than 80, our estimate, is 12; and we can say the sum of the deviations of the grades greater than 80, our estimate, is 5. Since $12 - 5 = 7$, the average will be $\frac{7}{6}$ less than 80. $80 - \frac{7}{6} = 78\frac{5}{6}$.
In order to understand the meaning of the word "deviation," we should know that this word is correctly used in such expressions as:

The deviation of 21 from 25 is 4.
The deviation of 60 from 50 is 10.
The deviation of $\frac{1}{3}$ from $1\frac{2}{3}$ is $1\frac{1}{3}$.

Example 2.

Estimate the average or the mean of the numbers 4, 7, 10, 11, 13, 25. Then compute the actual average of these numbers.
Because 25 is larger than the other numbers we might estimate the average to be 13.
The sum of the deviations of the numbers less than 13 is $9 + 6 + 3 + 2$ or 20.
The sum of the deviations of the numbers greater than 13 is 12.

The average is less than 13 but not much less.

$$\frac{4 + 7 + 10 + 11 + 13 + 25}{6} = \frac{70}{6} = 11\tfrac{2}{3}.$$

Using the statements above about deviations, we can check the result.

$20 - 12 = 8$. Since there were 6 numbers we divide 8 by 6. Since the sum of the deviations of the smaller numbers was more than that of the larger, we subtract, $13 - \frac{8}{6} = 11\frac{2}{3}$.

Example 3.

Average the whole numbers from 40 to 60 inclusive.

Let us assume the average is 50. The sum of the deviations of numbers less than 50 is

$$1 + 2 + 3 + 4 + 5 + 6 + 7 + 8 + 9 + 10.$$

The sum of deviations of numbers greater than 50 is

$$1 + 2 + 3 + 4 + 5 + 6 + 7 + 8 + 9 + 10.$$

Since the sums are the same, the average is 50.

EXERCISES

In Exercises 1 through 10 estimate the averages of the sets of numbers.

1. 40, 50, 60, 70, 80, 90
2. 1, 2, 3, 4, 5, 6, 7, 8, 9, 10
3. 93, 91, 89, 90, 90, 86, 84, 80
4. 216, 532
5. 199, 299, 399
6. 63, 66, 69, 72, 75, 78, 81, 84
7. 4.3, 4.4, 4.8, 4.7, 4.6, 4.5, 4.5
8. $\frac{1}{3}, \frac{1}{2}, \frac{1}{4}$
9. $1\frac{1}{2}, 2\frac{1}{2}, 3\frac{1}{2}, 4\frac{1}{2}, 5$
10. The whole numbers from 1 to 1000 inclusive. Hint: See the answer to Example 3.

For Exercises 11 through 20, compute the averages of Exercises 1 through 10. In Exercises 11 through 15 use two methods (the definition and deviations).

21. Find the average age of the students in your class. First find the age of each student to the nearest one-half year.
22. Find the average weight of the students in your class.
23. Find the average height of the girls in your class; the average height of the boys; the average height of the whole class.
24. Find the average grade on the last mathematics test given in your class.
25. The annual income of the families in the 1500 block on Q Street in Cedarville is:

$8000—3 families
$9000—4 families
$10,000—2 families
$11,000—2 families
$12,000—3 families
$15,000—1 family
$20,000—1 family

Find the average annual income of families in this block.

Quick Quiz No. 35

An *arithmetic sequence* of numbers is one in which each term may be obtained from the one which precedes it by adding a constant (the same number each time). The following is an arithmetic sequence:

5, 9, 13, 17, 21, 25.

In this sequence, 4 is added to each term to obtain the next term.

In Exercises 1 through 10 write the next two terms of each arithmetic sequence.

1. 4, 9, 14, 19, ____, ____.
2. 23, 34, 45, 56, ____, ____.
3. 312, 435, 558, 681, ____, ____.
4. $\frac{1}{2}$, $\frac{3}{4}$, 1, $\frac{5}{4}$, ____, ____.
5. 1.8, 2.6, 3.4, 4.2, ____, ____.
6. 0.08, 1.08, 2.08, 3.08, ____, ____.
7. 10%, $\frac{1}{4}$, 40%, 0.55, ____, ____.
8. 479, 580, 681, 782, ____, ____.
9. $\frac{7}{4}$, $\frac{25}{12}$, $\frac{29}{12}$, $\frac{11}{4}$, ____, ____.
10. -4, -2, 0, 2, ____, ____.

Other Measures of Central Tendency

The average or mean of a set of numbers is called a measure of *central tendency*. This term seems to be a good choice for in a sense the average is a number which is "central" in the set (from the point of view of deviations). The sum of the deviations of numbers less than the mean is equal to the sum of the deviations of the numbers greater than the mean.

Another commonly used measure of central tendency is the *median*. The median is the "central number" in a set when numbers are arranged in order of size.

Example 1.

Find the median of the set of numbers:

$$4, 10, 17, 83, 0, 6, 5, 51, 43$$

In order these numbers are: 0, 4, 5, 6, 10, 17, 43, 51, 83.
The median is 10. Would 10 be a reasonable estimate of the average of these numbers? Why not?

In Example 1, there is an odd number of numbers in the set. If there were an even number of numbers in the set, there would be no middle or "central" number. It is usually customary in sets with an even number of numbers to call the average of the two middle numbers the median.

Example 2.

Find the median of the set of 20 integers beginning in order with 107.

In a set of 20 numbers, the tenth and eleventh numbers are the two middle numbers. In this set the tenth number is 116 and the eleventh number is 117.

$$\frac{116 + 117}{2} = 116.5$$

The median is 116.5.

A third measure of central tendency is called the *mode*. The mode of a set is the member which occurs most frequently in the set. None of the sets considered so far in this section has a mode. In these examples each number in the set occurs only once in the set.

Example 3.

Find the mode of the set of numbers:

$$14, 15, 16, 16, 16, 17, 18, 18, 19, 50.$$

The mode is 16, since 16 appears three times in the set, and no other number appears more than twice.

Example 4.

Find the mean and the median of the set of numbers in Example 3.

Mean: Estimate 20

Sum of deviations of numbers less than 20:

$$6 + 5 + 4 + 4 + 4 + 3 + 2 + 2 + 1 = 31$$

Sum of deviations of numbers greater than 20: 30.

The mean is $20 - \dfrac{(31 - 30)}{10} = 19.9.$

Median: The fifth number in the set is 16.
The sixth number in the set is 17.
The median is 16.5.

The set of numbers in Example 3 was chosen so that the mean, the median, and the mode would all be different. Sometimes one of these measures of central tendency is better to use than another. We might observe that the mode does not have much significance unless there is a large number of items in the set and the more frequently occurring items are around the middle in order of size. If a teacher grades on the so-called "normal curve" she would give more C's than A's, B's, D's, or E's. The C-grade would be the mode. If there were about the same number of A's and B's as there are of D's and E's, the mode would have meaning in this kind of distribution as a measure of central tendency.

In Example 3, one number was much larger than any of the others and hence the mean is not a very good measure of central tendency in this case. The median gives a better indication of central tendency in this example. Suppose the median of a set of class grades is given. Your grade is the same as the median. You then know that there are as many students with a grade lower than yours as there are students with a grade higher than yours. In this case we can say the median is a satisfactory measure of central tendency.

EXERCISES

In Exercises 1 through 10 find the mean, median, and mode (if it exists) of the sets of numbers.

1. 10, 20, 30, 40, 50, 60, 70, 80, 90, 90, 100
2. 2, 5, 8, 11, 14, 17, 20
3. 3, 3, 3, 4, 5, 6, 6, 7, 8, 8
4. 1.1, 2.3, 4.5, 6.7, 8.9, 11.9, 13.9
5. 1309, 1310, 1311, 1414, 1415, 1419, 1410, 1310

6. $\frac{1}{2}, \frac{2}{3}, \frac{3}{4}, \frac{5}{6}, \frac{6}{7}$

7. The multiples of 5 less than 100.

8. The multiples of 7 between 50 and 100.

9. The two-digit whole numbers with unit digit 4.

10. $1\frac{3}{4}, 2\frac{1}{4}, 3\frac{3}{4}, \frac{7}{4}, 3\frac{1}{2}, 5\frac{1}{4}$, 1.75, 2.25

11. Find the mean and the mode of the ages of the students in your class.

12. Find the mean and the mode of the weights of the students in your class.

13. Find the mean and the mode of the grades on the last test in your class.

14. Supply a missing number so that the mean of the set will be 15:

    5, 10, 10, 12, 15, 16, 17, 18, 24, ____.

15. Find the median and the mode of the set of numbers in Exercise 14.

16. Will the set of numbers made up of the populations of the 50 states have a mode? Will the mean or the median be larger for this set of numbers?

17. Answer the questions in Exercise 16 using the set of numbers made up of the areas in square miles of the 50 states.

18. The *third quartile* of a set of numbers is a number such that $\frac{1}{4}$ of the numbers are greater than the third quartile and $\frac{3}{4}$ are less. What is the third quartile of the first 24 whole numbers? Ans. 18.5. In this case, many other numbers besides 18.5 would satisfy the definition.

19. Find the third quartile of the set of numbers:

    10, 40, 33, 36, 71, 82, 94, 107, 62, 93, 8, 14, 17.5, 50, 60, 70

20. Find the first quartile of the set of numbers in Exercise 19.

21. Find the mean and median of the set of numbers in Exercise 19.

Computation with Approximate Numbers

We have learned that all measures are approximate. When we say that a length is 15 inches, we mean that it is nearer 15 inches than it is 14 inches or 16 inches. We might say that the length is between 14.5 inches and 15.5 inches. Similarly, if we say that the

The Gemini Spacecraft I is wheeled out of work stand at Cape Kennedy, Florida. Mathematics is one of the basic elements in our space program.

population of a certain town is 13,500 to the nearest one hundred we know that the population is somewhere between 13,450 and 13,550.

When we compute with approximate numbers it is well to observe the effect of the approximate nature of measurement.

Example 1.

(a) Add the approximate numbers, expressed to the nearest tenth of a unit:

19.5; 20.2; 36.4; 41.1; 88.0; 106.5

(b) Use the "lower limit" of each number and find the sum.

(c) Use the "upper limit" of each number and find the sum.

(d) Compare the results of (a), (b), and (c) and state a conclusion.

(a)	(b)	(c)
19.5	19.45	19.55
20.2	20.15	20.25
36.4	36.35	36.45
41.1	41.05	41.15
88.0	87.95	88.05
106.5	106.45	106.55
311.7	311.40	312.00

Notice that the approximate number 19.5 represents a measurement between 19.45 and 19.55 units and that 20.2 represents a measurement between 20.15 and 20.25 units.

You probably see a shorter way in which the sums of (b) and (c) could have been obtained.

(d) The sum of the measurements given by the approximate numbers is somewhere between 311.4 and 312.0.

Multiplication of numbers representing measurements may give us a product which appears to be much more accurate than it actually is. This is shown in Example 2.

Example 2.

Find the area of a rectangle if the sides are found to be 15 and 23 inches respectively to the nearest inch. What error in the product may be due to the approximate nature of the measurement?

$$15 \times 23 = 345$$

$$14.5 \times 22.5 = 326.25$$

$$15.5 \times 23.5 = 364.25$$

Due to the approximate nature of the measurements the true area is somewhere between 326.25 and 364.25 square inches.

In each part of this chapter we have been concerned with estimating. Estimating may come into the work of this section in two ways. The sum or product of a number obtained by measurement is a kind of estimate (a reasonably close one) of the actual sum or product of the measures.

We can estimate the possible error in a product of numbers found by measurement. This is illustrated by Example 3.

Example 3.

An automobile is driven 42 miles an hour for 2.5 hours. The rate is expressed to the nearest mile per hour and the time to the nearest half hour. Estimate the possible error in the distance travelled, using these measurements.

$$42 \times 2.5 = 105$$

Using these measurements, the distance travelled is 105 miles. Since the rate is between 41.5 and 42.5 miles per hour, and the time is between 2.25 and 2.75 hours, the distance travelled is between 41.5×2.25 and 42.5×2.75 miles. We can estimate the possible error to be $0.5 \times 2.5 + 0.25 \times 42$. This is $1.25 + 10.5 = 11.75$. This estimate is based on the product

$$(42 + 0.5)\ (2.5 + 0.25).$$

Do you see why this provides a good estimate?

EXERCISES

1. If measurements are recorded to the number of units given below, between what numbers do the true measurements lie?

   (a) 47 (b) 1356 (c) 0.56 (d) 0.4

   (e) 23.478 (f) $3\frac{3}{4}$ (g) 4.0 (h) 0.019

2. What is the difference in meaning between a measurement of 4 inches and a measurement of 4.0 inches?
3. Compare the products: (45) (31) (44.5) (30.5) (45.5) (31.5)
4. The populations of 5 towns to the nearest 50 people are 950, 1100, 800, 1450, and 2350.
   Find the sum of these numbers. Between what two limits do the actual populations lie?
5. Find the areas of the triangle with altitude and base given.
   (a) h = 5 in., b = 10 in.
   (b) h = 2 ft., b = 4 ft.
   (c) h = 1.3 cm., b = 3.7 cm.
6. Between what two limits does each of the areas in Exercise 5 lie?

Review of . . .

ESTIMATING and CENTRAL TENDENCY

1. Estimate the answers to the nearest 10:
   (a) $423 + 589 + 699 + 877$ (b) $3701 - 1945$
   (c) 63×99 (d) $5624 \div 81$
   (e) 40% of 1100 (f) 150% of 75
   (g) $\frac{1}{2}$% of 444 (h) $1672 + 495 - 783$
   (i) $(\frac{3}{4})(48)(\frac{7}{8})(2\frac{1}{2})$
2. Find the mean and median of the following numbers:

   81, 85, 89, 93, 97, 101, 105
3. Find the appropriate number so that the mean and the median of the set of numbers are the same:

   6, 7, 8, 9, 10, 11, 12, 13, ____.
4. In Butler Junior High School, the ages of students to the nearest year are:

Age	*Number of Students*
10	2
11	15
12	406
13	450
14	410
15	30
16	3

What is the modal age, or mode of this distribution?

*5. Find the mean age of students in Butler Junior High School from the data given in Exercise 4.

6. If the mean is much greater than the median, what would you conclude about a set of data?

7. If your test score is above the median in the class would your grade also be above the mode or the mean? Why?

8. State in your own words the meaning of "central tendency."

9. If a measurement is recorded as 1353 feet, between what two actual lengths does the measurement lie?

10. Would the numbers 13 and 13.0 ever have different meanings?

11. Find the means of the following:
   (a) Whole numbers from 10 to 49 inclusive.
   (b) The multiples of 7 less than 100.
   (c) $\frac{1}{4}, \frac{1}{5}, \frac{1}{6}, \frac{1}{7}, \frac{1}{8}$.

12. Find the medians of the sets of numbers in Exercise 11.

Chapter Test

1. Estimate the product to the nearest 100: (42) (35) (89).

2. Estimate the quotient to the nearest 10: 6046 $\div$ 374.

3. Estimate what per cent 671 is of 932 to the nearest 5%.

4. Find the mean of the following set of numbers:

   41, 47, 51, 52, 53, 54, 70

5. What is the median of the set of all three-digit numbers ending in 0?

6. Consider the collection of numbers made up of the following three sets:

   Set A: even numbers less than 100
   Set B: multiples of 5 between 55 and 75
   Set C: multiples of 12 less than 144

   What is the mode of the collection which includes all numbers in Sets A, B, and C.

7. The length and width of a rectangle are measured to the nearest inch and found to be 5 inches and 4 inches respectively. Considering 5 and 4 to be approximate numbers, between what two areas, in square inches, is the area of the rectangle known to be?

Appendix ● ▲ ■ ⬢

More Addition Practice

Part I.

(1)	(2)	(3)	(4)	(5)
6	9	4	8	6
9	2	5	7	5
1	8	1	3	4
1	1	7	2	3
+4	+5	+3	+9	+2

(6)	(7)	(8)	(9)	(10)
9	8	9	8	9
9	3	6	2	6
2	2	7	5	7
1	1	4	1	5
+4	+5	+3	+4	+1

Part II.

(1)	(2)	(3)	(4)	(5)
24	26	48	49	93
65	46	51	56	84
93	58	63	35	75
+26	+42	+45	+42	+64

(6)	(7)	(8)	(9)	(10)
49	59	65	37	45
54	45	84	43	86
63	86	93	82	72
+51	+21	+22	+98	+94

(11)	(12)	(13)	(14)	(15)
57	89	87	89	86
84	49	93	46	95
63	72	45	57	47
24	65	87	83	36
+28	+85	+29	+96	+84

Reducing Fractions to Lowest Terms

1. $\frac{4}{8} = \frac{4 \div 4}{8 \div 4} = \frac{1}{2}$
2. $\frac{10}{15} = \frac{10 \div 5}{15 \div 5} = \frac{2}{3}$
3. $\frac{14}{21} = \frac{14 \div 7}{21 \div 7} = \frac{2}{3}$

It will sometimes save time to divide both numerator and denominator by the largest number that is contained exactly in both of them. If the numerator and denominator of a fraction are divided by the same number other than zero, the value of the fraction remains the same.

Reduce to lowest terms:

1. $\frac{5}{10}$	2. $\frac{6}{18}$	3. $\frac{8}{24}$	4. $\frac{9}{27}$	5. $\frac{7}{21}$
6. $\frac{10}{12}$	7. $\frac{15}{20}$	8. $\frac{6}{9}$	9. $\frac{14}{16}$	10. $\frac{24}{32}$
11. $\frac{12}{16}$	12. $\frac{7}{14}$	13. $\frac{3}{6}$	14. $\frac{4}{16}$	15. $\frac{4}{8}$
16. $\frac{6}{8}$	17. $\frac{11}{22}$	18. $\frac{21}{42}$	19. $\frac{25}{35}$	20. $\frac{17}{34}$

1. $8\frac{2}{4} = 8\frac{1}{2}$
2. $9\frac{10}{12} = 9\frac{5}{6}$

21. $9\frac{2}{4}$	22. $7\frac{4}{8}$	23. $9\frac{6}{12}$	24. $10\frac{7}{14}$
25. $3\frac{6}{8}$	26. $8\frac{4}{10}$	27. $5\frac{9}{12}$	28. $7\frac{5}{10}$

Improper Fractions and Mixed Numbers

Change to mixed numbers:

1. $\frac{5}{4}$	2. $\frac{7}{6}$	3. $\frac{6}{5}$	4. $\frac{9}{8}$	5. $\frac{7}{5}$
6. $\frac{10}{8}$	7. $\frac{12}{10}$	8. $\frac{14}{12}$	9. $\frac{8}{6}$	10. $\frac{9}{6}$
11. $\frac{13}{6}$	12. $\frac{19}{9}$	13. $\frac{23}{10}$	14. $\frac{29}{12}$	15. $\frac{35}{16}$
16. $\frac{18}{8}$	17. $\frac{14}{6}$	18. $\frac{40}{12}$	19. $\frac{25}{10}$	20. $\frac{54}{16}$

Change the improper fractions:

1. $14\frac{8}{6} = 15\frac{2}{6}$ or $15\frac{1}{3}$
2. $15\frac{15}{12} = 16\frac{3}{12}$ or $16\frac{1}{4}$

1. $10\frac{5}{4}$	2. $11\frac{7}{6}$	3. $12\frac{6}{5}$	4. $20\frac{6}{4}$
5. $11\frac{4}{3}$	6. $12\frac{10}{8}$	7. $10\frac{12}{10}$	8. $14\frac{14}{12}$
9. $9\frac{8}{6}$	10. $9\frac{10}{6}$	11. $7\frac{18}{20}$	12. $9\frac{16}{12}$
13. $18\frac{12}{8}$	14. $20\frac{24}{21}$	15. $7\frac{15}{9}$	16. $6\frac{21}{15}$

Addition of Fractions

Add the numbers in Parts I, II, and III:

Part I.

1. $\frac{1}{2} + \frac{1}{2}$	2. $\frac{1}{8} + \frac{5}{8}$	3. $\frac{4}{7} + \frac{2}{7}$	4. $\frac{2}{9} + \frac{2}{9}$

5. $\begin{array}{r} 2\frac{1}{3} \\ \underline{+1\frac{1}{3}} \end{array}$ 6. $\begin{array}{r} 4\frac{4}{5} \\ \underline{+3\frac{3}{5}} \end{array}$ 7. $\begin{array}{r} 8\frac{4}{9} \\ \underline{+2\frac{7}{9}} \end{array}$ 8. $\begin{array}{r} 5\frac{4}{5} \\ \underline{+3\frac{3}{5}} \end{array}$

9. $\begin{array}{r} 6\frac{1}{2} \\ 4\frac{1}{2} \\ \underline{+3\frac{1}{2}} \end{array}$ 10. $\begin{array}{r} 8\frac{2}{3} \\ 1\frac{1}{3} \\ \underline{+4\frac{2}{3}} \end{array}$ 11. $\begin{array}{r} 6\frac{3}{8} \\ 2\frac{5}{8} \\ \underline{+1\frac{1}{8}} \end{array}$ 12. $\begin{array}{r} 5\frac{11}{16} \\ 3\frac{3}{16} \\ \underline{+4\frac{5}{16}} \end{array}$

Part II.

1. $\begin{array}{r} 8\frac{3}{4} \\ \underline{+4\frac{1}{2}} \end{array}$ 2. $\begin{array}{r} 7\frac{7}{16} \\ \underline{+3\frac{3}{4}} \end{array}$ 3. $\begin{array}{r} 8\frac{3}{8} \\ \underline{+2\frac{3}{4}} \end{array}$ 4. $\begin{array}{r} 9\frac{5}{6} \\ \underline{+3\frac{1}{3}} \end{array}$

5. $\begin{array}{r} 8\frac{8}{9} \\ \underline{+2\frac{1}{3}} \end{array}$ 6. $\begin{array}{r} 7\frac{1}{5} \\ \underline{+3\frac{2}{15}} \end{array}$ 7. $\begin{array}{r} 9\frac{1}{2} \\ \underline{+10\frac{5}{6}} \end{array}$ 8. $\begin{array}{r} 7\frac{1}{3} \\ \underline{+13\frac{7}{12}} \end{array}$

Part III.

$$\begin{array}{rcl} 2\frac{1}{8} & = & 2\frac{3}{24} \\ 3\frac{1}{3} & = & 3\frac{8}{24} \\ 1\frac{1}{2} & = & \underline{1\frac{12}{24}} \\ & & 6\frac{23}{24} \end{array}$$

1. $\begin{array}{r} 3\frac{1}{6} \\ \underline{+4\frac{1}{5}} \end{array}$ 2. $\begin{array}{r} 8\frac{1}{8} \\ \underline{+2\frac{2}{3}} \end{array}$ 3. $\begin{array}{r} 4\frac{1}{2} \\ \underline{+9\frac{1}{7}} \end{array}$ 4. $\begin{array}{r} 8\frac{3}{4} \\ \underline{+2\frac{2}{3}} \end{array}$

5. $\begin{array}{r} 9\frac{1}{3} \\ 2\frac{1}{2} \\ \underline{+1\frac{1}{4}} \end{array}$ 6. $\begin{array}{r} 8\frac{1}{5} \\ 2\frac{1}{3} \\ \underline{+1\frac{1}{4}} \end{array}$ 7. $\begin{array}{r} 7\frac{1}{4} \\ 8\frac{1}{3} \\ \underline{+2\frac{1}{6}} \end{array}$ 8. $\begin{array}{r} 11\frac{1}{16} \\ 3\frac{1}{3} \\ \underline{+\ 1\frac{1}{2}} \end{array}$

Addition of Decimals

Part I.

Add:

1. $\begin{array}{r} 0.4 \\ 0.2 \\ \underline{0.3} \end{array}$ 2. $\begin{array}{r} 0.62 \\ 0.84 \\ \underline{0.35} \end{array}$ 3. $\begin{array}{r} 0.016 \\ 0.216 \\ \underline{0.945} \end{array}$ 4. $\begin{array}{r} 1.26 \\ 2.18 \\ \underline{4.15} \end{array}$ 5. $\begin{array}{r} 0.005 \\ 0.002 \\ \underline{0.009} \end{array}$

6. $\begin{array}{r} 2.75 \\ 1.23 \\ \underline{1.56} \end{array}$ 7. $\begin{array}{r} 0.2164 \\ 0.3172 \\ \underline{1.8176} \end{array}$ 8. $\begin{array}{r} 9.241 \\ 3.862 \\ \underline{8.754} \end{array}$ 9. $\begin{array}{r} 4.4367 \\ 1.2816 \\ \underline{3.1820} \end{array}$ 10. $\begin{array}{r} 12.2675 \\ 12.1672 \\ \underline{13.0072} \end{array}$

Part II.

Find the sum:

1. $0.6 + 0.4 + 0.8 + 0.9$
2. $1.7 + 2.9 + 3.7 + 1.6$
3. $0.29 + 0.76 + 0.07 + 12.$
4. $7.001 + 2.961 + 3.008$
5. $17.25 + 18.75 + 13.75$
6. $0.0124 + 0.0267 + 0.3876$
7. $4.0211 + 3.7762 + 3.8772$
8. $2.00002 + 3.00027 + 4.00472$
9. $65.751 + 100.256 + 0.751$
10. $18 + 7.0002 + 8.21 + 5.5$

Addition of Denominate Numbers

Add:

1. 4 qt. 2 pt. 6 qt. 1 pt. 5 qt. 2 pt.	2. 6 gal. 3 qt. 2 gal. 1 qt. 5 gal. 2 qt.	3. 3 bu. 2 pk. 4 bu. 1 pk. 8 bu. 3 pk.
4. 14 lb. 10 oz. 16 lb. 2 oz. 8 lb. 9 oz.	5. 3 T. 400 lb. 8 T. 500 lb. 5 T. 672 lb.	6. 3 ft. 2 in. 4 ft. 6 in. 8 ft. 9 in.
7. 3 yd. 2 ft. 4 yd. 2 ft. 6 yd. 1 ft.	8. 6 mi. 120 rd. 4 mi. 160 rd. 3 mi. 120 rd.	9. 6 hr. 10 min. 4 hr. 1 min. 8 hr. 6 min.

10. 6 ft. 2 in.; 3 ft. 4 in.; and 7 ft. 9 in.

11. 6 lb.; 8 lb. 1 oz.; 12 oz.

12. 3 yd.; 4 yd. 1 ft.; 6 yd. 2 ft.

See Appendix, pages 312-314 for Tables of Measure.

Units of Measure

Before we had standards for measuring, man used various objects as units of measure. Some early units of measure were:

	Unit	*What it is called*	*Approximate measure*
1.	The breadth of four fingers	Palm or hand	3 inches
2.	The length of first joint of thumb	Inch	1 inch
3.	The width of first finger	Digit	$\frac{3}{4}$ inch
4.	The stretch of open hand	Span	9 inches
5.	The length of forearm from elbow to tip of middle finger	Cubit	18 inches
6.	The stretch of outstretched arms	Fathom	6 feet
7.	The length of the foot	Foot	12 inches
8.	The length from nose to end of thumb when arm is stretched out full length	Yard	3 feet
9.	The length of the step	Pace	3 to 3.3 feet
10.	A thousand double paces	Mile	1 mile
11.	The length of the ploughman's goad stick	Rod	1 rod
12.	The length of a furrow	Furlong	$\frac{1}{8}$ mile

Let's see if we agree:

1. How many *digits* is the length of the page of this book?
2. How many *palms* or *hands* is the width of your desk?
3. How many *spans* is the length of your desk?
4. How many *cubits* is the width of the room?
5. How many *fathoms* is the height of the door?
6. How many *foot lengths* is your row of seats?
7. How many *nose yards* is a piece of string?

Did your measurements agree with all of your classmates'? Why is this true?

You can see how confusion resulted from this kind of measuring. The palm, the span, the cubit, and the other units of measure were not the same on different men. A king or ruler sometimes attempted to make these units of measure uniform by demanding for example, that the palm be the width of his hand. Thus, with each new king, the units of measures changed.

To avoid confusion in measuring, standards were worked out and adopted by governments. In the United States a model of each standard is kept in Washington, D. C., at the National Bureau of Standards. Copies of measures based on these standards are furnished each state and all the units of measure are based on these standards. An interesting report could be given on the National Bureau of Standards.

The tables of units of measure commonly used are found in the Appendix, pages 312-314.

What unit would you use to measure each of the following:

1. The width of a sheet of paper.
2. The height of the room.
3. The width of the front yard of a house.
4. The distance between two cities.
5. The length of material to make a dress.
6. The weight of a person.
7. The gasoline we put in our cars.
8. The sugar we buy.
9. The milk we buy or use.
10. The harvest from the wheat field.
11. The time spent in each class at school.

12. The amount of land in a farm.
13. The weight of a box of candy.
14. The weight of a letter.
15. The flour used in a cake.
16. The carrying capacity of freight boats.

Relationships Between Measures

Match the words in Column A with those in Column B:

Example:
1—g

Column A	Column B
1. One yard	a. 16 ounces
2. One foot	b. 4 quarts
3. One pound	c. 60 seconds
4. One mile	d. 8 quarts
5. One gallon	e. 2 cups
6. One quart	f. 144 square inches
7. One peck	g. 36 inches
8. One minute	h. 2000 pounds
9. One pint	i. $16\frac{1}{2}$ feet
10. One hour	j. 24 hours
11. One square foot	k. 5,280 feet
12. One ton	l. 4 pecks
13. One rod	m. 60 minutes
14. One bushel	n. 12 inches
15. One day	o. 2 pints

Using measures we frequently have to change from one unit of measure to another.

Changing to Smaller Units

3 yd. 2 ft. = 11 ft.	There are 3 ft. in 1 yd. so in 3 yd. there would be 3 × 3 or 9 ft.
	3 yd. 2 ft. = 9 ft. + 2 ft. or 11 ft.

List answers by Exercise number on a separate sheet of paper.

1. 7 ft. = ______ in.
2. 4 ft. 4 in. = ______ in.
3. 6 yd. = ______ in.
4. 4 yd. 2 in. = ______ in.
5. 3 gal. = ______ qt.
6. 2 gal. 3 qt. = ______ qt.
7. 4 lb. = ______ oz.
8. 3 lb. 2 oz. = ______ oz.
9. 3 bu. = ______ pk.
10. 4 bu. 1 pk. = ______ pk.
11. 4 hr. = ______ min.
12. 3 hr. 10 min. = ______ min.
13. 8 min. = ______ sec.
14. 6 min. 2 sec. = ______ sec.
15. 2 sq. ft. = ______ sq. in.
16. 3 sq. ft. 40 sq. in. = ______ sq. in.
17. 8 T. = ______ lb.
18. 3 pk. = ______ qt.
19. 2 T. 300 lb. = ______ lb.
20. 4 pk. 7 qt. = ______ qt.

Changing to the Units Given

70 min. = 1 hr. 10 min.	There are 60 min. in one hour. To find how many hours in 70 minutes divide 70 by 60. This would equal 1 hour and 10 minutes.

List answers by Exercise number on a separate sheet of paper.

1. 2 ft. 3 in. = ______ in.
2. 4 yd. 1 ft. = ______ ft.
3. 3 yd. 6 in. = ______ in.
4. 2 mi. = ______ ft.
5. 4 lb. 2 oz. = ______ oz.
6. 4 T. 300 lb. = ______ lb.
7. 2 sq. ft. = ______ sq. in.
8. 4 bu. 2 pk. = ______ pk.
9. 3 gal. 1 qt. = ______ qt.
10. 2 hr. 10 min. = ______ min.
11. 26 in. = ______ ft.
12. 8 ft. = ______ yd.
13. 13 pk. = ______ bu.
14. 5000 lb. = ______ T.
15. 70 min. = ______ hr.
16. 40 in. = ______ yd.
17. 24 oz. = ______ lb.
18. 19 pt. = ______ qt.
19. 106 qt. = ______ gal.
20. 17 qt. = ______ gal. ______ qt.

Comparing Units of Measure

Which is larger 4 bu. or 13 pk.?

To compare 4 bu. with 13 pk., we may change the 4 bu. to pecks.

4 bu. = 16 pk.

Comparing 16 pk. with 13 pk. we would say 4 bu. is larger than 13 pk.

Which is larger?

1. 2 ft. or 26 in.
2. 4 yd. or 126 in.
3. 3 yd. or 10 ft.
4. 33 oz. or 2 lb.
5. 3 T. or 5,000 lb.
6. 2 mi. or 10,000 ft.
7. 4 gal. or 24 qt.
8. 66 min. or 1 hour
9. 54 hours or 2 days
10. 6 pt. or 2 qt.
11. 5 bu. or 25 pk.
12. 4 cups or 3 pt.
13. 70 articles or 6 dozen articles
14. 25 inches or 2 ft.
15. 17 qt. or 2 pk.
16. 18 pt. or 2 gal.
17. 3 cups or 1 pt.
18. 600 sec. or 15 min.
19. 3 days or 80 hours
20. 692 days or 2 yrs.

Subtraction of Integers

Subtract and check:

1. 9,826 −4,613	2. 7,529 −7,421	3. 8,526 −8,520	4. 9,721 −9,721
5. 6,720 −1,738	6. 7,530 −2,896	7. 8,530 − 84	8. 9,640 −8,796
9. 8,200 −4,521	10. 3,700 − 896	11. 8,500 −3,841	12. 9,800 − 41
13. 8,000 −4,561	14. 7,000 −3,687	15. 9,000 − 21	16. 5,000 − 992

Copy in vertical columns, subtract, and check:

17. 7,629 − 42
18. 7,000 − 2,900
19. 80,000 − 7,962

Subtraction of Fractions

In Parts I, II, and III subtract and write answers in lowest terms:

Part I.

$$\begin{array}{r} 2\frac{5}{6} \\ -1\frac{1}{6} \\ \hline 1\frac{4}{6} = 1\frac{2}{3} \end{array}$$

1. $\frac{3}{8} - \frac{1}{8}$	2. $\frac{4}{5} - \frac{3}{5}$	3. $\frac{7}{8} - \frac{7}{8}$	4. $\frac{5}{9} - \frac{4}{9}$
5. $2\frac{7}{8} - 1\frac{3}{8}$	6. $4\frac{2}{3} - 1\frac{2}{3}$	7. $8\frac{5}{16} - 2\frac{1}{16}$	8. $9\frac{4}{9} - 2\frac{3}{9}$

Part II.

1. $7\frac{1}{2} - 6$	2. $4\frac{2}{3} - 3$	3. $7\frac{7}{8} - 5$	4. $9\frac{11}{16} - 4$
5. $7 - 2\frac{1}{2}$	6. $8 - 4\frac{3}{4}$	7. $9 - 6\frac{7}{8}$	8. $8 - 4\frac{3}{5}$

Part III.

1. $6\frac{1}{2} - 2\frac{3}{4}$	2. $7\frac{1}{3} - 3\frac{5}{6}$	3. $8\frac{1}{8} - 2\frac{3}{4}$	4. $7\frac{1}{16} - 3\frac{3}{8}$
5. $9\frac{1}{3} - 2\frac{3}{4}$	6. $5\frac{1}{12} - 3\frac{2}{3}$	7. $4\frac{1}{5} - 2\frac{1}{2}$	8. $4\frac{1}{3} - 2\frac{3}{4}$
9. $7\frac{1}{3} - 2\frac{1}{2}$	10. $4\frac{1}{6} - 3\frac{3}{4}$	11. $8\frac{2}{5} - 1\frac{2}{3}$	12. $2\frac{1}{12} - 1\frac{2}{5}$

Subtraction of Decimals

Subtract:

1. 8.0 − 2.25	2. 9.0 − 3.75	3. 10.0 − 2.19	4. 8.1 − 2.25	5. 7.5 − 1.45
6. 3.9 − 3.75	7. 0.821 − 0.756	8. 1.837 − 1.796	9. 0.0872 − 0.0796	10. 18.16 − 2.25
11. 27.59 − 1.45	12. 13.96 − 3.75	13. 0.0026 − 0.0019	14. 0.049 − 0.021	15. 7.0002 − 1.5675

Which is larger and how much, in the following?

1. 0.5 or 0.025
2. 0.75 or 0.075
3. 0.21 or 0.025
4. 0.6 or 0.06
5. 0.09 or 0.950
6. 0.84 or 0.039
7. 2.25 or 2.2
8. 8.5 or 7.476

Subtraction of Denominate Numbers

Subtract:

1. 17 ft. 2 in. − 3 ft. 9 in.
2. 2 yd. 1 ft. −1 yd. 3 ft.
3. 14 lb. 2 oz. − 6 lb. 10 oz.
4. 17 yd. 1 in. −11 yd. 20 in.
5. 3 gal. 1 qt. −2 gal. 3 qt.
6. 4 pt. −1 pt. 1 cup

Find the number of years, months, and days from the first date to the second, in Exercises 1 through 5.

1. From September 9, 1930, to June 1, 1955.

Year	Month	Day
	17	
1954	~~5~~	31
~~1955~~	~~6~~	~~1~~
1930	9	9
24 yr.	8 mo.	22 days

Count 30 da. = 1 month

2. From December 25, 1935, to July 4, 1940.
3. From August 2, 1930, to May 4, 1955.
4. From July 1, 1950, to January 1, 1970.
5. From July 4, 1776, to the date today.

1. How many hours and minutes are there from 9:30 a.m. to 2:45 p.m.?

```
 11
 12 hr. 60 min.
−  9 hr. 30 min.
   2 hr. 30 min. until noon

  2 hr. 30 min.
+2 hr. 45 min.
  4 hr. 75 min.
       or
  5 hr. 15 min.
```

2. How long is it from 6:30 a.m. until 5:45 p.m. the same day?
3. How long is it from 5:10 a.m. until 2:30 p.m. the same day?
4. How long is it from 6:30 p.m. until 4:30 a.m. the next day?
5. How long is it from 9:20 p.m. until 12:01 a.m. the next day?

Understanding the Multiplication Facts

Solve for N:

$6 \times 3 = 18$

$6 \times N = 18$

$N = 3$

$N \times 3 = 18$

$N = 6$

$\frac{1}{6}$ of 18 = ?

$\frac{1}{3}$ of 18 = ?

1. $4 \times N = 0$
2. $1 \times 9 = N$
3. $2 \times 7 = N$
4. $\frac{1}{2}$ of $18 = N$
5. $\frac{1}{2} \times 16 = N$
6. $7 \times N = 21$
7. $\frac{1}{3} \times 15 = N$
8. $N \times 3 = 27$
9. $\frac{1}{3} \times 24 = N$
10. $3 \times 4 = N$
11. $4 \times 6 = N$
12. $\frac{1}{4} \times 16 = N$
13. $N \times 4 = 28$
14. $9 \times N = 36$
15. $\frac{1}{4} \times 32 = N$
16. $5 \times N = 30$
17. $9 \times 5 = N$
18. $\frac{1}{5} \times 40 = N$
19. $\frac{1}{5} \times 15 = N$
20. $5 \times N = 35$
21. $6 \times N = 54$
22. $\frac{1}{6} \times 36 = N$
23. $\frac{1}{6} \times 42 = N$
24. $6 \times N = 48$
25. $7 \times 4 = N$

26. $7 \times N = 63$ 27. $N \times 7 = 56$ 28. $9 \times N = 63$ 29. $8 \times 8 = N$
30. $\frac{1}{8} \times 56 = N$ 31. $\frac{1}{8} \times 72 = N$ 32. $N \times 8 = 48$ 33. $9 \times 4 = N$
34. $N \times 9 = 54$ 35. $9 \times 9 = N$ 36. $7 \times N = 63$

Multiplying with Zero in Multiplicand

1. 303	2. 401	3. 1502	4. 7001	5. 8000
3	4	5	5	7
6. 5009	7. 7200	8. 709	9. 7020	10. 8190
9	8	6	8	9

Multiplying with Two-Digit Multipliers

1. 45	2. 96	3. 77	4. 83	5. 97
23	45	64	71	62
6. 821	7. 362	8. 4521	9. 8211	10. 9721
75	53	84	87	96

Multiplying with Zero in Multiplier

1. 25	2. 42	3. 81	4. 291	5. 845
50	70	60	90	80
6. 287	7. 986	8. 4728	9. 9876	10. 872
40	30	50	20	400

Multiplying with Zero in a Three-Digit Multiplier

Example					
526 506 3156 2630 266,156	1. 125 102	2. 342 204	3. 751 503	4. 962 602	5. 875 107
	6. 1241 609	7. 1205 808	8. 4962 407	9. 8702 504	10. 9736 906
8752 219 78768 8752 17504 1,916,688	11. 2576 123	12. 8945 465	13. 8729 527	14. 5726 375	15. 6182 928
	16. 7561 736	17. 4218 549	18. 8167 678		

Multiplying Fractions

$\dfrac{4}{\not{5}_{1}} \times \dfrac{\not{10}^{2}}{9} = \dfrac{8}{9}$

1. $\frac{2}{3} \times \frac{3}{5}$ 2. $\frac{4}{5} \times \frac{5}{6}$ 3. $\frac{7}{8} \times \frac{4}{9}$ 4. $\frac{3}{4} \times \frac{12}{17}$

5. $\frac{6}{7} \times \frac{3}{4}$ 6. $\frac{8}{9} \times \frac{1}{6}$ 7. $\frac{12}{15} \times \frac{3}{10}$ 8. $\frac{15}{16} \times \frac{24}{35}$

$\frac{3}{4} \times 5 = \frac{15}{4}$ or $3\frac{3}{4}$

9. $\frac{1}{4} \times 24$ 10. $\frac{3}{8} \times 16$ 11. $\frac{5}{6} \times 10$ 12. $\frac{9}{12} \times 15$

13. $\frac{8}{9} \times 20$ 14. $\frac{7}{8} \times 11$ 15. $\frac{9}{13} \times 26$ 16. $\frac{7}{15} \times 45$

$4\frac{2}{3} \times 12 =$

$\dfrac{14}{\not{3}_{1}} \times \not{12}^{4} = \dfrac{56}{1}$ or 56

17. $1\frac{1}{3} \times 12$ 18. $2\frac{1}{4} \times 16$ 19. $7\frac{1}{2} \times 20$

20. $10\frac{1}{2} \times 14$ 21. $8\frac{2}{3} \times 5$ 22. $6\frac{2}{3} \times 7$

$\frac{2}{3} \times 4\frac{1}{2}$

$\dfrac{\not{2}^{1}}{\not{3}_{1}} \times \dfrac{\not{9}^{3}}{\not{2}_{1}} = 3$

23. $\frac{3}{5} \times 7\frac{1}{2}$ 24. $\frac{5}{6} \times 1\frac{2}{3}$ 25. $\frac{5}{9} \times 2\frac{1}{5}$ 26. $6\frac{1}{2} \times \frac{4}{5}$

27. $\frac{7}{8} \times 2\frac{2}{3}$ 28. $\frac{15}{16} \times 1\frac{1}{7}$ 29. $3\frac{1}{2} \times \frac{8}{9}$ 30. $7\frac{2}{3} \times \frac{6}{9}$

$5\frac{1}{2} \times 1\frac{1}{4}$

$\frac{11}{2} \times \frac{5}{4} = \frac{55}{8}$ or $6\frac{7}{8}$

31. $2\frac{2}{5} \times 1\frac{1}{4}$ 32. $4\frac{1}{2} \times 1\frac{2}{3}$ 33. $8\frac{4}{5} \times 1\frac{1}{11}$

34. $9\frac{1}{2} \times 2\frac{2}{3}$ 35. $12\frac{1}{2} \times 1\frac{1}{5}$ 36. $22\frac{1}{2} \times 1\frac{4}{9}$

37. $8\frac{1}{3} \times 2\frac{2}{5}$ 38. $14\frac{3}{4} \times 1\frac{1}{5}$

$\begin{array}{r} 12 \\ \underline{7\frac{2}{3}} \\ 8 \\ \underline{84} \\ 92 \end{array}$

39. $\begin{array}{r} 15 \\ \underline{3\frac{3}{5}} \end{array}$ 40. $\begin{array}{r} 75 \\ \underline{12\frac{2}{5}} \end{array}$ 41. $\begin{array}{r} 81 \\ \underline{16\frac{1}{3}} \end{array}$ 42. $\begin{array}{r} 24 \\ \underline{16\frac{3}{4}} \end{array}$

43. $\begin{array}{r} 18\frac{2}{3} \\ \underline{6} \end{array}$ 44. $\begin{array}{r} 17\frac{1}{2} \\ \underline{8} \end{array}$ 45. $\begin{array}{r} 14\frac{3}{4} \\ \underline{12} \end{array}$ 46. $\begin{array}{r} 16\frac{1}{5} \\ \underline{25} \end{array}$

Multiplying Decimals

$\begin{array}{r} 0.126 \\ \underline{12} \\ 252 \\ \underline{126} \\ 1.512 \end{array}$ $\begin{array}{r} 457 \\ \underline{0.62} \\ 914 \\ \underline{2742} \\ 283.34 \end{array}$

1. $\begin{array}{r} 4.26 \\ \underline{8} \end{array}$ 2. $\begin{array}{r} 0.826 \\ \underline{5} \end{array}$ 3. $\begin{array}{r} 47.21 \\ \underline{21} \end{array}$ 4. $\begin{array}{r} 87.5 \\ \underline{16} \end{array}$

5. $\begin{array}{r} 875 \\ \underline{0.05} \end{array}$ 6. $\begin{array}{r} 876 \\ \underline{1.2} \end{array}$ 7. $\begin{array}{r} 756 \\ \underline{0.009} \end{array}$ 8. $\begin{array}{r} 297 \\ \underline{0.213} \end{array}$

$\begin{array}{r} 1.25 \\ \underline{2.7} \\ 875 \\ \underline{250} \\ 3.375 \end{array}$

9. $\begin{array}{r} 0.27 \\ \underline{0.09} \end{array}$ 10. $\begin{array}{r} 3.75 \\ \underline{1.2} \end{array}$ 11. $\begin{array}{r} 9.672 \\ \underline{0.06} \end{array}$ 12. $\begin{array}{r} 21.73 \\ \underline{0.045} \end{array}$

13. $\begin{array}{r} 2.761 \\ \underline{2.9} \end{array}$ 14. $\begin{array}{r} 0.427 \\ \underline{3.6} \end{array}$ 15. $\begin{array}{r} 296.1 \\ \underline{0.008} \end{array}$ 16. $\begin{array}{r} 43.18 \\ \underline{7.2} \end{array}$

Multiplying by 10, 100, and 1000

10 × 262.25 = 2622.5
100 × 262.25 = 26225
1000 × 262.25 = 262250

1. 10 × 29.1
2. 10 × 3.72
3. 10 × 0.063
4. 10 × 27
5. 10 × 0.0752
6. 10 × 0.271
7. 100 × 8.21
8. 100 × 75.2
9. 100 × 0.009
10. 100 × 0.9
11. 100 × 0.067
12. 100 × 21.7
13. 1000 × 2.1
14. 1000 × 0.097
15. 1000 × 7.67
16. 1000 × 0.002
17. 1000 × 2.47
18. 1000 × 91

Multiplying Denominate Numbers

$$\begin{array}{r} 3\text{ gal.}\quad 2\text{ qt.} \\ 5 \\ \hline 15\text{ gal.}\ 10\text{ qt.} \\ \text{or} \\ 17\text{ gal.}\quad 2\text{ qt.} \end{array}$$

1. $\begin{array}{r} 6\text{ ft. } 4\text{ in.} \\ 5 \\ \hline \end{array}$
2. $\begin{array}{r} 8\text{ yd. } 3\text{ ft.} \\ 6 \\ \hline \end{array}$
3. $\begin{array}{r} 4\text{ lb. } 7\text{ oz.} \\ 4 \\ \hline \end{array}$
4. $\begin{array}{r} 3\text{ hr. } 10\text{ min.} \\ 7 \\ \hline \end{array}$
5. $\begin{array}{r} 8\text{ T. } 45\text{ lb.} \\ 20 \\ \hline \end{array}$
6. $\begin{array}{r} 6\text{ bu. } \ 3\text{ pk.} \\ 12 \\ \hline \end{array}$
7. $\begin{array}{r} 9\text{ qt. } 1\text{ pt.} \\ 7 \\ \hline \end{array}$
8. $\begin{array}{r} 2\text{ mi. } 42\text{ rd.} \\ 9 \\ \hline \end{array}$

Dividing Integers

Divide and express the remainder as an integer in Parts I, II, III, and IV. In Part V, use a fraction in expressing the quotient. Check.

Part I.

1. $20\overline{)960}$
2. $30\overline{)750}$
3. $40\overline{)872}$
4. $50\overline{)1250}$
5. $60\overline{)1829}$
6. $70\overline{)1756}$
7. $80\overline{)25122}$
8. $90\overline{)27253}$
9. $60\overline{)27126}$

Part II.

1. $22\overline{)9064}$
2. $33\overline{)6996}$
3. $41\overline{)8721}$
4. $53\overline{)1679}$
5. $63\overline{)78214}$
6. $71\overline{)12871}$
7. $82\overline{)17216}$
8. $93\overline{)18421}$

Part III.

1. $29\overline{)9019}$
2. $37\overline{)7215}$
3. $49\overline{)2125}$
4. $57\overline{)6728}$
5. $68\overline{)12121}$
6. $77\overline{)14126}$
7. $85\overline{)96215}$
8. $96\overline{)12960}$

Part IV.

1. $125\overline{)27500}$ 2. $281\overline{)17141}$ 3. $396\overline{)87216}$ 4. $451\overline{)92183}$

5. $521\overline{)17256}$ 6. $641\overline{)38241}$ 7. $725\overline{)87450}$ 8. $972\overline{)23328}$

Part V.

1. $18\overline{)459}$ 2. $28\overline{)1050}$ 3. $30\overline{)2890}$

4. $49\overline{)1369}$ 5. $54\overline{)4128}$ 6. $66\overline{)5434}$

7. $750\overline{)90800}$ 8. $844\overline{)70096}$ 9. $900\overline{)28500}$

Practice with Zeros in the Quotient

Divide and check in Parts I and II.

Part I.

1. $15\overline{)309}$ 2. $25\overline{)1008}$ 3. $36\overline{)751}$

4. $48\overline{)1963}$ 5. $58\overline{)2851}$ 6. $63\overline{)1865}$

7. $76\overline{)15969}$ 8. $83\overline{)29070}$ 9. $92\overline{)41420}$

Part II.

1. $18\overline{)5508}$ 2. $24\overline{)5021}$ 3. $39\overline{)11934}$

4. $47\overline{)23786}$ 5. $521\overline{)104600}$ 6. $630\overline{)25300}$

7. $75\overline{)156210}$ 8. $81\overline{)249620}$ 9. $97\overline{)487216}$

Dividing Fractions

1. $6 \div \frac{2}{3}$ 2. $7 \div \frac{1}{2}$ 3. $9 \div \frac{2}{3}$ 4. $12 \div \frac{3}{4}$

5. $16 \div \frac{1}{8}$ 6. $18 \div \frac{1}{3}$ 7. $10 \div \frac{5}{6}$ 8. $21 \div \frac{3}{4}$

9. $\frac{3}{4} \div 3$ 10. $\frac{7}{8} \div 2$ 11. $\frac{15}{16} \div 5$ 12. $\frac{9}{16} \div 3$

13. $\frac{11}{12} \div 3$ 14. $\frac{4}{5} \div 4$ 15. $\frac{2}{3} \div 4$ 16. $\frac{5}{32} \div 10$

$$\frac{3}{4} \div \frac{1}{2} = \frac{3}{\cancel{4}_{2}} \times \frac{\cancel{2}^{1}}{1} = \frac{3}{2} \text{ or } 1\tfrac{1}{2}$$

or

$$\tfrac{3}{4} \div \tfrac{1}{2} = \tfrac{3}{4} \div \tfrac{2}{4} = \tfrac{3}{2} \text{ or } 1\tfrac{1}{2}$$

17. $\frac{1}{2} \div \frac{1}{4}$ 18. $\frac{7}{8} \div \frac{3}{4}$ 19. $\frac{9}{16} \div \frac{7}{8}$

20. $\frac{4}{5} \div \frac{1}{2}$ 21. $\frac{3}{4} \div \frac{2}{3}$ 22. $\frac{11}{12} \div \frac{2}{3}$

23. $\frac{5}{9} \div \frac{2}{3}$ 24. $\frac{5}{6} \div \frac{2}{3}$

$$3\frac{1}{3} \div \frac{2}{3} = \frac{\overset{5}{\cancel{10}}}{\underset{1}{\cancel{3}}} \times \frac{\overset{1}{\cancel{3}}}{\underset{1}{\cancel{2}}} = 5$$

or

$3\frac{1}{3} \div \frac{2}{3} = \frac{10}{3} \div \frac{2}{3} = \frac{10}{2}$ or 5

25. $7\frac{1}{2} \div \frac{1}{4}$ 26. $4\frac{1}{2} \div \frac{3}{4}$ 27. $12\frac{1}{2} \div \frac{5}{6}$
28. $5\frac{1}{3} \div \frac{1}{2}$ 29. $6\frac{2}{3} \div \frac{1}{4}$ 30. $8\frac{1}{3} \div \frac{3}{4}$
31. $3\frac{2}{3} \div \frac{5}{6}$ 32. $2\frac{7}{8} \div \frac{3}{4}$

$4\frac{1}{2} \div 4 = \frac{9}{2} \times \frac{1}{4} = \frac{9}{8}$ or $1\frac{1}{8}$

or

$4\frac{1}{2} \div 4 = \frac{9}{2} \div 4 = \frac{9}{2} \div \frac{8}{2} = \frac{9}{8}$ or $1\frac{1}{8}$

33. $2\frac{2}{3} \div 4$ 34. $3\frac{1}{3} \div 5$ 35. $7\frac{1}{2} \div 4$
36. $4\frac{1}{3} \div 3$ 37. $3\frac{1}{8} \div 2$ 38. $5\frac{1}{4} \div 3$
39. $1\frac{1}{8} \div 6$ 40. $5\frac{1}{2} \div 8$

41. $3\frac{1}{2} \div 1\frac{1}{4}$ 42. $5\frac{1}{3} \div \frac{5}{6}$ 43. $8\frac{2}{3} \div \frac{2}{3}$ 44. $3\frac{1}{5} \div 1\frac{1}{2}$
45. $6\frac{1}{3} \div 1\frac{1}{6}$ 46. $9\frac{3}{4} \div \frac{3}{8}$ 47. $2\frac{1}{2} \div \frac{7}{8}$ 48. $5\frac{5}{6} \div 2\frac{2}{3}$
49. $\frac{1}{2} \div 1\frac{1}{4}$ 50. $\frac{2}{3} \div 1\frac{5}{6}$ 51. $\frac{4}{5} \div 1\frac{1}{4}$ 52. $\frac{7}{8} \div 2\frac{1}{2}$
53. $\frac{15}{16} \div 3\frac{1}{2}$ 54. $\frac{11}{12} \div 2\frac{2}{3}$ 55. $\frac{5}{32} \div 1\frac{1}{4}$ 56. $\frac{5}{6} \div 3\frac{1}{2}$

Dividing Decimals

Divide and check.

1. $7\overline{)7.21}$ 2. $9\overline{)27.81}$ 3. $12\overline{)24.48}$
4. $16\overline{)0.048}$ 5. $25\overline{)0.375}$ 6. $42\overline{)9.156}$
7. $250\overline{)92.5}$ 8. $526\overline{)483.92}$ 9. $0.08\overline{)0.248}$
10. $0.009\overline{)2.736}$ 11. $0.18\overline{)0.5436}$ 12. $2.1\overline{)18.27}$
13. $0.35\overline{)3.360}$ 14. $7.2\overline{)48.96}$ 15. $1.25\overline{)6.125}$
16. $5.56\overline{)178.476}$ 17. $0.926\overline{)0.436146}$

Divide and check; express quotient to nearest tenth.

1. $7\overline{)11.1}$ 2. $0.8\overline{)20.6}$ 3. $1.4\overline{)10.2}$
4. $0.72\overline{)0.84}$ 5. $9.3\overline{)2.7}$ 6. $0.65\overline{)3.21}$
7. $1.31\overline{)0.28}$ 8. $75\overline{)61}$ 9. $124\overline{)181}$

Divide and check; express quotient to nearest hundredth.

1. $4\overline{)0.028}$ 2. $5\overline{)1.71}$ 3. $0.6\overline{)0.1}$
4. $29\overline{)8.2}$ 5. $8.6\overline{)21.3}$ 6. $0.71\overline{)8.22}$
7. $125\overline{)2.45}$ 8. $476\overline{)18.26}$ 9. $361\overline{)285}$

Divide and check; express quotient to nearest thousandth.

$$6\overline{)1.100}\quad 0.1833 \text{ rounds to } 0.183$$

Check: 0.1833
× 6
10998
+ 2
1.1000

1. $4\overline{)0.13}$ 2. $0.7\overline{)1.8}$ 3. $2.4\overline{)0.0016}$
4. $75\overline{)21}$ 5. $1.11\overline{)0.252}$ 6. $0.16\overline{)0.316}$
7. $9\overline{)12}$ 8. $45\overline{)36}$ 9. $81\overline{)18}$

Dividing by 10, 100, and 1000

1. $25 \div 10$ 2. $36 \div 100$ 3. $86 \div 1000$
4. $8.7 \div 10$ 5. $2.9 \div 100$ 6. $7.2 \div 1000$
7. $0.25 \div 10$ 8. $0.21 \div 100$ 9. $0.25 \div 1000$
10. $0.062 \div 10$ 11. $0.026 \div 100$ 12. $16.2 \div 1000$
13. $250 \div 10$ 14. $19.2 \div 100$ 15. $400 \div 1000$
16. $7.21 \div 10$ 17. $1.16 \div 100$ 18. $3261 \div 1000$

Changing Fractions to Decimals

Express as decimals to the nearest hundredth.

1. $\frac{1}{7}$ 2. $\frac{4}{5}$ 3. $\frac{3}{11}$ 4. $\frac{1}{25}$ 5. $\frac{1}{30}$
6. $\frac{9}{11}$ 7. $\frac{5}{4}$ 8. $\frac{6}{5}$ 9. $\frac{8}{7}$ 10. $\frac{4}{3}$

Practice Dividing Denominate Numbers

1 ft. $6\frac{1}{3}$ in.
6)9 ft. 2 in.
6
3 ft. = 36 in.
38 in.
36
$\frac{2}{6} = \frac{1}{3}$

1. 5)6 hr. 10 min. 2. 6)37 min. 6 sec.
3. 8)10 hr. 12 min. 4. 3)4 gal. 1 qt.
5. 3)6 qt. 1 pt. 6. 7)16 lb. 1 oz.
7. 3)4 T. 100 lb. 8. 3)5 yd. 3 in.
9. 2)3 mi. 10 rd.

Changing Decimals to Per Cents

Write as per cents.

1. 0.06 2. $0.09\frac{1}{3}$ 3. 0.075 4. 0.082
5. 0.13 6. 0.24 7. $0.26\frac{2}{3}$ 8. $0.83\frac{1}{3}$

9. 0.125	10. 0.625	11. 0.375	12. 0.333
13. 1.25	14. 2	15. 1.5	16. 3.8

Changing Fractions to Per Cents

Write as per cents.

1. $\frac{3}{5}$	2. $\frac{1}{20}$	3. $\frac{1}{10}$	4. $\frac{1}{25}$
5. $\frac{1}{50}$	6. $\frac{1}{4}$	7. $\frac{7}{10}$	8. $\frac{9}{25}$
9. $\frac{20}{20}$	10. $\frac{25}{20}$	11. $\frac{9}{4}$	12. $\frac{3}{2}$
13. $\frac{5}{8}$	14. $\frac{1}{9}$	15. $\frac{1}{7}$	16. $\frac{1}{15}$
17. $\frac{3}{11}$	18. $\frac{8}{15}$	19. $\frac{7}{10}$	20. $\frac{5}{12}$
21. $\frac{9}{8}$	22. $\frac{7}{6}$	23. $\frac{10}{9}$	24. $\frac{16}{15}$

Changing Per Cents to Decimals

Express as decimals.

1. 3%	2. 7%	3. $9\frac{1}{3}$%	4. $7\frac{1}{2}$%
5. 80%	6. 90%	7. 24%	8. 32%
9. $13\frac{1}{3}$%	10. 118%	11. 240%	12. 300%

Changing Per Cents to Fractions

Express as fractions.

1. 5%	2. 2%	3. 6%	4. 7%
5. 90%	6. 80%	7. 85%	8. 72%
9. 11%	10. 22%	11. 36%	12. 52%
13. $12\frac{1}{2}$%	14. $87\frac{1}{2}$%	15. $16\frac{2}{3}$%	16. $33\frac{1}{3}$%

Per Cent Problems

Find:

1. 6% of $700	2. 1% of $1000
3. 82% of 225 mi.	4. 75% of 320 mi.
5. $33\frac{1}{3}$% of 672 lb.	6. $66\frac{2}{3}$% of 420 lb.
7. $12\frac{1}{2}$% of 40.8 mi.	8. $37\frac{1}{2}$% of $20.40
9. $16\frac{2}{3}$% of $4.80	10. $8\frac{1}{3}$% of $.48

What is $1\frac{1}{2}\%$ of \$820?		What is $2\frac{1}{3}\%$ of \$200?	
$N = 0.015 \times 820$	\$820	$N = 0.02\frac{1}{3} \times 200$	\$200
$N = 12.3$	.015	$N = 4.67$	$0.02\frac{1}{3}$
$1\frac{1}{2}\%$ of \$820 is \$12.30.	4100	Answer: \$4.67.	$66\frac{2}{3}$
	820		400
	\$12.300		$\$4.66\frac{2}{3}$

In Exercises 11 through 20 round to nearest cent in finding:

11. $2\frac{1}{2}\%$ of \$720
12. $4\frac{1}{2}\%$ of \$480
13. $1\frac{1}{2}\%$ of \$25
14. $3\frac{1}{2}\%$ of \$15
15. $3\frac{1}{4}\%$ of \$30
16. $4\frac{1}{4}\%$ of \$120
17. $2\frac{1}{3}\%$ of \$50
18. $2\frac{2}{3}\%$ of \$100
19. $4\frac{3}{4}\%$ of \$8
20. $2\frac{4}{5}\%$ of \$70

Per Cents Greater than 100%

What is 105% of \$400?	
$N = 1.05 \times 400$	\$400
$N = 420$	1.05
	2000
Answer: \$420.	400
	\$420.00

What is:

1. 106% of \$200
2. 120% of \$40
3. 125% of \$220
4. 104% of \$160
5. 150% of \$480
6. 175% of \$370
7. 300% of \$12
8. 400% of \$700

Per Cents Less than 1%

What is $\frac{1}{3}\%$ of \$900?	
$\frac{1}{3}\%$ means $\frac{1}{3}$ of 1%	\$900
$N = \frac{1}{3} \times 0.01 \times 900$	0.01
$N = 3.00$	\$9.00
	$\frac{1}{3}$ of \$9.00 = \$3.00
Answer: \$3.	

What is:

1. $\frac{1}{2}\%$ of \$450
2. $\frac{1}{3}\%$ of \$960
3. $\frac{1}{5}\%$ of \$5
4. $\frac{1}{4}\%$ of \$10
5. 0.9% of \$60
6. 0.8% of \$90
7. 0.3% of \$450
8. 0.1% of \$80

Finding the Per Cent

\$15 is what % of \$20?	
$15 = N \times 20$	
$\frac{15}{20} = N$	$\frac{15}{20} = \frac{3}{4}$ or 75%
$75\% = N$	

1. \$25 is what % of \$30?
2. \$400 is what % of \$600?
3. 18 bu. is what % of 54 bu.?
4. 36 in. is what % of 54 in.?
5. \$9 is what % of \$13?
6. \$75 is what % of \$120?
7. \$10 is what % of \$4?
8. \$.80 is what % of \$50?
9. 24 games is what % of 50 games?
10. \$.75 is what % of \$3?

\$8 is 20% of what amount?

$8 = 0.20 \times N$

$\frac{8}{0.20} = N$

$40 = N$

$0.20\overline{)\$800}$ = \$40.

Answer: \$40.

\$6 is $66\frac{2}{3}$% of what amount?

$6 = \frac{2}{3} \times N$

$\frac{6}{\frac{2}{3}} = N$

$9 = N$

$6 \div \frac{2}{3} = \overset{3}{\cancel{6}} \times \frac{3}{\underset{1}{\cancel{2}}} = \$9$

Answer: \$9.

1. \$150 is 25% of what amount?
2. \$320 is 75% of what amount?
3. 12 in. is 20% of how many inches?
4. 15 yards is $33\frac{1}{3}$% of how many yards?
5. \$1.25 is 20% of what amount?
6. \$3.75 is 5% of what amount?
7. \$84 is $16\frac{2}{3}$% of what amount?
8. \$480 is $12\frac{1}{2}$% of what amount?
9. 16 pupils is 10% of how many pupils?
10. 420 pupils is $66\frac{2}{3}$% of how many pupils?

Finding Commission

Find 2% commission on a \$4000 sale.

What is 2% of \$4000?

$N = 0.02 \times 4000$

$N = 80$

$$\begin{array}{r} \$4000 \\ 0.02 \\ \hline \$80.00 \end{array}$$

The commission is \$80.

1. Find 1% commission on a \$8000 sale.
2. Find 3% commission on a \$500 sale.
3. Find $1\frac{1}{2}$% commission on a \$1200 sale.
4. Find 5% commission on a \$7000 sale.
5. Find 2% commission on a \$800 sale.
6. Find 6% commission on a \$75 sale.
7. Find $\frac{1}{2}$% commission on a \$100,000 sale.
8. Find $\frac{3}{4}$% commission on a \$200,000 sale.

Finding the Net Amount

What is the net amount if a 5% commission is allowed on a \$12,000 sale?

What is 5% of $12,000?

$N = 0.05 \times 12{,}000$ | $\begin{array}{r}\$12{,}000\\ 0.05\\ \hline \$600.00\end{array}$

$N = 600$

$12,000 − $600

$11,400 net amount.

Find net amount on each of the following:

1. 3% commission on $8000
2. 5% commission on $120,000
3. $3\frac{1}{2}$% commission on $4200
4. $\frac{1}{2}$% commission on $800

Finding the Rate of Commission

Mary received $10 commission for selling a $200 picture. What was the rate of commission?

$10 is what % of $200?

The ratio of $10 to $200 $= \frac{10}{200} = \frac{1}{20}$

$\frac{1}{20} = 5\%$

$10 is 5% of $200.

Find the rate of commission on the following:

1. $8 commission on $100 sale
2. $150 commission on $3000 sale
3. $900 commission on $6000 sale
4. $10 commission on $5000 sale

Finding the Total Sales

A salesman making 5% commission received $750. What were his total sales?

$750 is 5% of what amount?

$750 = 0.05 \times N$

$\frac{750}{0.05} = N$

$\begin{array}{r}\$15000.\\ 0.05\overline{)\$750.00}\end{array}$

Answer: $15,000.

Find the total sales in the following, if:

1. 6% commission on sales = $360
2. 2% commission on sales = $1440
3. $1\frac{1}{2}$% commission on sales = $150
4. $\frac{1}{2}$% commission on sales = $220

Discount Problems

How much is a 10% discount on a $27 dress?

What is 10% of $27?

$N = 0.10 \times 27$

$N = 2.70$

Answer: $2.70.

$\begin{array}{r}\$27\\ 0.10\\ \hline \$2.70\end{array}$

Find the discount.

1. Original price—$14
   Rate of discount—2%
2. Original price—$1.50
   Rate of discount—10%

3. Original price—\$240
   Rate of discount—8%
4. Original price—\$30.20
   Rate of discount—4%

What will you pay for a \$50 coat if the discount is 15%?

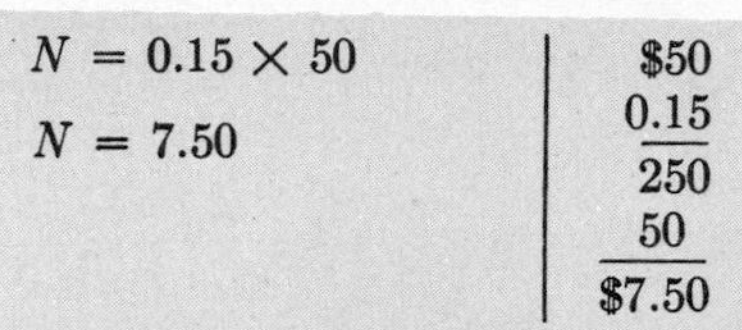

$N = 0.15 \times 50$

$N = 7.50$

$$\begin{array}{r} \$50 \\ 0.15 \\ \hline 250 \\ 50 \\ \hline \$7.50 \end{array}$$

$N = 50 - 7.50 = 42.50$

$N = \$42.50$ is the net amount.

Find the net amount.

1. Original price—\$40
   Rate of discount—10%
2. Original price—\$100
   Rate of discount—2%
3. Original price—\$5
   Rate of discount—8%
4. Original price—\$14.20
   Rate of discount—6%

Symbols

Symbols are used to express ideas. The symbol "=" means "is equal to" and "6 + 3 = 9" is read "Six plus three is equal to nine." The symbol "≠" means "is not equal to" and "6 + 3 ≠ 10" is read, "Six plus three is not equal to ten."

EXERCISES

Copy the following exercises, selecting the symbols which make the statements true:

(1) $299 + 28 \genfrac{}{}{0pt}{}{=}{\neq} 327$

(2) $492 - 167 \genfrac{}{}{0pt}{}{=}{\neq} 245$

(3) $64 \times 23 \genfrac{}{}{0pt}{}{=}{\neq} 209$

(4) $2911 \div 71 \genfrac{}{}{0pt}{}{=}{\neq} 41$

(5) $2\frac{2}{3} + 1\frac{1}{2} \genfrac{}{}{0pt}{}{=}{\neq} 4\frac{1}{6}$

(6) $17 - 3\frac{4}{5} \genfrac{}{}{0pt}{}{=}{\neq} 14\frac{4}{5}$

(7) $1\frac{4}{5} \times 6 \times \frac{2}{3} \genfrac{}{}{0pt}{}{=}{\neq} 7\frac{1}{5}.$

(8) $14 \div \frac{2}{7} \genfrac{}{}{0pt}{}{=}{\neq} 4$

(9) $0.6 + 2.6 + 0.7 + 8.0 \genfrac{}{}{0pt}{}{=}{\neq} 9.9$

(10) $400 - 22.6 \genfrac{}{}{0pt}{}{=}{\neq} 174$

(11) $26^2 \genfrac{}{}{0pt}{}{=}{\neq} 676$

(12) $2(100) + 3(10) + 6 \genfrac{}{}{0pt}{}{=}{\neq} 236$

(13) 23 ft. 6 in. + 22 ft. 12 in. $\genfrac{}{}{0pt}{}{=}{\neq}$ 46 ft. 8 in.

(14) 44 gal. 1 qt. − 21 gal. 2 qt. $\genfrac{}{}{0pt}{}{=}{\neq}$ 22 gal. 3 qt.

(15) 4 bu. 3 pk. $\times$ 4 $\stackrel{=}{\neq}$ 17 bu. 2 pk.

(16) 16 hr. 10 min. $\div$ 2 $\stackrel{=}{\neq}$ 8 hr. 5 min.

(17) $9\frac{1}{3} + 6\frac{2}{3} + 7\frac{1}{2} \stackrel{=}{\neq} 6\frac{2}{3} + 9\frac{1}{3} + 7\frac{1}{2}$

(18) $452 \times 126 \stackrel{=}{\neq} 126 \times 452$

(19) 10% of \$90 $\stackrel{=}{\neq}$ \$900

(20) $1\frac{1}{2}\% \stackrel{=}{\neq} .015$

The symbol "$<$" means "is less than." The statement "$6 < 4 + 3$" is read "Six is less than four plus three." The symbol "$>$" means "is greater than" or "is more than." The statement "$8 > 6 + 1$" is read "Eight is greater than six plus one."

EXERCISES

Copy the following exercises, selecting the symbols which make the statements true:

(1) $19 + 4 \lessgtr 17 + 5$

(2) $142 - 67 \lessgtr 55$

(3) $24 \times 18 \lessgtr 17 \times 25$

(4) $1826 \div 21 \lessgtr 94$

(5) $8\frac{2}{3} + 1\frac{1}{2} \lessgtr 9\frac{1}{3}$

(6) $2\frac{7}{8} - 1\frac{1}{4} \lessgtr 1\frac{1}{2} + \frac{3}{4}$

(7) $9\frac{7}{8} \times 2 \lessgtr 20$

(8) $14\frac{7}{8} \div \frac{1}{2} \lessgtr 7$

(9) $0.8 + 0.2 + 0.1 \lessgtr 0.75 + 0.16 + 0.09$

(10) $0.7 - 0.4 \lessgtr 0.83 - 0.16$

(11) $0.62 + 1.6 \lessgtr 0.16 \times 0.62$

(12) $1.429 \div 0.25 \lessgtr 8$

(13) $25^2 \lessgtr 2 \times 25$

(14) $\frac{42}{84} \lessgtr \frac{1}{3}$

(15) $\frac{1}{2} \lessgtr \frac{4}{7}$

(16) $\frac{2}{3} \lessgtr 0.6$

(17) $12\frac{1}{2}\%$ of $88 \lessgtr 10$

(18) 6% of \$2.52 $\lessgtr$ \$15.12

(19) $0.66 \lessgtr \frac{2}{3}$

(20) $66\frac{2}{3}\%$ of $300 \lessgtr 100$

Practice with Symbols

Copy, using one of these symbols to make the statement true.

$=, \neq, <, >$

(1) $25 + 48 \quad 73$

(2) $19 \times 6 \quad 104$

(3) $75 \div \frac{1}{3} \quad 25$

(4) 9% of \$250 \$22.40

(5) $10^2 \quad 20$

(6) $8^3 \quad 512$

(7) $3.72 + 1.64 + 2.11 \quad 8.07$

(8) $3.9 \times 4.2 \quad 16.38$

(9) $17\frac{3}{4} + 16\frac{1}{4} \quad 34$

(10) $29\frac{2}{5} \div 29\frac{2}{5} \quad 1$

(11) $14 \times 14 \times 14 \quad 14^3$

(12) If $r = 3$, $\pi r^2 \quad 3.14 \times 3 \times 3$

(13) If $s = 9$, $s^2 \quad 18$

(14) If $l = 19$ and $w = 11$, $lw \quad 209$

(15) The ratio of 14 to 7 $\frac{1}{2}$

(16) The ratio of 10 to 20 $\frac{1}{2}$

(17) $\frac{81}{109} \quad \frac{3}{4}$

(18) $\frac{4}{9} \quad \frac{24}{54}$

(19) $60 \div \frac{1}{2} \quad 60 \times 2$

(20) $\frac{4}{5} \div \frac{2}{3} \quad \frac{4}{5} \times \frac{3}{2}$

The symbol "( )" is often used to make clear a mathematical statement. The following statement is true:

$8 + (6 \div 3) = 10$ The parentheses are used to show that 8 is added to the quotient of $6 \div 3$.

Can you tell why these statements are true?

$$(8 \div 2) \times 6 = 24$$
$$7 + (6 \times 2) = 19$$

EXERCISES

Solve the following:

(1) $18 \div (9 \div 3)$

(2) $27 \div (6 \div 2)$

(3) $(9 + 4) \times 2$

(4) $(38 - 14) \div 2$

(5) $(1\frac{1}{2} + 2\frac{1}{2}) \times 3$

(6) $(7\frac{2}{3} - 1\frac{1}{3}) \div 4$

(7) $(3\frac{1}{2} \div \frac{1}{2}) + 2\frac{1}{2}$

(8) $(1\frac{1}{8} \times 1\frac{1}{2}) + 6\frac{1}{4}$

(9) $414 - (125 \div 25)$

(10) $(0.6 + 0.8) \div 2$

(11) $(9.2 - 1.6) \div 4$

(12) $(0.9 \times 0.6) \times 3$

(13) $(2.5 \div 0.5) + 6$

(14) $(1 + 4)^2$

(15) \$100 + (10% of \$100)

(16) \$45 − ($33\frac{1}{3}$% of \$45)

(17) 100% − (10% + 22%)

(18) 50% − (6% + 1.5%)

(19) ($\frac{1}{2}$ of $100)^2$

(20) ($\frac{1}{3}$ of $18)^3$

EXERCISES

$C = \pi d$	$P = 2(l + w)$	$A = bh$
$A = s^2$	$P = 4s$	$A = \pi r^2$
$A = \frac{1}{2}bh$	$A = lw$	$P = 5s$

Match the above formulas with these statements:

1. The area of the interior of a square is equal to the square of the measure of the side.
2. The circumference of a circle is the product of π and the measure of the diameter.
3. The perimeter of a regular pentagon is equal to the product of 5 times the measure of a side.
4. The area of the interior of a triangle is equal to $\frac{1}{2}$ the product of the measure of the base and the measure of the altitude.
5. The area of the interior of a circle is the product of π and the square of the measure of the radius.
6. The area of the interior of a rectangle is the product of the measure of the length and the measure of the width.
7. The perimeter of a square is the product of 4 times the measure of a side.
8. The area of the interior of a parallelogram is the product of the measure of the base and the measure of the height.
9. The perimeter of a rectangle is equal to 2 times the sum of the measure of the length and the measure of the width.

Tables of Measure

Linear Measures

12 inches (in.) = 1 foot (ft.)
3 feet = 1 yard (yd.)
$5\frac{1}{2}$ yards = 1 rod (rd.)
$16\frac{1}{2}$ feet = 1 rod
320 rods = 1 mile (mi.)
1760 yards = 1 mile
5280 feet = 1 mile

Square Measures

144 square inches (sq. in.) = 1 square foot (sq. ft.)
9 square feet = 1 square yard (sq. yd.)
$30\frac{1}{4}$ square yards = 1 square rod (sq. rd.)
160 square rods = 1 acre (A)
43,560 square feet = 1 acre
640 acres = 1 square mile (sq. mi.)

Cubic Measures

1728 cubic inches (cu. in.) = 1 cubic foot (cu. ft.)
27 cubic feet = 1 cubic yard (cu. yd.)

Liquid Measures

2 cups = 1 pint (pt.)
2 pints = 1 quart (qt.)
4 quarts = 1 gallon (gal.)

Dry Measures

2 pints = 1 quart (qt.)
8 quarts = 1 peck (pk.)
4 pecks = 1 bushel (bu.)

Weight Measures

16 ounces (oz.) = 1 pound (lb.)
100 pounds = 1 hundredweight (cwt.)
2000 pounds = 1 ton (T.)

Time Measures

60 seconds (sec.) = 1 minute (min.)
60 minutes = 1 hour (hr.)
24 hours = 1 day (da.)
7 days = 1 week (wk.)
365 days = 1 year (yr.)
366 days = 1 leap year
12 months (mo.) = 1 year

Days of the Months

Thirty days have September,
April, June, and November.
All the rest have thirty-one,
Except February, which has twenty-eight in line
'Till leap year makes it twenty-nine.

(All years divisible by 4 are leap years except those century years like 1900 which are not divisible by 400. The year 2000 will be a leap year.)

Metric Measures of Length

10 millimeters (mm.) = 1 centimeter (cm.)
10 centimeters = 1 decimeter (dm.)
10 decimeters = 1 meter (m.) (about 39.37 in.)
1000 meters = 1 kilometer (km.) (about $\frac{5}{8}$ or 0.6 mi.)

Commonly Used Equivalents

1 bushel of potatoes weighs about 60 pounds
1 bushel of apples weighs about 48 pounds
1 cubic foot of water weighs about 62.5 pounds.

1 cubic foot has a capacity of approximately 7.5 gallons.
231 cubic inches has a capacity of 1 gallon.

Index

Index ● ▲ ■ ⬣

A

Abacus, 8
Abscissa, 268
Addition:
  addends, 45
  decimal fractions, 63-65
  denominate numbers, 66-68
  estimating, 46
  fractions, 58-59, 60-61
  grouping, 46
  review, 68-69
  sum, 45
Angles:
  acute, 34
  adjacent, 39
  central, 240, 257-258
  complementary, 40
  degree, 33
  drawing and measuring, 37-38
  interior, 96, 242
  kinds, 34
  naming, 36
  obtuse, 34
  reflex, 36
  review, 43
  right, 31-34
  rotation, 31-33
  sides, 32
  straight, 34
  supplementary, 40-41
  symbol for, 36
Angles (*Cont.*):
  vertex, 32
  vertical, 39
Arc, 227, 258-259
Areas:
  circles, 234-235
  defined, 172
  dimensions, 169
  parallelograms, 176-180
  rectangles, 173-175
  review, 180-182
  solids, rectangular, volume of, 243-246
  squares, 172-175
  triangles, 179-180

B

Bisect, defined, 23

C

Central tendency:
  approximate numbers, computation with, 284-287
  averages, 278-281
  mean, 282
  median, 282
  mode, 282
  quartile, 284

Central Tendency (*Cont.*):
review, 287-288
Chapter tests:
addition (4), 69-70
angles, exploring (3), 44
circle, exploring the (13), 237-238
division (8), 153-154
estimating and central tendency (16), 288
graphs (15), 273-274
lines, exploring (2), 29-30
multiplication (7), 121-122
numbers, the basis of (1), 17-18
per cent, business uses of (12), 226
per cents, exploring (11), 208-209
perimeters and areas (10), 182
polygons and rectangular solids (14), 247-248
quantities, comparing (9), 165-166
subtraction (5), 90
triangles and quadrilaterals (6), 100
Chord, 228
Circle:
arc, 227, 258-259
area, 234-235
chord, 228
circumference, 227, 232-233
defined, 227
diameter, 228
finding the circumference, 232-233
graphs, 256-262
pi, 230-231
radius, 228
review, 236-237
sector, 259-260
semi, 228
Circumference, 227, 232-233
Commission, figuring, 211-215
Constructing, explained, 23
Coordinate, 263
Cubic units, 244

D

Decimals, 63
addition, 63-65
changing to fractions, 149
changing to per cents, 186
division by, 140-141
division of, 138-139
fractions, changing to decimals, 147-148
multiplication, 116-117
per cents, changing to decimals, 188
rounding, 142-144
subtraction, 80-82
Degree, 33
Descartes, René, 10-11, 262
Diameter, 228
Discount, figuring, 216-219
Division:
arithmetic processes, and other, 124
averages, finding, 129-130
of decimal fractions, 138-139
by decimals, 140-141
defined, 123
denominate numbers, 151-152
dividend, 124
divisor, 124
estimating quotients, 126
fractions, 133-138
methods, 127
quantities, comparing, by, 156-157
quotient, 124
remainder, 125
review, 152-153
rules, 57-58
short, 131-132
by 10, 100, or 1000, 145-147
with whole numbers, 130-131

E

Egyptian number system, 3-5
Estimating:

Estimating (*Cont.*):
in addition, 46
in division, 126
in multiplication, 103
with per cents, 277-278
review, 287
in subtraction, 72, 73
sums and products, 275-277
Exponents, 10-13
using, to write numbers in polynomial form, 12-13

F

Formulas:
area:
circle, 235
parallelograms, 178
rectangle, 173
square, 174
triangle, 179
circumference, finding the, 232
defined, 167
interest, 222
perimeter:
polygons, regular, 242
rectangle, 169
square, 168
triangle, 170
volume of rectangular solids, 245
Fractions:
addition, 58-59, 60-61
changing to decimals, 147-148
changing to per cents, 187-188
decimal, 63
decimals, changing to fractions, 149
denominator, 55
division, 133-138
equivalent, 56
improper, 55
simplifying, 58
like, 58
changing to, 59-60
meaning of, 54
mixed numbers, 58
Fractions (*Cont.*):
multiplication, 108-112
numerator, 55
per cents, changing to fractions, 188-189
proper, 55
reducing to lowest terms, 56-58
subtraction, 76-79

G

Geometry, coordinate, 262-263
Graphs:
abscissa, 268
axis, 265
bar, 161-164, 251-253
broken-line, 254-256
circle, 256-262
arc, 258-259
central angle, 257-258
making, 260-262
sectors, 259-260
lines in a plane, 265-268
the number line, 262-265
numbers, assigning, to points on a plane, 268-270
ordered number pairs, 268
ordinate, 268
pictographs, 249-251
review, 270-273

H

Hexagon, 239, 241
Hindu-Arabic number system, 7-10

I

Interest:
amount, 220
defined, 220
finding the amount, 221-222

Interest (*Cont.*):
finding, time given in days, 224
formula for finding, 222-224
principal, 220
rate of, 220
time, 220

L

Lines:
bisecting:
with compasses and straight edge, 24
with ruler, 23-24
constructing:
perpendicular, with straight edge and compasses, 27
segments of certain length, 22-23
drawing:
parallel, with ruler and right angle, 28
perpendicular, with straight edge and right angle, 26
horizontal, 19
intersecting, 20
the number, 262-265
oblique (slanting), 19
parallel, 20
perpendicular, 21
in a plane, 265-268
plumb, 19
review, 28-29
vertical, 19

M

Mean, 282
Measure, tables of, 312-314
Median, 282
Mode, 282
Multiplication:
decimal fractions, 116-117
denominate numbers, 119

Multiplication (*Cont.*):
factors, 102
fractions, 108-112
integers, 103-104
mixed numbers, 113-114
multiplicand, 101
multiplier, 101
partial products, 104
product, 101
review, 120-121
by 10, 100, and multiples of 10 and 100, 104-106, 117-118

N

Net proceeds, 212
Numbers:
approximate, computation with, 284-287
assigning, to points on a plane, 268-270
changing, from base five to base ten, 15-16
denominate:
addition, 66-68
division, 151-152
multiplication, 119
subtraction, 83-84
directed, 263
Egyptian system, 3-5
Hindu-Arabic system, 7-10
history, 1-10
mixed, 58
multiplication, 113-114
the number line, 262-265
numerals, 2-3
ordered number pairs, 268
polynomial form, 8-10
positional notation, 9-10
reading large, 49-50
review, 16-17
Roman system, 5-7
rounding, 52-54
verbal expression, 1-3
Numerals, 2-3

O

Octagon, 239
Ordinate, 268

P

Parallelograms:
- altitude, 176
- area, 176-180
- base, 176
- definition, 176
- height, 176
- rectangle, 98
- rhomboid, 178
- rhombus, 178
- square, 98

Pentagon, 239
Per cents:
- changing to decimals, 188
- changing to fractions, 188-189
- commission, 211-215
- decimals, changing to per cents, 186
- discount, 216-219
- equivalents, table of, 189
- estimating with, 277-278
- etymology, 183
- explanation, 183-186
- figuring, of a quantity, 191-195
- figuring to the nearest per cent, 200-201
- finding, 199-200
- finding total amounts with, 202
- fractions, changing to per cents, 187-188
- greater than 100%, 195-197
- of increase and decrease, 204-205
- interest, 220-225
  - finding the amount, 221-222
  - finding, time given in days, 224
  - formula for finding, 222-224
- less than 1%, 197-198

Per cents (*Cont.*):
- reviews, 198, 207-208, 225-226
- solving problems, 189-191
- in sports, 206-207

Perimeters:
- defined, 167
- polygons, regular, 242-243
- rectangles, 169-170
- review, 180-182
- squares, 167-169
- triangles, 170-171

Pi, 230-231
Plane surface, 91
Polygons:
- central angles, 240
- defined, 239
- hexagon, 239, 241
- octagon, 239
- pentagon, 239
- perimeter, 242-243
- quadrilateral, 239
- regular, 240
- review, 246-247
- triangle, 239

Polynomial form, 8-10
- grouping by fives, 13-15
- using exponents, 12-13

Practice in:
- addition, 48-49, 289
  - decimals, 65-66, 82-83, 291
  - of denominate numbers, 292
  - fractions, 61-62, 79, 290-291
- commission, 307-308
- decimals, 118-119
  - addition, 65-66, 291
  - changing to per cents, 304-305
  - division, 303-304
  - multiplication, 118-119
  - subtraction, 82-83, 297
- denominate numbers, 292-296
  - division, 304
  - subtraction, 298
- discount, 308-309
- division, 131, 301-302, 304
  - decimals, 303-304
  - fractions, 149-150
- formulas, using, 312

Practice in (*Cont.*):
fractions:
addition, 61-62, 79, 290-291
changing to decimals, 304
changing to per cents, 305
division, 149-150
improper, and mixed numbers, 290
multiplication, 114-115, 300
subtraction, 79, 297
reducing to lowest terms, 290
mixed numbers, 290
multiplication, 107, 298-299
decimals, 118-119
fractions, 114-115, 300
per cents, 202-203, 305-307
changing to decimals, 305
changing to fractions, 305
subtraction, 74-75, 296
decimals, 82-83, 297
denominate numbers, 298
fractions, 79, 297
of measures, 87
symbols, problems using, 309-311

Q

Quadrilaterals:
defined, 96
diagonals, 96
interior angles, 96
parallelograms, 96, 97-99
rectangle, 98
review, 99-100
square, 98
trapezoid, 97
Quantities, comparing:
bar graphs, 161-164
by division, 156-157
ratio, 157-160
review, 164-165
by subtraction, 155-156
Quartile, 284
Quick Quizzes (*See also* Review tests), 25, 38-39, 51-52, 60, 66, 75-76, 78, 89, 107-108, 112-113, 120, 138, 147, 150-151, 160-161, 175-176, 180, 191, 199, 203-204, 205-206, 207, 215-216, 219, 229-230, 233, 235-236, 242, 246, 251, 253-254, 256, 265, 270, 281

R

Radius, 228
of a line, 23
Ratio, 157-160
Rectangles, 98
area, 173-175
perimeter, 169-170
solids, rectangular (*See* Solids, rectangular)
Reviews:
addition, 68-69
angles, 43
circles, 236-237
division, 152-153
estimating and central tendency, 287-288
graphs, 270-273
lines, 28-29
multiplication, 120-121
numbers, 16-17
perimeters and areas, 180-182
per cents, 207-208
per cent, using, 225-226
polygons and rectangles, 246-247
quadrilaterals, 99-100
quantities, comparing, 164-165
subtraction, 89-90
triangles, 95-96
Review tests (*See also* Quick Quizzes), 62, 79-80, 115-116, 133, 193
Rhomboid, 178
Rhombus, 178
Roman number system, 5-7

S

Sectors, 259-260
Solids, rectangular:
  cubic units, 244
  review, 247
  volume, 243-246
Square measure table, 300
Squares, 98
  area, 172-175
  perimeter, 167-169
Standard time, 84-86
Subtraction:
  additive process, 73-74
  check, 72
  decimal fractions, 80-82
  denominate numbers, 83-84
  fractions, 76-79
  measure of time, 84-86
  minuend, 72
  quantities, comparing, by, 155-156
  remainder, 72
Subtraction (*Cont.*):
  review, 89-90
  subtrahend, 72
  take away process, 72

T

Trapezoid, 97
Triangles:
  acute, 93
  area, 179-180
  base, 94
  base angles, 94
  constructing, 92
  defined, 91
  equilateral, 92
  isosceles, 92
  obtuse, 93
  perimeter, 170-171
  review, 95-96
  right, 93
  scalene, 92
  vertex angle, 94

1 2 3 4 5 6 7 8
65 66 67 68